HUNTING FOR
FOSSILS

HUNTING FOR

FOSSILS

A Guide to Finding & Collecting Fossils in All Fifty States

by MARIAN MURRAY

Drawings by Madge Perry

COLLIER BOOKS
A Division of Macmillan Publishing Co., Inc.
NEW YORK

Library of Congress Catalog Card Number: 67–22402

Hunting for Fossils is also published in a
hardcover edition by Macmillan Publishing Co., Inc.

Macmillan Publishing Co., Inc.
866 Third Avenue, New York, N.Y. 10022
Collier-Macmillan Canada Ltd., Toronto, Ontario

First Collier Books Edition 1974

Printed in the United States of America

*To all those who delight
in the fascinating pastime of
hunting for fossils*

Acknowledgments

I N THE PROCESS OF COLLECTING MATERIAL ABOUT THE
fossil picture throughout the United States, I have had reason to be deeply grateful to a great many men and women
on the staffs of geological surveys, museums, libraries (both
public and institutional), colleges, and universities. They
have answered technical queries, directed me to popular and
scientific publications, and lent unpublished studies or texts
peculiarly difficult to obtain. When no printed material on
fossil sites was available, geologists and paleontologists have
sometimes compiled data specifically for use in this book. In
a number of instances specialists have checked passages
intended for inclusion and have otherwise been helpful in a
manner far beyond the call of any possible duty.

I am especially grateful to Allen F. Agnew, state geolo-
gist, State Geological Survey, South Dakota; H. V. Andersen,
curator, Geology Museum, Louisiana State University; Mar-
vin J. Andresen, assistant professor of geology, University of
Alaska; Harlan P. Banks, professor of botany, Cornell
University; Herman F. Becker, research associate, New York
Botanical Garden; H. K. Brooks, Department of Geology,
University of Florida; the late Barnum Brown, curator
emeritus of paleontology, American Museum of Natural
History; Frank Byrne, chairman, Department of Geology,
Idaho State College.

Charles L. Camp, Museum of Paleontology, University
of California at Berkeley; J. R. Chelikowsky, head, Depart-
ment of Geology and Geography, Kansas State University;
J. M. Chelini, Bureau of Mines and Geology, State of Mon-
tana; Jane Cheney, director, Children's Museum, West
Hartford, Connecticut; Stephen G. Conrad, assistant state
geologist, Division of Mineral Resources, North Carolina;
Charles W. Copeland, Geological Survey of Alabama; Dan
A. Davis, district geologist, United States Geological Survey,
Hawaii; Charles G. Doll, state geologist, State of Vermont;

G. M. Dow, research assistant, Illinois State Geological Survey;

Robert J. Floyd, principal geologist, Department of Conservation, State of Tennessee; Gary Gautier, student, Idaho State College; Marion L. Gilbert, curator of records, State Museum, University of Nebraska; John J. Groot, state geologist, Delaware Geological Survey; G. F. Hanson, state geologist, University of Wisconsin; Robert L. Heller, head, Department of Geology, University of Minnesota; H. Garland Hershey, director, Iowa Geological Survey; F. D. Holland, Jr., professor of geology, University of North Dakota; Fred S. Honkala, chairman, Geology Department, Montana State University; Nicholas Hotton III, associate curator, reptiles and amphibians, Smithsonian Institution; Leo W. Hough, state geologist, Louisiana Geological Survey; Francis M. Hueber, associate curator, paleobotany, Smithsonian Institution; Marshall T. Huntting, supervisor, Division of Mines and Geology, State of Washington; Henry S. Johnson, Jr., geologist, State Development Board, South Carolina;

Robert W. Kelley, research geologist, Department of Conservation, State of Michigan; Porter M. Kier, associate curator, invertebrate paleontology, Smithsonian Institution; John W. Koenig, geologist, Division of Geological Survey and Water Resources, State of Missouri; John C. Kraft, acting chairman, Department of Geology, University of Delaware; John H. Lewis, assistant professor of geology, Colorado College; Joseph Lintz, Jr., Nevada Bureau of Mines, University of Nevada; Tracy W. Lusk, state geologist, Mississippi Geological Survey; Preston McGrain, assistant geologist, Kentucky Geological Survey, University of Kentucky; Paul O. McGrew, Department of Geology and Mineralogy, University of Wyoming; William J. McMannis, associate professor of geology, Montana State College; T. R. Meyers, geologist, New Hampshire State Planning and Development Commission; Grace Muilenburg, public information director, State Geological Survey, University of Kansas; John D. Naff, associate professor of geology, Oklahoma State University; Stuart A. Northrop, chairman, Department of Geology, University of New Mexico; I. Edgar Odom, Educational Extension Division, State Geological Survey, Illinois; Robert T. O'Haire, assistant mineralogist, Bureau of Mines, University of Arizona; Stanley J. Olsen, Florida Geological Survey; Garland Peyton, director, Department of Mines, Mining, and Geology, Georgia;

R. Dee Rarick, Office of Educational Services, Indiana Geological Survey; Clayton E. Ray, associate curator, vertebrate paleontology, Smithsonian Institution; Charles A. Repenning, United States Geological Survey, Menlo Park, California; Salem J. Rice, assistant mining geologist, State of California; E. F. Richards, head, Department of Geology and Geography, University of Alabama; Peter Robinson, curator of geology, University of Colorado Museum; Ivan T. Sanderson, author and zoologist; John T. Sanford, professor of geology, Wayne State University, Michigan; R. A. M. Schmidt, chief, Mineral Classification Section, USGS office, Anchorage, Alaska; W. Cullen Sherwood, Virginia Council of Highway Investigation and Research; Charles J. Smiley, College of Mines, University of Idaho; Laurence L. Smith, head, Department of Geology and Geography, University of South Carolina; Edward A. Stanley, associate research professor, Department of Geology, University of Delaware; Philip J. Sterling, geologist, Arkansas Geological and Conservation Commission; Robert E. Stevenson, chairman, Department of Geology, State University of South Dakota; William Lee Stokes, head, Department of Geology, University of Utah; Myrl V. Walker, director of museums, Fort Hays Kansas State College; John W. Wells, professor of geology, Cornell University; Kemble Widmer, state geologist, Department of Conservation and Economic Development, New Jersey.

Of course, the majority of the foregoing have doctorates, and certain ones may be identified by lengthy strings of letters after their names. Moreover, during the period necessary for publication of this book, many of them have no doubt acquired additional degrees, some have gone farther up the academic ladder, and at least a few have changed from one geological survey or college or museum to another. I note here the affiliation and status each held at the time we were in correspondence, and have not indicated academic honors. For these omissions and any errors, I ask pardon.

For firm moral support, and assistance in the laborious and sometimes very difficult task of organizing and checking material, deepest gratitude and appreciation to my friend Margaret Wood.

Contents

Introduction

IT GOES WITHOUT SAYING THAT THIS BOOK IS NOT FOR professionals but for amateurs—for the astonishing number of persons who have already been introduced to the joys of fossil collecting and, in addition, for those who are likely to become addicts. The second category certainly includes thousands upon thousands who at the moment may have no thought of ever becoming involved in that delightful pastime. But it is a very strong-minded person indeed who can resist the temptation to go a-hunting when he finds himself in a region where fossils are common, or when he, or someone he knows, makes a dramatic discovery. The virus is a persistent one—as bad as that for golf or bridge; and once infected, man, woman, or child will find it lingering in his bloodstream, despite all efforts to recover.

I myself have never been free from it since the day, after I came to live in Florida, when I seated myself in a friend's lanai, next to a strange-looking object that turned out to be a mastodon bone that had been found in front of her house. My addiction became complete a few years later, after I had casually found a walrus tusk that turned out to be from *Trichecodon huxleyi*—an extinct European species. Mine was the only fossil of this or any other kind of walrus known from Florida soil, and the second *Trichecodon* ever reported in the United States (with the first found near Charleston, South Carolina, about a hundred years ago, written about by the great Joseph Leidy, and later lost). My find was so important that Harvard's Museum of Comparative Zoology put out a special bulletin about it.

As is evident, I am not a professional scientist, and in this book have not tried to speak like one. Except where there is no common name, or where specific identification is essential, I do not use the scientific designations. The inexperienced hunter may come to all that when he feels ready for it.

Despite the nonscholarly manner in which much of this

material is presented, it has been prepared with conscientious care, in an attempt not only to be accurate but to make each statement conform as closely as possible to present thinking on the subject. Because, however, of the rapid change in all scientific thought, and the number of other sciences on which paleontology is dependent, it is doubtless inevitable that between now and the time when this book appears there will be changes that came too late to be recognized here. Moreover, it would be too much to hope that there will be no errors of fact. I merely hope that they will be few, and that those who read will be lenient.

All of us who have had a hand in creating this book have done so with the clear knowledge that the person who pokes around looking for fossils without really knowing what he is doing is at best a nuisance and often a menace to serious paleontologists. Most of the scientists would be much happier if uninformed amateurs would stay out of the way, and often say so.

Paleontologists in Utah cried out in anguish in November 1965, when irresponsible hunters went into a very important dig the scientists had left unfinished and messed the whole thing up. As a result, to hunt fossils in Utah one must have both a state and a county permit, and there is a heavy fine for infringement. It is interesting to note also that a committee was appointed in Utah in 1966 to cooperate with the American Geological Institute and the Department of the Interior in a nonschool education program. In New York, one must have a permit to dig near any state highway. Several other states have similar laws, and additional states will undoubtedly follow suit, but (as Utah realized) laws about permits will not be enough.

Widespread dissemination of information may well be the answer.

Children in school are being taught more and more about the earth sciences and in the process are acquiring at least a little knowledge of paleontology—although, to be sure, they may think that any fossil bone they pick up is that of a dinosaur.

Adults may have more opportunity to get facts, but have

less chance of assessing them correctly, unless they have access to interpretations not usually given (or not given accurately) in newspapers or news magazine reports. Adults, too, should know more than most of them do. The state of Connecticut will have a dinosaur park, all because a young man who ran a bulldozer for a construction company saw something he thought might be significant and reported it immediately (see p. 114).

There is no doubt that almost anyone possessed of curiosity, imagination, and interest in the strange is fascinated by fossils. The number of those who make a hobby of collecting them increases every day, and will keep on increasing, whether the professionals like it or not.

Some of the searchers have the erroneous idea that fossil finds may make them rich. A paleobotanist at our National Museum tells of his own sorrow and frustration when he was not able to acquire a fossil of a theretofore unknown species because the farmer who had picked it up thought he should receive a very large sum and destroyed the record when he couldn't get what he wanted.

Sadly enough, there will of course always be a few collectors who are selfish or even ruthless. But most persons can learn to obey the rules, as they have learned to pay attention to traffic lights. The more the general public learns about the lack of commercial value of those records in the earth, and the more it knows about what such records may mean to science, the less likely the average person is to overestimate the barely possible monetary value, to ignore what he has found, or to destroy it. The more the public knows on the subject, the more a fossil is likely to be treated with respect.

The person who pursues the hobby for any length of time is bound to find his interest and curiosity expanding. He wants to know more about what those bits of ancient plant and animal life really are, how they happened to be where he found them, how old they are, and what phases of evolution they represent. He feels an increasing urge to discover something unusual, something that will be exciting to the scientists. And if he is about to decide on a career, he may well come to the conclusion that he wants to be a professional paleontologist.

Within the scope of paleontology, he can, of course, become any one of many kinds of specialists—with his interest ranging from what one of the foraminifers or some other minute form divulges under a microscope to what the location of a given specimen reveals about the distribution of species throughout the world in any past era.

The field offers all sorts of exciting and romantic possibilities. Mysteries that baffle the experts are waiting to be solved. An incredible number of recognized gaps are yawning—ready to be filled by new fossil finds. Lucky discoveries may indicate that known phases were once connected by unsuspected links, or even suggest that some accepted theory must be discarded or modified. In paleontology, initiative, originality, and imagination are as important as perseverance and hard work.

Authorities say, for example, that they expect some brilliant young man or woman to come up with solutions to such mysteries of extinction as why the giant reptiles disappeared; why the horse and camel underwent most of their evolution on this continent and then vanished from our land but went on in other parts of the globe; whether there is, somewhere on earth, still hidden in the rock, a fossil ancestor of the "Dawn" horse, *Eohippus;* what happened to *Smilodon* and the other saber-tooths, or to *Eremotherium* and the rest of the ground sloths, which roamed this continent, and one of which apparently was domesticated in Argentina; how it happened that the plesiosaurs and other sea monsters disappeared; why the true opossum lives on only in North and South America, though most of his marsupial relatives are now confined to Australasia; what happened to certain marine invertebrates that used to be abundant.

Scientists want answers to all sorts of "whys." Why is the early Permian marine life found in Texas so much like that on the Indonesian island of Timor? Where and how did the modern corals originate? What was the function of those two knobs on the lower jaw of the giant piglike creature that roamed our plains in the early Miocene? Why did some

mastodons have tusks that curved backward, whereas others
had straight ones? Just how and why did the whale go back
to the sea after he had become a land dweller?

Certain periods, say the geologists, need more study
than they have had; and more fossils (sometimes from
specific regions) should be collected to represent those
periods. Among the periods that will best repay study are the
Silurian in the western part of North America; the Mesozoic
(for marine invertebrates) on the Pacific Coast; the late
Triassic and early Jurassic in places where more may be
learned about dinosaurs; interglacial ages all over the world,
to obtain more exact knowledge about temperatures at those
times of melting.

Between the Devonian and the Pennsylvanian, there
may be deposits that will explain what happened then to insects. Someone may find a great deposit of Mississippian
strata which will throw more light on the development of amphibians. Somewhere on this continent, perhaps from the
Cretaceous, there may be complete skulls, or even whole skeletons, which will show what the ancestors of all later mammals were like. In some part of the earth there are fossils to
fill in areas in the still incomplete sequence that started with
some sort of primate and has ended, so far, with *Homo
sapiens*.

Some of those reading this book may be among those
very ones who will answer the questions, make the important
discoveries, and solve the mysteries. In hunting the past,
they may also help toward an understanding of the present,
and give some insight into what the future may have to
offer.

Here and there throughout this text, the reader will find
a suggestion that he consult some professional. It is, to be
sure, always helpful to the nonprofessional to consult someone who is an authority. Nonetheless, let the suppliant be
imaginative enough to realize how loaded with work professionals are likely to be, and how kind they are when they
spend precious time helping the amateur. Many of them
have done as much for me, and I thank them with all my
heart.

This book goes forth with the hope that it may be of practical help to those who want to pursue the hobby of collecting fossils and that it may also be of sufficient interest to encourage some of my readers to make the hobby into a career.

MARIAN MURRAY

Sarasota, Florida
February 1, 1967

Warning to Fossil Hunters

BOTH THE AUTHOR AND THE PUBLISHERS WISH TO STRESS the fact that, except for limited areas of undistributed public domain controlled by the federal government,* the entire land surface of the United States is private or corporate property. Even roads, railroad tracks, and embankments are either privately or publicly owned.

As a result, though picking up small fossils along roads and railroads is only technically stealing, any unauthorized digging on or in such embankments and cuts constitutes a serious misdemeanor, quite apart from the fact that it is potentially dangerous to others. An undermined road may cause rock falls, washouts, or even more serious collapse, which in turn may cause severe accidents.

Therefore, before doing any collecting, and especially any digging, anywhere, one should be sure to ascertain who owns the property and obtain permission to collect and/or dig. This goes not only for private property but also for that owned by townships, and local, state, or federal government agencies. Also, the fossil hunter should *not* forget that there are laws against trespass.

Moreover, fossil hunters, like rock-hounds, cave explorers, and others engaged in field hobbies, *must* bear in mind the precepts of conservation. There is no longer any justification for the removal of any important natural object from its indigenous site. If any specimen larger than a detached object transportable by a single person is found, it should be marked, and reported to both the owner of the land *and* the nearest headquarters of the U.S. or state geological survey.

* *Under the purview of the Federal Antiquities Act.*

GEOLOGIC TIME SCALE

ERA	PERIOD	EPOCH	BEGINNING OF INTERVAL (MILLIONS OF YRS.)	IMPORTANT EVENTS
CENOZOIC (about 2%)	Quaternary	Recent	.01	Man becomes abundant
		Pleistocene	1–3(?)	First man; many mammals vanish
	Tertiary	Pliocene	13	Mammals reach their maximum diversity
		Miocene	25	
		Oligocene	36	Spread and diversification of mammals
		Eocene	58	
		Paleocene	63	
MESOZOIC (about 5⅓%)	Cretaceous		135	Flowering plants become dominant. Dinosaurs continue abundant then vanish
	Jurassic		181	First birds; dinosaurs increasingly abundant and diverse
	Triassic		230	First mammals. First dinosaurs
PALEOZOIC (about 12⅔%)	Permian		280	
	Carboniferous		345	First reptiles; first insects
	Devonian		405	First amphibians
	Silurian		425	First land life (plants and invertebrates)
	Ordovician		500	First fishes
	Cambrian		600	Marine invertebrates abundant
Basal and Proterozoic make up Precambrian (approximately 80% of the history of life)				First life—perhaps 3 billion years ago

Based in part on Chart Prepared by Smithsonian Institution, Department of Paleobiology

AS MAY BE SEEN IN THE GEOLOGIC TIME SCALE, THE BIL-lions of years before the Cambrian period may be simply lumped together as Precambrian. Sometimes all of that section of time is divided into three parts, which, starting with the oldest, are most commonly called: Archeozoic (Keewatin and Timiskaming); Proterozoic (Huronian and Keweenawan); and Precambrian, without further division. In general there seems to be a trend toward calling all that unimaginably long portion of infinity Precambrian, and making three divisions under that heading: Lower (Keewatin), Middle (Timiskaming), and Upper (Huronian and Keweenawan).

The Pleistocene, which very recently was stretched back to a beginning something like two million years earlier than the one million at which it had previously been reckoned, was the time of the so-called Ice Age, or, better, Ice Ages. It was a time of alternate glaciation and melting. Four main glacial ages and three interglacial are recognized: Nebraskan glacial, Altonian interglacial, Kansan glacial, Yarmouthian interglacial, Illinoian glacial, Sangamonian interglacial, and Wisconsin glacial, which is itself divided into five subdivisions. The Recent epoch is dated as beginning with the latest retreat of the glaciers, and of course it may be an interglacial age in which we ourselves are living.

How Geologic Periods Got Their Names

CAMBRIAN—named in 1835 by the Rev. Adam Sedgwick (professor of geology at Cambridge University) from Latin name for Wales, where rocks of that age were first recognized.

ORDOVICIAN—named in 1879 by Prof. Charles Lapworth (pioneer stratigrapher) for a Celtic tribe, the Ordovices, that once lived in Wales.

SILURIAN—named by Sir Roderick Impey Murchison (British geologist) in 1838, for another Celtic tribe, the Silures, that had lived in Wales and southern England.

DEVONIAN—from the county Devonshire, in western England. Sedgwick and Murchison invented the term to mean the rock system there, and between 1837 and 1839 were persuaded by William Lonsdale, English specialist on corals, to apply it to rocks halfway between the Silurian and Carboniferous. (In the U.S. the Carboniferous is divided into the Mississippian and the Pennsylvanian.)

MISSISSIPPIAN—name (because of deposits in the central Mississippi Valley) introduced in 1869 by Alexander Winchell (then professor of geology at the University of Michigan), but made effective in 1891 by Henry Shaler Williams, then with the USGS.

PENNSYLVANIAN—from the state; named by Williams.

PALEOZOIC (ancient life)—named in 1838 by Sedgwick, who included in the era only Cambrian through Silurian.

PERMIAN—named in 1841 for the province of Perm in the Ural Mountains of Russia, by Murchison, who decided that this period should be considered part of the Paleozoic.

TRIASSIC—from Latin *triad,* meaning a group of three; name suggested in 1834 by the German Friedrich August von Alberti, alluding to tripartite development of the rock system in Germany.

JURASSIC—named in 1799 by Friedrich Heinrich Alexander von Humboldt, German scientist, explorer, and natural philosopher; from the Jura mountains in France and Switzerland.

CRETACEOUS—from Latin *creta,* meaning chalk; named in 1822 by a Belgian, d'Halloy.

MESOZOIC (pertaining to middle life)—term devised in the early nineteenth century by John Phillips (nephew of William ["Strata"] Smith, see p. 28). The era originally included Cretaceous, Jurassic, Triassic, and part of Permian, but Phillips revised the stratigraphy and proposed the terms now in use.

TERTIARY (third)—introduced during the eighteenth century to mean rocks overlying earlier ones then called "primary" and "secondary." The period was divided into epochs through study of rocks in the Paris Basin, and names were derived from the Greek: Paleocene—"ancient recent"; Eocene—"dawn recent"; Oligocene—"scant recent"; Miocene—"less recent"; and Pliocene—"more recent."

QUATERNARY (fourth)—applied by French and German geologists to unconsolidated materials (like those deposited by streams, lakes, and glaciers) which covered Tertiary rocks.

PLEISTOCENE (most new)—term invented by Sir Charles Lyell, famous English geologist, who divided the Pliocene into Newer and Older and gave this name to the Newer.

CENOZOIC (pertaining to recent life)—name invented by John Phillips in 1840 or 1841 to include Tertiary and Quaternary.

Classification

THE SCIENTIFIC TERMINOLOGY BY WHICH PLANTS AND animals are classified was first established in the eighteenth century by the Swedish botanist Carl von Linné, who called himself Carolus Linnaeus, using Latin because it was the closest to a universal language. Linnaeus grouped plants and other living things into genera, and later scientists have followed his method. Nowadays, however, many names are derived from Greek, and may be taken from any language, or even just made up. However, following the system laid down by Linnaeus, they are always treated as if they were Latin words.

To the uninitiated, the whole system of nomenclature seems exceedingly complex. However (although complications have been added by the fact that with the growth of knowledge an enormous number of species have been added), it is really simple enough once a person has learned the key. And he will want to do that if he is going to read much about fossils.

The name of any group, from the kingdom down

through the subfamily, is a single capitalized word, *not* italicized. The name of the genus is *always* italicized *and* capitalized; that of the species is italicized but *not* capitalized. Frequently the name of the person who first identified the genus or species is appended and capitalized, but in upright type, and occasionally the date is added. It goes thus: Linnaeus set up a genus *Sciurus* to contain all squirrels and chipmunks, but it became evident that it held too much, and other genera were invented. A chipmunk genus *Tamias* is *Tamias* Illiger 1811, as having been set up by Illiger in that year. One species is *Tamias striatus* (often shortened to *T. striatus*). Or it may be *T. striatus* (Linnaeus), with parentheses around "Linnaeus" to indicate that changes have been made since Linnaeus assigned chipmunks as well as squirrels to the genus *Sciurus*, which is now a family, including all the *Sciurus*-like animals. Sometimes the date, 1758, is added, either inside or after the parentheses in which Linnaeus' name appears, to show when he made the original assignment.

Instead of appending the name of the person who first identified the species (a method that may sometimes appear conceited), discoverers of new fossil types have a habit of naming a species in honor of someone else—usually an important figure in the field. In that instance the species name becomes a Latinized, noncapitalized version of the name, as *copei* (for Cope) or *leidyi* (for Leidy).

Usually the reader will find that identifications consist only of the genus and species, as *Homo sapiens*.

CLASSIFICATION
The Systematic Hierarchy *

Kingdom—Animalia

Phylum—Chordata

Subphylum—Vertebrata

Superclass—Tetrapoda

Class—Mammalia

Subclass—Theria

Infraclass—Eutheria

Order—Primates

Suborder—Anthropoidea

Superfamily—Hominoidea

Family—Hominidae

Subfamily—Homininae

Genus—*Homo*

Subgenus—*Homo* (*Homo*)

Species—*Homo sapiens*

Subspecies—*Homo sapiens sapiens*

* Example of classification from *Life: An Introduction to Biology,* by G. G. Simpson, C. S. Pittendrigh, and L. H. Tiffany (New York, Harcourt, 1957).

HUNTING FOR
FOSSILS

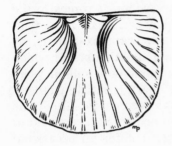 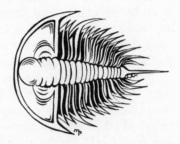

CHAPTER I

What Fossils Are All About

HOW OLD IS THE EARTH?
WHEN DID LIFE BEGIN?
HOW DID LIFE DEVELOP?

THE PERSON WHO LETS HIMSELF BECOME FASCINATED BY fossils will certainly want to know the answers to these questions. There will be many others, but these come, perhaps, first of all.

As of 1974, the age of the earth is thought to be somewhere between 4 and 5 billion years. As for the beginning of life—nobody knows when it occurred except that it was at some time after the earth had become the right temperature to support it, sometime more than 3 billion years ago. On the third question—all scientists agree that life developed from the simple to the complex, with unsuccessful experiments dying out along the way, and many apparently successful

Illustration above shows a Brachiopod and a Trilobite.

ones being discontinued. As we know it now, the progress was from the simplest of one-celled creatures to man himself.

What does this have to do with fossils?

Obviously the age of the earth could not have been established on the basis of nothing but those remains of once-living plants and animals. And when it comes to the question of the beginning of life, they can do no more than help because, except for a very few rare examples, the earliest fossils we know came from the Cambrian, which is now estimated to have opened about 600 million years ago. With the exception of extraordinary isolated instances, only the hard parts of any animal become fossilized; the soft-bodied living things that swam or floated or crawled in the water left almost no records, except for an occasional track or impression. When it comes to the *development* of life, however, the fossil record is the dictionary, encyclopedia, and bible of the paleontologist. Without that record we should have had nothing but academic guesswork about how the chain of development progressed from a protozoan to that thinking animal known as man.

The story of life is written in its fossils.

But just exactly what is a fossil?

The word itself comes from the Latin *fossilis*, meaning "dug up." And today the geologist or paleontologist will tell you that a fossil is *the remains or traces of any organism preserved in the rocks of the earth's crust.* One must note, however, that when the geologist says "rock" he doesn't necessarily mean "stone." From his point of view rock is any deposit that makes up the outer portion of the globe, which he calls the crust. When he says "rock" he may mean stone, sand, silt, shale, gravel, coal, clay, tar, or even ice or the permafrost (permanently frozen ground) of Siberia and other places in the far north. A fossil may, therefore, be anything from the print of a leaf to the bones of a man, and be found almost anywhere.

Sometimes fossils are buried deep in the rock, sometimes lying in plain sight; but it was thousands of years after man became *Homo sapiens* that he began to recognize them for what they are.

When the physical sciences were in their infancy certain philosophers and observers not only saw such strange objects but also tried to figure out some reason for their existence, and through the centuries individuals now and then wrote down their conclusions. All the same, it was the eighteenth century before scientists began to formulate theories that led toward what we now believe, and the middle of the nineteenth before Charles Darwin developed an overall theory of evolution and presented it to the general public in terms the common man could understand. Even then it was difficult for most persons to accept a supposition that one must think in terms of millions of years rather than a few thousand.

In mid-seventeenth century the Irishman James Ussher, archbishop of Armagh, had worked on the "begat"s and other Biblical data, to conclude that the earth had been created in the year 4004 B.C., "upon the entrance of the night preceding the twenty third day of Octob." Thereafter, for a long time, the date was printed in the margin of the Authorized Version of the Bible. It took courage indeed for anyone to suggest that the story of creation could not be accepted with entire literalness; and when scientists did begin to question it, and to imply that man was only another animal, the popular reaction (which hasn't entirely subsided yet) was what Loren Eiseley calls "the sick revulsion of the wounded human ego."

By the time of Darwin natural scientists had begun to upset the so-called cataclysmic theory, which tried to admit scientific evidence without denying Christian theology. According to that theory there had been a number of earlier Creations, but in each instance God decided He didn't like the results, destroyed them by some cataclysm, and started over again. On that basis, if a person came across the remains of some monstrous creature, he could tell himself that this was only a model the Creator had tried out and rejected. Or (in that version of science fiction) he could even surmise that it had come from some other part of the universe.

Geology did not begin to be much of a science until the beginning of the nineteenth century, when William ("Strata") Smith figured out a theory to explain the meaning of the layers of sediment he saw in England. Smith established a system on which others could progress, and by the time Darwin made his epochal voyage on the *Beagle* he was able to take along with him Charles (later Sir Charles) Lyell's *Principles of Geology* which denied cataclysms and propounded what is known as Uniformism, or Uniformitarianism (that the present is the key to the past—which is to say that geologic changes in the earlier ages came about in the same way they occur at present). Darwin could correlate these principles with what he himself observed, and try to relate to geologic periods the fossils he was assiduously collecting on his trip around the world.

Now, a century after Darwin, through the efforts of thousands of dedicated scientists (frequently assisted by amateurs), enough fossils have been found and identified to make it possible to read in them the basic story of life. The record is not complete, and never will be, for only a small proportion of living things ever become fossilized, and only a tiny percentage of those fossils has been or is likely to be found.

Though, generally speaking, the earliest fossils are from the Cambrian period, in 1962 Dr. Elso S. Barghoorn (professor of botany in Harvard's department of biology, and curator of the paleobotanical collections in the university's Botanical Museum) found Proterozoic fossils of 2-billion-year-old primitive blue-green algae in the Gunflint chert of the Canadian Shield of Ontario.

That rocked the geological world. And *then,* in February 1965, in the eastern Transvaal, near Daylight Mine, near Barberton, South Africa, he found fossil microorganisms that turned out to be *three* billion years old! In an article in *Science* magazine (May 6, 1966) he told of the tests he had made, and summed up the significance of his discoveries thus: "The occurrence of bacterium-like microfossils, presumably biogenic organic filaments, and complex biologically important hydrocarbons in the Early Precambrian Fig Tree chert establishes that organisms were in existence at least 3.1 billion years ago, and indicates that life on earth must have originated during the preceding 30 percent of the earth's history."

In this instance, the age given by other studies was confirmed by the rubidium-strontium whole-rock method—one of several ways of trying to establish how old a fossil is. For determining age up to possibly 50,000 years, carbon-14 is the customary method. For much older objects, there is, among others, the potassium-argon test, by which age was predicated for such things as the bones of the man-creature *Zinjanthropus*, found in the Olduvai Gorge in Africa by the Leakeys, and most recently dated as 1.850 million years old (see p. 19). These so-called atomic clocks depend on the decay of radioactive materials in the substance being tested.

Such microfossils as Dr. Barghoorn found are so tiny, and so hard to collect (not to speak of examining), that the amateur may certainly assume none will ever come *his* way. The earliest fossils he is likely to find are of those segmented arthropods known as trilobites, and of a type of bivalve called a brachiopod. Both these creatures existed in Precambrian times, but are seldom found in earlier than Cambrian sediments. However, if the fossil hunter finds trilobites or brachiopods, he must by no means assume that they belong to a time as long ago as the Cambrian, for trilobites kept on wriggling around for 300 million years, and brachiopods still thrive in our seas. To ascertain the age of a specimen, the simplest procedure is to compare it to types known to have existed at given periods. Perhaps it is fortunate that when a species becomes extinct it never reappears.

For many reasons, determining the age of a deposit in which he is digging isn't always easy for the person who doesn't know a great deal about geology. Fortunately, as Smith noted, there are sometimes index fossils. An index fossil is a form that appears *only* in rock of the same geologic age, because it lived in only one comparatively small portion of time and became very prolific. If a person finds the shell *Mac-*

lurites magnus, for example, he suspects immediately that the rock around about is Ordovician. If he comes on the coral *Pachyphyllum* he can be sure that the rocks are of the late Devonian. Some types of those abundant, astonishingly varied, and almost always very tiny fossils, the Foraminifera (foraminifers, forams, or "oil bugs") are found only in certain sediments, and are small enough to be caught up in the experimental cores that an oil geologist brings to the surface in an attempt to discover what formations he has penetrated in his drilling. The kind of foram he finds in a core helps to tell him whether to continue to drill or to move on. Reading up on index fossils may be good leisure work for the aspiring amateur fossil hunter whether his interests are practical or theoretical.

There is more and more experimental research on the origin of life, especially since we entered the age of extra-terrestrial space exploration, and that research is of great moment to the paleontologists. It used to be stated simply that "life began in the sea." Now, taking into account knowledge about the nucleic acids (DNA and RNA) and what they have divulged concerning genetics, and relating this knowledge to conclusions about the place oxygen has played in the development of life, Lloyd V. Berkner and Lauriston C. Marshall in a 1966 article present a theory that life evolved with explosive suddenness as soon as the necessary fuel became available in usable form. They say that the first one-celled organisms might have originated "on the bottoms of pools, ponds, or shallow lakes, or shallow protected seas fed perhaps by hot springs from thermal sources rich in nutrient chemicals" and that "this model of primitive ecology calls for pool depths sufficient to absorb the deadly ultraviolet but not so deep as to cut off too much of the visible light." Such a genesis, they find, agrees with what is indicated by the fossil record.

While, in the ancient waters, life was developing with infinite slowness from the first one-celled creature to increasingly more elaborate plant and animal forms, the land was bare. There were vast new shallow seas, however, in which life could develop better than before.

Sea plants became varied during the Ordovician, and there were such invertebrates as corals, starfish, many kinds of "shells," and the eurypterids—sea scorpions that could be as much as twelve feet long. Before the next period, the Silurian, was over, the first fishlike vertebrates had appeared. Here were the earliest obviously vertebrate ancestors of man.

Early Fish

Berkner and Marshall believe their research supports the theory that the first land animals appeared at about the same time as the plants—160 million years or so after multicelled life first appeared in the water, which was, itself, about 2.5 billion years after the one-celled organisms appeared. As aquatic plants stuck their heads above water, it seems evident, these men say, that spores were blown onto the land, "and then plants from those spores on the land provided a means of sustenance for animals that could then evolve ashore, finding there a physiological advantage over life in the water."

Just how life came ashore is still something for the specialists to argue. It seems certain, however, that any living thing moving out of the water faced at least these two basic problems—how to establish a satisfactory residence, and how to get enough oxygen to keep going. The progress of land plants was surely from very simple forms that were only slightly dependent on the surrounding atmosphere.

The earliest land plants so far found as fossils are related to the seaweeds of shallow seas and probably simply spread lichenlike films over the rocks. And then came psilopsids, which had no real roots and put forth only tiny leaves. Very soon, as geologic time goes, the land was sustaining plants that had developed vascular tissues, which strengthened them so that they could grow very tall.

Progress was toward sexual reproduction, which is as important for evolution in plants as in animals. A creature then has *two* parents, and inherits from both of them, thus making possible all sorts of combinations.

Among the animal pioneers onto the land was a fringe- or lobe-finned fish, a crossopterygian, which possessed unusually sturdy fins, and which had already developed (as well as gills) a swim-or-air bladder, which it was able to adapt into an air-breathing device. The fins were as important as the breathing apparatus, because they contained bones that made them helpfully rigid. *Osteolepis*, one of the fringe-fins, was especially important because his fins were so strong and stubby that he could bumble across land on them if need arose. When there was a drought and the patch of water in which he was living dried up, with luck he could make his way to a wetter place.

Eventually fins developed into legs, complete with feet and toes, and the most adaptable among these fish became amphibians, which could exist and move on land as well

Amphibian

as in water. In the process many types evolved, some of which still looked much like fishes, and some of which grew to a great size. The most successful branch was that of the labyrinthodonts, which in Triassic times adapted themselves to all manner of conditions. Strange to say (and no one knows why) though these creatures lived at least part of the time on land, many of their descendants forsook the land entirely and went back into the sea. Other branches developed into terrestrial quadrupeds.

Comparatively few fossil amphibians of any kind have been found, though some have come from late Devonian sediments. But the halfway creatures between amphibians and reptiles are even rarer. As usually happens in the evolutionary record, there was a good deal of overlapping, with forms we can call reptiles emerging even while amphibians were at their height. The emerging forms had stronger legs, and skin better adapted to life out of the water; they laid eggs that would hatch on land, bringing forth young that never needed any water at all, except to drink.

The first known of these halfway creatures—possibly the earliest to lay eggs with shells—is the Permian *Seymouria*, so-called because it was found near Seymour, Texas. Neither thoroughly amphibian nor yet quite reptile, it has been a headache to classify. One of the first *true* reptiles —famous for many years—was found in Pennsylvanian sediments near Linton, Ohio. More recently, others have been found near Linton, and parts of a dozen individuals have come from near Garnett, Kansas.

By the time those early reptiles had lived and died, land vegetation was not only varied but most luxuriant, falling into the swamps year after year, there to be acted on by bacteria, and at last becoming coal, which is often full of fascinating plant fossils.

From the Carboniferous rocks have come fossils of an incredible number of living things—both plant and animal. Moving among the vegetation were primitive spiders, the first true scorpions, several hundred kinds of dragonflies (some of them enormous), and more than eight hundred species of cockroaches.

When the Permian arrived, reptiles were already beginning to come into their own, and thereafter they had everything their own way during the whole Mesozoic era. Some
of the Cretaceous gentry were certainly the most vicious
animals that ever walked the earth. On the other hand,
though the name "dinosaur," given to these strange creatures
in 1842 by Sir Richard Owen, famous British paleontologist,
means "terrible reptile," some of these reptiles were no bigger
than chickens, and a goodly proportion wouldn't have eaten
meat if it had been offered to them.

Stegosaurus

Basically, dinosaurs are divided into two types: the
saurischians (with three-pronged pelvis) and the ornithischians (with four-pronged, called "birdlike," though they
look no more like birds than their cousins do). Saurischians
divide into theropods, those that walked on their hind legs
(like *Tyrannosaurus* and *Allosaurus*), which were carnivorous; and sauropods, those that walked on all fours (like the
brontosaurs), which were herbivorous. In general, the carnivores had bigger brain cases than the plant eaters did; but

the herbivorous types couldn't have been so desperately stupid, for they managed to survive for 100 million years or so. The ornithischians make things somewhat confusing because, though all of them seem to have been herbivorous, some walked on four feet and some on two. It is easy to see why the subject of fossil reptiles is sufficiently complex to demand a lifetime of study.

Moreover, though so many types have been known for many years, the story is added to every now and then. The scientific world gasped in astonishment and applauded in delight when Roy Chapman Andrews and his group from the American Museum of Natural History found dinosaur eggs along with other fossils in the Gobi desert in the 1920s. Now, in three summers—1963, 1964, and 1965—Polish-Mongolian expeditions into the Gobi have dug up some thirty-five tons of bones, which have included, among other wonders, the most nearly complete dinosaur skeletons ever discovered. There were eleven complete or almost complete dinosaurs, one of which (a carnivore, perhaps of a new family) had forelimbs more than twice as long as those of *Tyrannosaurus;* another, an herbivorous sauropod, not unlike a brontosaur, was sixty-five feet long.

Incredibly strange modifications came about in dinosaur forms between the Permian and the end of the Cretaceous. There were types with huge heads and short tails, tiny heads and long tails, paddles like fins, and webbed feet, and even one that wore a huge fan along its spine. Duckbills had crests in various odd shapes and sizes, including one that looked like a snorkle but was probably only part of the creature's smelling apparatus. One type had a thick mass of bone on top of its ugly head. Triceratops wore three horns and had a huge protective frill above the back of the neck. The ankylosaurs had plate armor, and sometimes spikes on their tails.

As might be expected, the herbivores such as the one known as *Brontosaurus*, which grew to a length of as much as ninety feet and had a weight of between thirty and forty tons, spent most of their lives floundering around in the swamps, whereas the carnivores (like the somewhat smaller but very unpleasant *Tyrannosaurus*) dashed about wherever there might be prey to be devoured.

Before the day of the dinosaurs was over, certain varieties were modified. Some spent most of their lives in trees. And a few went into the air to become forerunners of the birds, which are really nothing but reptiles with special

Tyrannosaurus

scales called feathers. And then, by the end of the Cretaceous, the majority of the Mesozoic reptiles, both large and small, including more than half of the major groups then in existence, had vanished utterly. By the time the Cenozoic really got into its rhythm, the only reptiles left on the ground were snakes, lizards, turtles, and crocodiles.

Why the dinosaurs disappeared in such fashion has always been one of the great mysteries of paleontology, and innumerable theories have been propounded to account for it. At the present time, authorities seem to believe that it may well have been a combination of several factors. One of

these may have been the strong environmental change—
from an even climate to marked extremes in both temperature and rainfall, especially in all middle and high latitudes
—that took place at the end of the Cretaceous. This change
was made worse by the fact that mountains were building all
over the globe. Because reptiles have what we call cold
blood and are dependent on outside warmth, dinosaurs must
have had great difficulty in maintaining enough body heat to
keep going. This would perhaps affect the smaller types first,
so that the big carnivores could leap on the logy small creatures and polish them off, until that source of food was
exhausted and they themselves began to starve. In addition,
they themselves could eventually have become so lackadaisi-
cal that they lost their initiative. There may well have been
fewer swamps and less plant life in general; but even if there
were plenty of plants around, the herbivores could have died
because they were too torpid even to eat enough.

Whatever happened took some 100 million years, and
undoubtedly conditions were much more unpleasant in some
regions than in others—one place too cold, another too hot.
It is known that too much heat can make reptiles temporarily
sterile, and if this happened at significant periods it would
certainly have affected the continuation of the race. Undoubtedly the dinosaurs moved around to take advantage of
the most hospitable places, but the game of survival was
going against them.

There were also biological changes in the environment.
Some of these resulted in the emergence of those strange
new creatures, the mammals, which originally were insect
eaters, but developed new dietary habits that put them into
competition with the hard-pressed dinosaurs. Their growth
may have been the strategic move that led to check-
mate.

The matter of climate is one that fascinates all paleontologists, because, of course, climatic conditions had a fundamental influence on what kind of living things existed at any
given time, and perhaps had equally much to do with the
direction in which those living things evolved. There were
warm, mild climates during the Ordovician, when the first

true vertebrates began to develop in the seas. During the Devonian, when amphibians had begun to lumber around the lakes and ponds, and plants were established on land, there were alternate periods of heavy rainfall and aridity. In the Jurassic, climates were uniformly mild almost from pole to pole, and the same kinds of animal and plant life were found from one end of the earth to the other. In the Miocene, moderate seasonal changes created gloriously lush vegetation—with mighty forests, new kinds of grass on great rolling plains, and broad pastures where hordes of mammals grazed among the blossoms of the angiosperms. There was plentiful and beneficent rainfall over all for some 12 million years. And then in certain regions came the Pliocene drought when deserts came into being and forests shrank, so that some of the animal population changed its habits, and left fewer records for us.

Back in the seas of the Mesozoic, there were reptiles as monstrous looking as some of the dinosaurs. One of the most spectacular is the Jurassic (and Triassic) *Plesiosaurus*, with a short, thick, flat body and a long neck and tail. And there were the mosasaurs (actually early relatives of lizards and snakes), and *Ichthyosaurus*, the "fish lizard."

And mammals were coming along.

Of course, like other forms of life, mammals didn't suddenly appear in finished form out of their ancestral stock, any more than amphibians had done from fishes. Again there was a great deal of overlapping. The biological class known as Mammalia had begun to emerge long before the great reptiles disappeared. In fact, some mammals appeared as early as the first dinosaurs.

Up to very recently the earliest mammal known was a tiny shrewlike creature from the Jurassic of England, but new light may be thrown on the whole picture by finds made in the Gobi desert by the Polish-Mongolian expeditions, which found, in addition to dinosaurs, fossils of rodents, insectivores, and a very early placental mammal skull in an excellent state of preservation.

Search into the ancestry of mammals has led comparative anatomists to those (usually carnivorous) reptiles of the late Carboniferous and early Permian, the pelycosaurs—and their descendants.

Fossil teeth are always important. Even a trained paleontologist may have difficulty deciding whether a big leg bone belonged to a mastodon or a mammoth, but show him (or even an amateur) just a piece of a tooth of one of them, and he will identify it without a moment's hesitation.

Although man has only thirty- two teeth, the basic mammal set-up is for forty-four—incisors, canines, premolars, and molars, acquired in two sets. Mesozoic reptiles varied as much in their jaws and teeth as they did in their sizes. *Tyrannosaurus* and his ilk had fangs that moved in a scissorlike motion. One beaked dinosaur had a jaw that worked like a nutcracker, with a hinge below the tooth sockets. An aquatic variety had several overlapping rows of rather small lozenge-shaped teeth—as many as two thousand—which were replaced as they wore down. In most reptiles, all teeth were more or less alike, but pelycosaurs began to change the pattern, and it kept changing.

The most significant descendants of the pelycosaurs in the evolutionary line appear to have been the theriodonts, which really branched out to develop tooth patterns and other characteristics that led straight toward "mammalhood." They had small front teeth, daggerlike weapons next along the jaw, and large, broad back teeth—all very much as mammals do. Although this pattern was not seized on immediately, it became an acceptable one for later development.

The theriodonts and some of their relatives also changed their vertebrae, shoulder blades, legs, feet, and neck. What happened in the neck was very important because it consisted of the development of a double-ball joint connecting the head and spine, instead of the single condyle at the base of the skull, which was characteristic of the reptiles. The new joint permitted the theriodonts to move their heads as we do ours. Moreover, in addition to all this, by the time mammals were fully developed, they had acquired an internal thermostat (lacking in the reptiles), which man finds very convenient.

Both pelycosaurs and theriodonts were carnivorous, and we might as well accept the fact right here that every single step in the evolution of mammals has been along the line of predatory flesh-eaters. This, alas, may help to support the distressing contention of some ethologists that aggression is one of the basic instincts in man.

The modifications that little by little created mammals out of reptiles took something like 200 million years, during which various changes kept moving them a little farther along the route. The Eocene is known as the Age of Mammals; and by the time that epoch came along, many forms had already died out, originally small ones had grown to immense sizes and fantastic shapes, and certain ones— already large—were becoming larger still. Wherever there were no land connections, distinctive forms evolved on the various continents.

A great deal is known about the Eocene, and one of the reasons for that lies in what happened in the Geisel valley, Germany.

Once in a while there is some sort of geologic miracle, and zoological and botanical remains are preserved in a state of almost unbelievable perfection. Such a miracle occurred in the Geisel valley, near Leipzig. In a deposit that came to light in the 1920s, there was almost every type of life that flourished in the Eocene. Not only bones and exo-skeletons were found, as is customary, but soft parts. Frogs retained their brains, spinal cords, and skin; fish and mammals still had muscles and cartilaginous tissue; birds had feathers and bits of skin; plants retained their chlorophyll. There were even stomach contents, and microscopes revealed such amazing details as the minute structure of leaves, scales, and feathers. In certain instances, beetles had even kept the color of their carapaces.

The record in our own country seems nowhere to be so detailed, but it has provided enormous numbers of familiar creatures, and some that defy belief.

Nobody is sure whether the horse appeared first on this

continent or in Europe, because the same kind of early fossil has been found in both places—named *Hyracotherium* in Europe, and *Eohippus* here. In any event, *Eohippus* survived here to the end of the Eocene, and his descendants continued into the Pleistocene, gradually reducing three toes into one, and finally becoming *Equus*, the modern horse. Vast herds of wild horses ran all over this country, but vanished during the late Pleistocene, after which horses were seen here no more until the Spaniards brought them back in. This is another of those puzzling mysteries.

According to some authorities, the most ancient ancestor of the camel sprang to life on our own continent; others think he or one of his early descendants reached here as an immigrant. In any event, it is known that the family had a representative in North America at least as early as the Eocene, that it developed here through many stages leading to the modern camel, and that the Pliocene form went from here to South America and Asia during that epoch. Thereafter, the camel flourished in other parts of the world and disappeared from our land at some time during the Recent.

That's strange enough, but it seems even more astonishing that during the Oligocene true rhinoceroses roamed our western plains along with other huge, nightmarish creatures, all of which became extinct.

The Oligocene has given up an extraordinary number of kinds of fantastic monsters, but the Pleistocene also had quite a few. There were then lions, wolves seven feet long, saber-toothed cats, mammoths, mastodons, huge ground sloths, and hundreds of other kinds, some large, some small. Most of them were gone before the Pleistocene was over, but a few lingered on into the Recent, and occasionally left their bones along with those of man. Some of the Pleistocene animals we still see today, and we have especially complete knowledge of certain extinct types.

Another kind of miracle took place sometimes in the Pleistocene, with the preservation of animals in the permafrost. The most famous of these animals is known as the Beresovka Mammoth. It has been written of by various authors, and versions vary slightly, but the story seems to have gone somewhat like this:

In August 1900, a Russian hunter was following a deer on the Beresovka River (a tributary of the Kolyma) about sixty miles from the Arctic Circle, when he saw the head of a mammoth sticking out of the ground. The rest of the body was buried. He chopped off a tusk and sold it to a Cossack, who reported the matter to the governor of Yakutsk. The governor sent word to the Russian Academy of Sciences in St. Petersburg, and in the spring of 1901 the academy sent out an expedition led by Otto Herz, curator of the academy museum. After a harrowing three-thousand-mile trip, taking months, by all sorts of uncomfortable conveyances, and the last stages on foot, the party reached the site.

One version says that by the time they got there the mammoth's head had been chewed off, and a terrible stench permeated the air; another says that the meat was still red, and in such good condition that the dogs ate some of it. In any event, the scientists analyzed the contents of the thirty-three-pound stomach, dismembered the carcass, and shipped it back to St. Petersburg, where it was reconstructed in the zoology museum of the Academy of Sciences. Pieces of the dry flesh and a portion of the woolly skin on which blood had clotted were given to the U.S. government and are in our National Museum.

As most zoologists reconstruct the incident, the animal had fallen into a crevasse, injuring itself badly, but had fought desperately to get out. Many thousands of years later, when it was found, its forelegs were still flexed and clutching at the sides of the crevasse. Though it must have struggled for a long time, eventually it gave in and fell back and soon afterward was covered and frozen. The pelvis, several ribs, and a shoulder blade were broken, and there was clotted blood on the chest, but food still lay in the jaws and stomach. The permafrost had preserved a moment in time.

When it comes to the fossils of man himself, most contemporary thinking seems to support the thesis that both he and the apes sprang from some common ancestor, possibly a creature not unlike *Proconsul*, whose skull and jaws were found in 1948 in the Olduvai Gorge of Tanganyika (now Tanzania) by Mary Leakey.

The story of the finding and recognizing of fossils that point the way to modern man began sometime more than a hundred years ago and has had its most dramatic chapters in Asia and Africa. The fossil record in Africa seems to comprise the earliest, and to be the most comprehensive and prolific—at least to date. It seems to have proved that, as Darwin predicated, the origin of man was on the African continent.

Mrs. Leakey and the late Dr. Louis S. B. Leakey, noted anthropologists who dug persistently in the Olduvai Gorge for decades, eventually discovered bones and artifacts that pushed back the date for the genesis of true man by hundreds of thousands of years. In 1959 they found the jaw and parts of the skull of a creature they named *Zinjanthropus,* now thought to be less significant than he appeared to be, because apparently he did not make the tools found near him, as was at first supposed. Then, in 1960 (announced early in 1964), not far from the burial place of *Zinjanthropus,* the Leakeys came on teeth and certain other bones of several individuals—a child, a young woman, an older woman—and parts of two other individuals of a pygmy species they called *Homo habilis.* Perhaps *Homo habilis* made the tools found in 1959; when Dr. Leakey announced the find he said that he felt sure this early man was a toolmaker and perhaps could talk, because he had a jaw that could have formed words.

The search, in its larger sense, is not only for the earliest ancestor of man, but for the common ancestor of both apes and men. More and more fossils important in each category keep on being unearthed in Africa.

In 1969, Richard Leakey, true son of his parents, found in the desert east of Lake Rudolph a skull, incredibly like that of *Homo sapiens.* Atomic and other tests have proved the skull to be at least 2.6 million years old.

Back not many years ago, for a brief time, it was thought that the North American continent might take its place along with Asia and Africa as having fostered a very,

very early type. Then the fossil record was discovered to have been falsely interpreted (see p. 188).

Before that, for a long time, it had been assumed that man came to this continent no earlier than ten thousand years ago, and the type when first found was named Folsom Man because his artifacts were unearthed near Folsom, New Mexico. Now it seems to have been proved that men came across the Bering Strait or a Siberian-Alaskan isthmus at least thirty thousand years ago, spreading from there into our Southwest. And at any moment someone *may* discover a cache of fossils and artifacts that will prove it was even earlier.

One of the most exciting things about fossils is that, when it is least expected, almost anyone may come across some relic of past life that turns an accepted theory topsy-turvy and creates a frenzy among paleontologists, anthropologists, and archaeologists as they try to develop a satisfying new one.

CHAPTER II

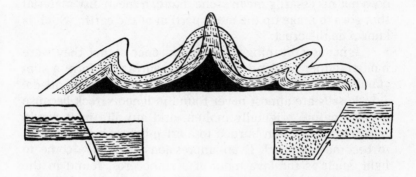

The Rock and How It Got There

WHETHER HE WANTS TO OR NOT, THE PERSON WHO becomes even the most amateur of paleontologists must learn at least a little about geology—the science that treats of the history of the earth as recorded in its rocks.

Not only must he become familiar with the divisions of the geologic time table (see p. xx) and understand what kinds of rock *may* contain fossils if conditions are right, he should know also what deposits were laid down in the area where he is searching and which of them are likely to be productive. In certain states, such as West Virginia, the problem will be simple because the greater part of the sediment is of the period known as Carboniferous, in which little is to be found except plant fossils. But when it comes to states like New Mexico or California, deposits are of such varied ages that almost any form of life *may* be lying there.

Illustration above shows Folds and Faults.

Whether it *is* there or not depends on a great many factors.

Basically, there are three types of rock: igneous, metamorphic, and sedimentary. And remember here that "rock" does not necessarily mean stone, but can mean any material that goes to make up the outer portion of the earth, which is known as the crust.

Igneous (meaning fiery) rocks, once so hot they were molten, either hardened beneath the surface to form a substance such as basalt, or flowed forth as lava to cool outside.

Fossils are almost never found in igneous rock because it is by nature originally molten, and any life in it would inevitably have been burned to a crisp before it could begin to become fossilized. Even impressions that have come to light, such as the lava mold of a rhinoceros, found in the state of Washington, at Blue Lake near the Grand Coulee Dam (see p. 280), are immense curiosities. The chances of some record being left are a little better if a volcano erupts so violently that the lava is blown out as tuff, or volcanic ash, which sometimes falls with deathly speed over a vast area, burying everything in its path—both plant and animal.

On a very small scale, that is what happened in Pompeii in A.D. 79. Despite the fact that the city was rediscovered a mere 1,700 years later—in geologic time, less than the flick of an eyelash—there were remains there that are considered fossils. In one villa buried under the ashes from Vesuvius, thirty-four skeletons were found. Water from above had solidified the fine white ash, so that it retained molds of the whole bodies, and in many cases it was possible to make casts of the bodies by filling those molds.

It was also in volcanic ash, in Africa, that anthropologists found the exceedingly controversial skeleton of some kind of man-creature in 1959.

Metamorphic rocks are those that have been changed over from other types by heat and pressure. They include quartzite, formed from sandstone; marble, from limestone or dolomite; schists, from sandy shales. Slate is metamorphic rock that has not been entirely changed, and granites and other rocks of lower density than the basalts are now considered to be the end products of a form of metamorphosis of very ancient volcanic outpourings through a process of chemical separation. The place to look for fossils is in sedimentary chalk, dolomite, shale, and sandstone and in combinations—known as conglomerates—that are made up of fine and coarse elements, as is the "puddingstone" seen near Boston, Massachusetts.

In sedimentary rocks, there is always the possibility of finding fossils—which, one must remember, are defined as "the remains or traces of any organism." On that basis, a fossil may be anything from the print of a leaf, or the path a worm made, or the footprint of a dinosaur, to the complete skeleton of a man. The actual bones of an animal remain sometimes in their exact shapes though the organic part of their composition has been largely replaced by minerals. On the other hand, a leaf may sometimes be found completely unmineralized, in a peat bog. A shell itself may sometimes have entirely disappeared, but left a cast of its internal form, or a mold of its outer one, composed of a substance such as limestone. Coprolites—indigestible portions of food an animal excreted—are also considered fossils.

Paleontologists are concerned chiefly with deposits created millions of years ago and laid down, by either water or wind, onto what was, at any given time, the surface of the globe.

Here may be a good place to digress for a moment to consider some of the theories about the make-up of the planet on which we live. The basic assumption nowadays is that there is a surface called the *crust,* averaging 20 to 30 miles in depth; inside it is the *mantle,* which goes down another 1,800 miles; and at the center, the *core,* of metal, where the pressure is tremendous. The crust, which is what most concerns the majority of us, is composed of the continental blocks and the oceans.

There has long been a theory that when land first formed there was one world continent, labeled Gondwana by its advocates, or, according to another school of thought, two huge continents (Gondwana and Laurasia), later pulled apart to make the land masses we know. Though that idea was pooh-poohed for a long time, it seems to be accepted now by almost everyone. And that thesis fits well into the widely accepted contemporary assumption that the globe, instead of starting hot and growing cooler, originated in the accumulation of small solid fragments, inhospitably cold, which gradually warmed up until the mass of them was capable of supporting life.

The reasoning by which scientists evolved this theory is most elaborate. It is based on the discovery that rocks making up the earth's interior are likely to contain radioactive elements; the knowledge that heat would have been generated by radioactive decay; and the hypothesis that possibly when the earth's core was cold it was not iron but rock in a metallic phase, which was not concentrated in the center but evenly distributed, and only gradually sank into its present position.

From this assumption (concerning which some persons of course have reservations, while others wish to add to and/ or subtract from it) specialists go on to suggest that here may have been the kind of evolution that would have caused the day to shorten bit by bit throughout geologic ages, as most specialists now believe it did (see p. 214).

The oldest surface rock on our earth is the heart of a continent—what is known as the shield—found, for example, in North America as the Laurentian Plateau. It is believed now that the Laurentian Plateau was formed in mid-Archean times, and that thereafter the heights were eroded, so that a half-billion years or so later, when the land rose again, the result was like new mountains.

That process of mountain building (called orogeny) went on for millions and millions of years, with the original mountains in several areas worn down (peneplained) and uplifted again. Erosion is still going on, of course, and activity deep in the earth (indicated by occasional earthquakes and eruptions) reminds us that mountain building also is continuing in its slow but inevitable fashion.

Geologists have names for the periods of mountain building, know a great deal about what happened and why, and what the results were for the entire continent. The Taconic Orogeny is the name for what went on in America during the Cambrian and Ordovician; the Acadian Orogeny, for the Devonian period; the Appalachian, for the Permian; the Nevadian, for the Jurassic; the Laramide, for the Cretaceous. Two great geosynclinal troughs were created very early, and thereafter the topographical aspects of the whole continent were constantly changing. Geosynclines are great elongated basins of sedimentation, formed along the margins of more stable regions, and are themselves capable of giving rise to mountain chains, as they have done all over the world. The whole process of orogeny springs from the subsiding of a geosyncline. That subsiding results in various elaborate movements both below and above the surface, some of which are still not yet entirely understood. By mid-Cambrian, the region of our Grand Canyon had not only risen but had been peneplained, and other mountains, known as the Killarneys, had thrust their peaks toward the sky in a line that reached more than seven hundred miles up into Ontario from Wisconsin and the Upper Peninsula of Michigan. The most important section of Cambrian rock in the world had been laid down under a sea where the Canadian Rockies now lie.

In those days, the edges of our continent were vastly different. On the east side, reaching for an unknown distance into the Atlantic, was what is now assumed to have been an island area that geologists call the Land of Appalachia. There, by mid-Cambrian, mountains had several times been uplifted and lowered. Off the west coast, beyond the mountain ranges, was a corresponding area, the Land of Cascadia, which frequently changed its topography and, in the Cambrian, was comparatively low except for occasional peaks known as monadnocks. From Louisiana and the southern part of Arkansas, the Land of Llanoria stretched southward into the Gulf of Mexico.

A large part of those fringe areas then above sea level is now a part of the continental shelf—that sloping underwater region that goes to a depth of something like six hundred feet and then plunges abruptly down the continental slope toward the abyss, which is now known to be 36,560 feet below sea level in the Marianas Trench in the Pacific.

The fact that much land now submerged as the continental shelf along our Atlantic coast was once dry land has been proved in dramatic fashion by fossils found recently all the way from Virginia to Cape Cod. Various kinds of Pleistocene remains have come up—some in the nets of trawlers, others in samplings of the sea bottom taken by the USGS and the Woods Hole Oceanographic Institute, as part of a five-year project devoted to looking for mineral deposits as well as remains of former land organisms. Late in 1966, a report mentioned especially the teeth of mastodons and mammoths found on the shelf—in one instance 40 miles off Cape Cod, where the water is 120 feet deep.

Paleontologists say that the teeth are often very well preserved, and have added to knowledge of the "Ice Age" on our continent. These teeth show that the mastodon that once lived along the fringe of the continent was identical with the forms that have been deduced from fossils found in many places, but that the mammoth must have been different from the kind heretofore known to have lived on our 48-state mainland, looking more like the frozen woolly mammoth of Alaska and Siberia.

The amateur fossil hunter may find something once in a while in shallow water, but most of his hunting will be done ashore.

Actually, of course, the sea has been his greatest friend —not only because it fostered the earlier forms of life and helped to set in motion a chain of living things that, so far at least, has culminated in man, but because it has swept back and forth across the land, again and again and again, always leaving potentially fossiliferous deposits.

In the Cambrian period, the seas invaded the two great north-south geosynclinal troughs, and in the Ordovician at least half of the continent was submerged, with an east-west seaway known now as the Ouachita Trough. It is said that in the greatest inundation of all, one could have sailed a boat from the Atlantic to the Pacific, and from the

Arctic to the Gulf. As the seas moved back and forth, later sediments were deposited on top of earlier ones, to form strata of what we call the geologic column. Sometimes they remained where they were deposited, sometimes they were swept away again. Or, during any given period, there may not have been any marine deposits because the sea didn't reach that area. For example, after, let's say, the Permian, there may be a gap of more than 220 million years, with nothing on top until we come to the Pleistocene.

It is easy to understand that because of the greater or lesser inundations, and because the land has risen and fallen so many times, in so many places, the antiquity of fossils found in any portion of the United States (or elsewhere) will vary astonishingly. For example, though there are Ordovician sediments in Alabama, the earliest at the surface in nearby Florida are Eocene (and only a bit of them). In addition, erosion almost inevitably complicates the matter even more.

Moreover, all over the globe, as the crust has intermittently shifted about, the layers of sediment have been moved also, so that sometimes their present position bears only the vaguest relationship to what obtained when they were originally laid down. Here and there the whole column has been tipped over on a slant; sometimes it may have been tipped completely upside down.

Basically, the two topographical changes that upset the level of any area are folds and faults. Pressures can cause a section to move upward, making a kind of loop, called a *fold*. But if the strata under pressure don't have enough room to curve, or are too rigid to bend, they will break, to create a *fault*. When the strata break, results may be very complex. For example, suppose there were three strata, originally lying on top of each other. The top one breaks, letting the second protrude at the surface. Later, the second layer breaks, letting the third one appear, and perhaps push up into a tall peak. If the thrust that produced the fault is exerted at a vertical angle, the result may be what is called an overthrust, in which the second layer is forced over onto the first, and the third onto the second, leaving the strata in reverse order. Or the strata may sideslip in opposite directions, in a process known as shearing.

There is a great variety of faults, but technically they are divided into two types: tension and pressure. The kind that breaks the loop of a fold is a pressure fault. In a tension fault, the force of a pull makes the earth's surface crack open, so that blocks (great or small) drop between the cracks. This is also known as block faulting and is the kind that occurred in the Tularosa valley, New Mexico. If blocks left reaching toward the sky (and adjacent to those that fell) are big enough, they are block mountains. Sometimes, when there is pressure *after* the tension, one block is squeezed up and that on the other side drops, so that the ends of the areas that were originally adjacent no longer meet, and the result looks as if someone had done a poor job of carpentry. When the area is eroded (after folding or faulting, or both), it is often like working out a jigsaw puzzle to figure how the various strata got where we find them.

At the beginning of the nineteenth century, the Englishman William Smith, called the founder of stratigraphic geology, and nicknamed "Strata," observed such phenomena, recognized the different characters of the earth layers, realized that certain fossils appeared only at certain levels, and saw how important they could be in identifying zones of sediment. In fact, he published a memoir entitled, in the longwinded manner of his time, "Strata Identified by Organized Fossils, Containing Prints on Coloured Paper of the Most Characteristic Specimens in Each Stratum." In another volume he described some seven hundred fossils, which he gave to the British Museum.

Though he was a keen observer, Strata Smith of course had no real idea of why the layers of sediment came to be arranged in the fashion in which he found them, or what the fossils in them could eventually mean to science.

Today, a geologist may spend his life trying to create a definitive picture of what happened in one small section of the geologic column. And many geologists are working all the time, with relentless tenacity, to solve old problems, to relate new material to what is already known, and to support shaky theories or find clues that will lead to new significant conclusions.

Some aspect of the geologic and paleontological record must be looked at anew, with disconcerting frequency. The change in dating of a fossil may necessitate a change in the date accepted for the deposit in which it was found, and thereby may upset some cherished belief or theory of the earth scientists.

In general, of course, the amateur will be digging in deposits concerning which there is no important question of age. But even then he will almost certainly consult some technical literature before he goes very far, and there are many geological terms with which he must familiarize himself.

Before anyone begins to read geological bulletins or guides he should know that he will be seeing a lot about what the scientists call *formations.* A formation is one unit in a series of stratified rocks, and itself is made up of an aggregation of layers, which are separated by surfaces known as bedding planes, along which the layers may be easily divided. Usually a formation has a geographical name, such as Green River, Bone Valley, Niobrara, Denver. It may be hundreds of feet thick, consisting of layers called *members,* which also have individual names. Then the members may be divided into *beds* (also named), or (if they are less than one centimeter thick) into *laminae.* If two or more adjacent formations have common features, they may be lumped together as a *group,* such as the Newark Group, formed in the Triassic period, running up the eastern part of our continent between the Carolinas and Nova Scotia.

One of the most confusing aspects of the formation picture is that certain formations run across or into several states. The Denver, for example, is met in Colorado, Iowa, Kansas, Nebraska, New Mexico, Texas, Utah, Wyoming, and the Dakotas. Some formations extend even farther.

To understand the intricacies of geological conditions, even in one locality, is usually far beyond the scope of the person who looks on paleontology as a hobby. And further complications are added by the fact that there are various reasons why a formation (or some of its members) very often does not go along in neatly stacked sections. Erosion may have shaved off certain layers before later ones were added, resulting in gaps known as unconformities or disconformities, according to the type of distortion.

And there are additional intricacies within these layers-upon-layers. In the larger sense, each bed or group of beds has typical organic remains, as Strata Smith discovered. By considering such key fossils, it is possible to judge the geologic age of the beds and also to correlate rocks in various parts of the world.

Ideally, one must remember, the so-called geologic column would consist of one layer after another, superimposed in order of age, with each of those layers known as a stratum. Unfortunately, however, the layers are not only frequently disturbed in their vertical continuity, but never continue indefinitely in any direction horizontally. The fossil hunter cannot expect that if he finds a nice fossiliferous bed of limestone he may go up the road a half mile and find the same limestone, and therefore the same group of fossils. The limestone up the road may be either higher or lower; and the original patch may have gradually faded out altogether and merged, on its own level, into sandstone or some other material, with completely different remains in it.

Sometimes there is an abrupt interruption of the horizontal continuity, making a rapid differentiation of fossils and a mystifying change in what is found. Some breaks of this kind are purely local; others extend over a wide area. Such horizontal changes create what are known as *facies*.

All beds, in addition to changing their facies, have to taper out somewhere, of course. Wherever the tapering occurs, it is caused partly by the fact that all deposits are shaped something like thin-edged pancakes of different sizes, which have been spread out and subsequently flattened from the top by the pressure of later deposits. Then, too, not only is each pancake a facies, but each in itself contains a number of smaller facies.

Moreover, suppose one of these pancakes was created by a lake bordered in different directions by a desert, a bog, a forest, and a prairie. Each of those environments would have contained different animals, all living at the same time. In the lake there would have been littoral, shallow-water, and deep-water animals; and entirely different kinds of animals would have lived around the mouth of any fresh-water stream running into it. Moreover, fresh-water streams may run into such a body of water as Lake Walker in Nevada, which itself is salt, and therefore salt-water and fresh-water animals may be there now in the same type of deposits. And the creatures that moved throughout the surface waters would have rained down on all these facies of the lake. Such a lake is somewhat like an ocean with its surrounding seas, though on a small scale.

Let us assume that as the water of our lake dried up, it did so gradually. Therefore, the desert encroached from one side, the forest perhaps from another (probably via the swamps, which would increase as the waters receded). The possibilities and combinations of possibilities are almost infinite, and each would have led to a different fauna and a different type of deposition. Nobody should be surprised at anything he finds anywhere, within the general limits of the stratum he is investigating.

An understanding of facies may help the amateur to comprehend why we may find marine shells in coal beds. They are there, of course, because salt water flowed over the bed at some time or times, and receded quickly, leaving a thin deposit of marine sediment, in which, naturally, there may well be marine fossils.

At the risk of sounding discouraging, one must admit that the names of deposits are themselves confusing. A section of Triassic rock in Connecticut may have one name; in adjacent Massachusetts, it may have quite another. Perhaps it is a good thing that, at first, the amateur fossil hunter is likely to confine his activities to one area, and doesn't care too much, anyhow, about what official name is given to the rock, as long as he has a chance of finding something exciting in it.

CHAPTER III

The Backboneless Ones

BECAUSE MAN HAS A BACKBONE, HE IS QUITE SURE THAT the development of a vertebrate skeleton was *the* truly significant process in all evolution, and that creatures belonging to the Chordata should be recognized automatically as of a higher order than those whose bodies function in some other fashion.

He may be right. But if adaptability and survival over long ages is any criterion, man is far surpassed by the cockroach, which began to scuttle around some 300 million years ago and is equally at home at this moment in a jungle or a New York apartment, without even having changed his appearance much, except in size, and sometimes the color of his jacket. Or if numbers count for anything, man should know that he is incalculably surpassed by the overwhelming multiplicity, taken as a whole, of those creatures who have

Illustration above is of a Crinoid.

managed very neatly without spines. Although there are great numbers of vertebrate animal bones in some places, the fossil hunter is immensely more likely to find remains of invertebrate ones. In fact, 99 per cent of all fossils are of something we loosely call a "shell," and invertebrates comprise twenty out of the twenty-one phyla into which scientists now arrange all animals.

Why their fossils are so abundant and so prevalent is obvious, once one stops to think about it. In the first place, the majority of invertebrates, except for arthropods, are aquatic animals—most of them marine. Under water, conditions for fossilization are much more favorable than they are under air (i.e., on land), where almost anything can happen to a carcass before "dirt" of some kind covers it, and where the material that does cover it is of a kind that will harden fairly rapidly. Water—especially sea water—tends to protect and preserve. And in addition, since the beginning of life there has been a great deal more sea than land.

Inasmuch as they make up twenty phyla, invertebrates naturally vary greatly in the structure and composition not only of the soft parts of their bodies but of the hard parts also. The integuments of insects, crustaceans, and so on are made of chitin—a horny and fairly sturdy substance, which does not dissolve quickly, so that integuments are much more likely to fossilize than the soft parts are. However, some of the coverings or supports are so fragile that even under the best conditions they get broken up and disappear as the softer tissues do.

The majority of invertebrates that have come down to us as fossils were protected by coverings containing carbonate of lime, occurring as either aragonite or calcite (or sometimes both together), in the form of shells. Aragonite shells are opaque, compact, and have a chalky appearance. However, though they are harder and heavier than those of calcite, they dissolve rather quickly. The calcite ones are translucent, with a porous interior, but despite their apparent greater delicacy, stand up much better.

Though one-celled animals such as Foraminifera and Radiolaria (nowadays usually called protists) do have hard shells, and have been preserved by the trillions, study of them constitutes a whole separate science, and often a life work. For purely practical reasons (including the fact that most of the one-celled animals are microscopic), the amateur fossil-hound had better ignore those creatures and concern himself with the more easily observed invertebrates that are known to have left fossils. These are Porifera (sponges), Coelenterata (corals, hydroids, jellyfishes, sea anemones, and allied forms), Bryozoa (moss animals), Chaetognatha (arrow worms), Brachiopoda (lampshells), Annelida (segmented worms), Echinodermata (crinoids, starfish, sea urchins, and so on), Mollusca (mollusks), and Arthropoda (arthropods—such as trilobites, crustaceans, horseshoe crabs, insects, and spiders). It goes without saying that these are divided into classes, orders, genera, and species, to constitute a filing system that will make the layman feel he has become involved with a computer.

These creatures usually appear in scientific publications under rather intimidating names, and sometimes there *are* no other names for them. But popular writers, and even some scientists, are often content to be less technical, and will unblushingly use a common word—if there is one. Even in textbooks, for example, creatures that belong to the phylum Brachiopoda will appear as brachiopods or (less frequently) as lampshells, and the Crinoidea as sea lilies.

Ignore, if you will, the fact that the phylum Porifera comprises four classes. But remember that there are now some 4,500 living species, and nobody knows how many extinct ones, and that sponges vary as greatly in their forms and the complexity of their structure as they do in size. They may be tubular, globular, cuplike, fan shaped, discoidal, vaselike, or in various other forms, each with some sort of skeleton. They live in colonies (in salt or fresh water), and nearly all of them are attached to some object that is fixed to the bottom. Types that have either siliceous or calcareous skeletons are known in their fossil manifestations; but in anything made up of spicules of silica, the spicules tend to scatter, so that siliceous sponges are very rare; and though the calcareous ones fossilize much more easily, the resultant

forms are lumps that look as if they might be almost anything, and are exceedingly hard to identify. The person who
hunts in an area where such remains have been found would
do well to take a look beforehand at some of them in a
museum.

Sponges are among our oldest fossils, and have persisted, certainly from the Cambrian, and probably from the
Archean of the Proterozoic, to our own time. In the scheme
of life, they are close to the one-celled animals and are in a
way only vast colonies of single cells.

The Coelenterata also were growing in the Precambrian, and are almost all marine, with some nine thousand
living species known, in three orders (all of which have
made fossils). Members of this phylum are radially symmetrical, and have only one internal cavity, which opens to
the exterior by the mouth. The body consists of outer and
inner layers of cells (ectoderm and endoderm), with a
gelatinous layer in between. Included among them are such
things as corals, sea plumes, and fresh-water jellyfishes
(Hydrozoa) and Scyphozoa, sometimes called the only "true"
jellyfishes.

Almost anyone who looks around may pick up fossil
coral, somewhere. And corals are so varied and so beautiful
that even after they have been weighed down by tons of
earth for millions of years, and perhaps battered about, to
boot, they still make wonderful specimens. Just as there are
whole coral reefs and even islands, terrestrial formations
sometimes contain strata composed entirely of corals. These
anthozoans are first known from the Cambrian, and are still
building their limy mountains in the sea today. They can be
dome shaped, or dish shaped, or look like trees, groups of
branches, honeycombs, or cornucopias; and the single animals of which colonies are made also come in a wide variety
of forms.

As with any other aspect of paleontology, classification
of corals has changed a good deal during the past few years,
and the amateur who wants to understand them, and con-
sults the books, will find himself faced by a bewildering
number of terms, and sometimes by conflicting statements.

One acceptable division is into (1) horn corals (the subclass Rugosa or wrinkled, which includes the tetracorals)—common first in the Paleozoic; (2) the reef-building hexacorals (sceleratinians—first known from the Middle Triassic, and still continuing; and (3) the colonial tabulates (the subclass Tabulata, generally making prisms, and including schizocorals, the sometimes honeycombed favosites, and other genera)—from late Ordovician to early Devonian. All sorts of forms, some of them with deviations from what would seem to be normally included, go under these headings.

Graptolites (Graptolithina—"written stones" because they look like pen or pencil marks) used to be placed among the Hydrozoa, but it has now been decided that they are not related to the coelenterates at all, but to the Pterobranchia, which in turn appear to be distantly connected to the Chordata. In any event, graptolites are found *only* in lower Paleozoic rocks, where they most often occur in black carbonaceous shales, and occasionally in sandstones and limestones. Two of the five orders (Dendroidea, which were late Cambrian to Mississippian; and Graptoloidea, Ordovician to Devonian) are especially significant as fossils. Because of their limited appearance on the stage of life, and because they are found in great abundance all over the world, graptolites are of incalculable help to the stratigraphic geologist. They are compound animals, of many shapes, but often look like a stem of grass with little cuplike structures along one or both sides. Each of these structures was apparently a separate animal, although all of them were connected by thin links of cellular material. Almost nothing is known of the make-up or function of these creatures as individuals; but as a group they appear to have been an unsuccessful "experiment," dropping out from the main line that finally made the grade as vertebrates.

The Bryozoa (moss animals, with about six hundred living species) have lived and still live in sea water, and all of them are colonial—that is to say, they always gather in an undifferentiated contiguity like that of a subway car at

rush hour; and individuals are equally anonymous. Most of
the individual animals are submicroscopic, but the colonies
may form large mats or filigree encrustations on other objects, such as seaweeds, shells, corals, or even the bottoms of
boats. Other colonies grow as masses of gelatinous material.
Bryozoans began to appear in the Ordovician, still persist,
and are comparatively common as fossils. The horny or limy
structures that housed the multitudinous individuals appear
as fossils in such forms as bushes or fans, or what are known
as "Archimedes' screws."

When the amateur fossil hunter picks up a shell, he
may recognize it as one of the brachiopods, or lampshells, if
it looks symmetrical when he lays it on its smaller valve.
Seen sidewise, it is lopsided. Some thirty thousand species
of fossil brachiopods have been identified, with the oldest
ones, so far, found in the Cambrian. Zoologists divide the
phylum into two classes, the Articulata and the Inarticulata.
Inarticulate shells are those in which nothing but muscle
makes a hinge between the two valves, which are composed
of chitin and calcium. In the articulated (much more common in all sediments except very early ones), there are teeth
along the hinge, to help hold the two shells together. Generally, brachiopods are only an inch or so in diameter, but
in Paleozoic times some of them grew to be as much as nine
inches.

One of the fossil hunter's most rewarding bits of luck is
to find a mass (or even one) of those peculiarly lovely fossils
known as crinoids or sea lilies—one of the major kinds of
echinoderms. Among the echinoderms (many of which are
covered by limy plates) are also the starfishes, sea cucumbers, sea urchins, brittle stars, and three extinct types: the
"bladderlike" cystoids (Cambrian to Devonian), the "bud-
like" blastoids (mid-Devonian to late Permian), and the
edrioasteroids (seated stars—Cambrian to Mississippian).
Technically, the phylum Echinodermata (spiny-skinned
animals) is divided into eight common classes, and for us
the most important of these animals are the crinoids, and the
echinoids and their relatives, because they have lasted long-

est and their fossils are easier to find. These have persisted ever since the Ordovician. Like the chordates, echinoderms develop an internal skeleton—but then they hide inside it!

A crinoid looks like a flower, with the calyx waving on a long stalk. These sea lilies may be found all over the world, growing even in the waters of the abyss. Though they started early, they are highly complex animals, which have always lived in colonies, where they build up beds of limestone. The calyx is made up of plates—very small in the oldest and most primitive, but later becoming larger and more complex, as other portions of the animal have done. Some five thousand species have been found as fossils.

Any fossil that looks something like a starfish may be classed as one of the Stelleroidea (starlike creatures), which now are divided into the asteroids, ophiuroids, and somasters. It is thought that all of these evolved from Cambrian crinoids that lost their stems and started to crawl on tube feet. We may find true starfishes (asteroids, which began in the Paleozoic and are rather rare), brittle stars (ophiuroids— first in the Ordovician, and less frequent in later sediments), some of the sea stars (somasters—early Ordovician to late Devonian), echinoids (sea urchins, which nowadays may be picked up alive or recently dead on many beaches, and as fossils from Devonian to Pleistocene), and sea cucumbers (holothuroids—found very rarely as fossils, and usually only as pieces, which are exceedingly small—beginning with the Mississippian).

In all animal life, few, if any, phyla as a whole have ever become extinct, though within a phylum portions of various groups have died away, while some have been replaced by others.

When we come to the Mollusca we find an absolutely bewildering number of creatures, most of which construct "shells." Nowadays, the phylum is divided into five major classes: (1) the "snails" or Gastropoda; (2) bivalves or Pelecypoda; (3) the Cephalopoda, a class that contains the octopuses, squids, cuttlefish, nautilus-like forms and ammonoids; (4) the tusk-shells or Scaphopoda; (5) the hinge-shelled Amphineura. To these used to be added a sixth—the incredibly ancient and basic Monoplacophora.

The majority of mollusks are marine, but countless millions of them live on land and countless more in fresh water. Some 150,000 living species are known, and there are several hundreds of thousands of fossilized forms. In size, the mollusks range from species that are almost microscopic to those such as the giant clam, which may weigh five hundred pounds. Certain mollusks came along early in the Paleozoic, and many species are useful as keys to the ages of strata. Modern shell books may be of help for identification—though not, of course, for geologic age. Such books, naturally, are not enough for the student of fossils. The published scientific records of when this, that or the other mollusk became extinct are not to be completely trusted, especially since the initiation of modern scientific deep-sea investigations. These have already brought up things supposed to have disappeared millions of years ago, and some forms with peculiarities that have upset established beliefs.

Whether or not we accept the Monoplacophora as a full class of the animal kingdom, the creatures the name was created for are close to the bottom of the molluscan family tree, from the point of view of evolution. One of these creatures is *Neopilina*, which, to the great astonishment of everyone concerned, was dredged up alive in the east Pacific by a Danish expedition in 1952, turning out to be a near relative of certain Silurian forms that were thought to have become extinct in the mid-Devonian! It really is not safe nowadays to say flatly that *anything* is extinct.

More than fifty thousand species are included in the Gastropoda—a class that typically have eyes, a mouth, tentacles, a broad foot, and a lid called an *operculum*, which can be used to close their single valve's opening. Limy shells protect most of these animals, which include the snails, turret shells, whelks, conchs, and similar forms that we pick up on our beaches. In addition to the seagoing varieties, there are numerous fresh-water gastropods, and many others (usually very "snailish" looking) that are terrestrial. Some gastropods are peculiarly nasty creatures, which use their sharp tongues to bore through other shells and commit a little cannibalism. The earliest known forms are from the Upper Cambrian.

Pelecypods (elsewhere in the world, lamellibranchs), some forms of which first appeared in the Ordovician, are the bivalved mollusks, such as clams, oysters, mussels, and scallops, and are very common as fossils. Most of them lived, and live, on the bottom, and certain types fasten themselves onto other objects. When the shell of a pelecypod opens, the animal may stick out a foot or a siphon. The fossil hunter will have a fascinating but frustrating time with reference books that describe these multitudinous animals, and in trying to identify them.

Not all of the various kinds of creatures that go into the class of Cephalopoda (some of which have been found first in the Lower Cambrian) have shells. Some have no shell at all; others have a "shell" on the inside. A cephalopod may be straight, curved, or coiled. The class, we should remember, is divided into octopuses, squids, cuttlefish, and such nautilus-like forms as nautiloids and ammonoids; and the over-all name means that they are "head-footed," as is displayed by the octopus, with its eight waving tentacles surrounding its head. The fossil hunter is perhaps most likely to find something of the nautiloid variety, which sometimes looks like a snail but is quite different in structure.

A nautiloid (horn-shell), which is likely to be coiled (at least somewhat) is also very different in its internal structure from an ammonite, though the two may look much alike from the outside—at least at first glance, and especially in the earlier forms. Ammonites appeared in the Silurian and became extinct at the end of the Cretaceous; *Nautilus* is the only living member of the Nautiloidea. Classification of this whole group was changed in 1925, so that the person trying to identify one of these shells from printed material must watch carefully or he will find himself in a state of utter confusion. In general, he may be able to tell the difference between a nautiloid and an ammonoid by looking at the surface "suture" lines marking the septa, or chambers, inside. Ammonites may be very large indeed, and their shells have curving suture lines that often make intricately complex patterns, in contrast to the more simple lines of the nautiloids. A nautiloid is a handsome object; but a well-preserved ammonite, polished and displaying all over it those "foliaceous" lines that look like incredibly delicate lace, is one of the most beautiful of all fossils. As might be expected, those lines became more and more complex during the evolution of the order, and thus provide a helpful hint as to the geologic age of the specimen.

Though the ink-squirting, torpedo-shaped squids called belemnites swam in Mississippian seas, they did not become plentiful until late Triassic time; then they flourished astonishingly in the Jurassic, diminished in the Cretaceous, and seem to have died out before or during the Eocene. A belemnite body contained an inside shell, called a phragmocone. Fossils are found along our eastern and Gulf coasts, from New Jersey to Texas, and thousands of forms have been identified, worldwide.

Scaphopods (tusk-shells) developed few genera (all marine) in Silurian times, but were much more prevalent in the Cenozoic, though they have always been rare as fossils.

And now for the arthropods, which have segmented bodies and paired limbs that are jointed. Trilobites, it will be recalled, were arthropods, which probably appeared before the Cambrian period; innumerable types were developed, but, for no reason that we know, the trilobites disappeared in the Permian. Their chitinous exoskeletons made their preservation readily possible, so that trilobite fossils are common in many parts of the country. So many have been found, and in such varieties, that their development may be traced from such simple forms as *Olenellus* of early Cambrian to the highly elaborate, spiny, possibly twenty-seven-inch-long, multiple-limbed *Teratapsis* of Middle Devonian. Some of them burrowed; some of them swam; and some of them appear to have drifted among the primitive sargasso weed of the ancient seas.

Trilobites constitute a vast subject in themselves. The basic classes alone are impressive enough: Onychophora—

wormlike creatures that seem to be offspring of annelid worms; Trilobita—trilobites; Crustacea—brine shrimps, water fleas, copepods, cirripedes (barnacles), sow bugs, prawns, lobsters, crabs, and the like; Arachnida—eurypterids (sea scorpions), horseshoe crabs, spiders, scorpions, daddy longlegs, mites, ticks, etc.; Chilopoda—centipedes (from at least as early as the Silurian); Diplopoda—millepedes (same age as centipedes); and Insecta—of which there are almost four times as many species as of all other living animals put together.

As to how ancient the Arachnida are: eurypterids range from the Ordovician to the Permian; horseshoe crabs from the upper Paleozoic; scorpions from the Silurian; Araneae (spiders) since the Permian. Daddy longlegs have been found in Pennsylvania deposits, but probably developed long before.

The insects, as one might expect, are extraordinarily difficult to disentangle—what with more than 900,000 known living species, divided into a great number of living orders. Typically, an insect has a head, thorax, and abdomen, one pair of antennae, three pairs of legs, and either one or two pairs of wings, though some are wingless. Textbooks mention the Apterygota, a group of very small, wingless insects, oldest of all, of which a few Devonian fossils are known, and which includes the silverfish, from the Triassic or possibly earlier. If one wants to be scientific, the class may be divided into the following orders: (1) Orthoptera (cockroaches—since upper Paleozoic, and grasshoppers—since Permian or Pennsylvania); (2) Isoptera (termites); (3) Dermoptera (earwigs); (4) Ephemerida (May flies—since the Permian); (5) Plecoptera (stone flies); (6) Odonata (dragonflies—since the Permian); (7) Heteroptera (true bugs very much like those we have today); (8) Homoptera (cicadas and aphids—from the Permian); (9) Mecoptera (scorpion flies); (10) Neuroptera (with folded wings, as the lacewings—since the Permian); (11) Tricoptera (caddis flies); (12) Coleoptera (beetles—since late Permian, but not abundant until the Mesozoic); (13) Lepidoptera (butterflies and moths—since the Eocene); (14) Diptera (ordinary flies, with two wings, but whose four-winged ancestors have been found in the Permian); (15) Hymenoptera (ants, bees, and wasps—most kinds from the Tertiary, but some from early Permian).

All insects are rare as fossils, and finds are of great interest to naturalists. Many of the Insecta have changed their forms little since the late Paleozoic; but, of course, identifying their fossils is complicated by the fact that insects indulge in polymorphism, whereby they look quite different at different stages in their existence.

Invertebrate paleontology is several sciences within itself. It includes not only the study of fossils of the bodies or parts of bodies of what once were actually "animals without backbones" but also the study of other types of fossil remains. One must take into account, for example, what are known as worm casts and trails. Such records of worms are apparently nearly all of the order Polychaeta, because those creatures lived in tubes of lime, chitinous material, or cemented sand which were sturdy enough to survive. Then, too, there were those small, mystifying, strangely shaped objects that look like teeth or jaws and are called conodonts. It is known, to be sure, that they became extinct during the Triassic, but no one is at all certain what they are or what function they performed when they were part of some living creature. And *there* is another problem for someone to solve.

Of course such a problem, posed by any individual aspect of paleontology, is only one of the thousands upon thousands presented by all branches of the science, which is itself a peculiarly brilliant product of man's curiosity, intelligence, and ingenuity.

CHAPTER IV

They Made Food, Shade, and Beauty

THE FIRST FOSSILIZED PLANTS TO ATTRACT WIDESPREAD
public attention were so-called petrified forests, which
aroused great wonder and excitement. Fossilized wood is
often exceedingly beautiful, and even in this day of marvels
a mighty tree frozen into rocklike permanence is still an awe-
inspiring phenomenon.

Although paleobotanical specimens are found much
less frequently than those of animal life, plant fossils have
been coming to light for centuries, in all sorts of sizes and
shapes, ranging from a gigantic *Sequoia* to microscopic pollen and spores, and from the three-dimensional solidity of a
branch to the mere shadow of a leaf. A searcher may come
across the remains of an entire plant, including woody parts,
leaves, and fruit; or of such members separated from their
fellows; or impressions left where any part or parts have
lain.

Illustration above shows Plant Forms.

44

In a rather special way, such remains sometimes act as peculiar kinds of index fossils. Late discoveries occasionally can upset supposedly established conclusions, but in general the periods in which various kinds of plants were thriving seem to have been firmly determined. Because that is so, the geologic age or physical character of a member of the animal kingdom can sometimes be estimated from the fossil plants among which it appears. Such a deduction is acceptable because scientists agree that if any creature follows a certain life pattern nowadays, the chances are that it lived in very similar fashion in the past.

A study of paleobotany is important for other reasons also. Both plant and animal life have always been, as they are now, dependent not only on each other but on climate. As more knowledge about fossil plant life is acquired it will almost certainly broaden our understanding of what climates were like in any part of the world at any given time. In general, we now know much more about plants that grew in the lowlands than we do about those of the uplands, because valleys, estuaries, and lake basins were better places to preserve fossils. Up to the present, in most parts of the world, only fragments have come from what were uplands when the plants were growing. Such a statement may seem inconsistent when we remember that one of the great sources for fossil plant life—the Florissant locality (see p. 107)—is today high in the Colorado mountains near Pikes Peak. But in Oligocene times, when those plants were alive, Florissant was a basin in an almost flat, sea-level countryside. The original Rockies had been peneplained and were not to rise again until the Pliocene.

Elaborate changes have been made in the classification of plants. Not so long ago four phyla—Thallophyta, Bryophyta, Pteridophyta, and Spermatophyta—supposedly covered all of them. Now Thallophyta (which was used for seaweeds, their allies, and the fungi) is split up into five phyla for the algae, and a sixth phylum for the fungi. Tracheophyta is used as a cover-all phylum for *everything* higher than the lowly Bryophyta (liverworts, hornworts, and mosses), and is split into four subphyla: Psilopsida, Lycopsida, Sphenopsida, and Pteropsida. All the way up, of course, there are a bewildering number of classes, genera, and species.

The person hunting fossils *might* find the remains of certain algae, and he might perhaps somewhat more easily come on liverworts and mosses. But his most likely finds will be among the Tracheophyta—the vascular plants.

As we all should know by this time, new finds may make any statement about fossils outdated. For generations it was thought that the *Metasequoia* was an extinct plant. And then someone found it blithely growing in China! But according to rather recent information, several varieties of vascular plants are known *only* from fossils. They include Psilophytales, which belong to the Psilopsida; Lepidondrales and Pleuromeiales of the Lycopsida; Hyaniales, Sphenophyllales, and Calamitales of the Sphenopsida; Coenopteridales of the Filicineae, or true ferns; Cordaitales, Pteridospermae, Cycadeoidales, and Caytoniales of the Gymnospermae. None of the angiosperms has yet become extinct.

Just as anyone who collects fossils of any kind finds that he must know something about geology, and inevitably gets involved in it more deeply as he goes along, so the person who becomes interested in plant fossils will scarcely be able to avoid at least a superficial consideration of the evolution of plant life, if he wants to identify what he has in his collection. In general, as with animal life, development is from the simple to the complex, and part of the problem becomes that of knowing what *is* simple and what complex.

One of the basic touchstones for giving any plant form its place in the evolutionary scheme is how it reproduces. Spores, for example, came before seeds and are less complex. Typically, a spore is a unicellular body—consisting of a nucleated mass of protoplasm surrounded by a cell wall—from which a new plant may grow. Actually, the matter is far from simple because in the various types of spore-bearing plants, spores are produced in different ways, and function differently. A seed is typical of the "higher" plants, and is usually taken to mean the matured ovule, surrounded by a protective covering, and containing a mass of food that will help it to develop into an individual similar to that from which it came. A seed comes into being when two different gametes, or sex cells, unite and grow into an embryo.

We often say that algae, lichens, and fungi are primitive forms. "Primitive" isn't a very good word for these plants, however, because in many instances they are far from primitive—actually highly complex in structure and behavior.

The bryophytes—Hepaticae (or liverworts), Anthocerotae (hornworts), and Musci (mosses)—are really lowly plants, although they produce chlorophyll and the most advanced develop structures superficially like roots, stems, and leaves. Fossil mosses are fairly abundant. (And here is a word of caution for the novice. There are some most beautiful forms of the mineral known as agate that look exactly like mosses preserved in a clear amorphous mass. These are most reasonably called moss-agate; but they are not fossils. They were caused by the formation of crystals of various materials such as manganese dioxide—in the manner that frost crystallizes on a windowpane—at the time when the main body of the agate was hardening from a jelly-like mass of silica.)

Abundant plant life grew in some parts of the Proterozoic seas, and calcareous algae from that era have been found in such places as the Grand Canyon. The earliest true land plants, however, probably were soft forms like algae or liverworts. It was not until well along in the Paleozoic era, however, that plants became firmly established on land and the major groups became differentiated. Among them were the tracheophytes, which grew vascular tissues.

Just when vascular land plants first appeared seemed to have been neatly settled way back in the early days of paleobotany. Because they had long been found in nothing earlier than authenticated Devonian sediments, scientists naturally ascribed their genesis to that period.

And then someone found vascular plant fossils in Australia in sediments that were considered to have been deposited during the Silurian—a period now said to have covered the 20 million years before the Devonian! The

Australian sediments had been identified as Silurian because they contained a type of graptolite (index fossils) that was ascribed to that division of geologic time. So everybody had to change his thinking on the subject, though some persons were not too happy about it.

Then, in 1962, a German paleobotanist, H. Jaeger, announced the results of investigations showing that the supposedly Silurian graptolites weren't Silurian at all, but Devonian! So everybody was right back where he started.

Dr. Harlan P. Banks of Cornell, in a 1966 report on Devonian plant fossils in New York state, in the Geogram published by the state's geological survey, explained that interest in Devonian flora was naturally great in the early days, when it was thought that vascular plants had appeared for the first time on the land surface during the Devonian period, and he reminded his readers that "several hypotheses concerning the early evolution of land plants have been predicated on the possibility that very simple vascular plants appeared first and then evolved into higher groups."

When the Australian discoveries seemed to show supposedly *earlier* plants more complex than later ones, that upset traditional theories about their evolution and made it necessary to try to develop new ones to account for the strange evidence.

"At the present time," Dr. Banks sums up the latest conclusions, "there is no widely accepted report of vascular plants older than beds that are transitional between Silurian and Devonian time and plants found in them are truly simple. Currently, therefore, we are back at the stage where we believe that simple land plants did [first] appear in the Devonian Period, and did evolve into more complex forms." *Exactly* when they came along won't be known, he says, until stratigraphers decide on a specific boundary between the two periods. But that's really an academic question, anyhow.

Anyone writing just before Dr. Jaeger's report came out must feel that his own timing was very bad. Something of how disconcerting that report must have been is indicated, for example, by the fact that, in a highly authoritative book published in 1962, Dr. Theodore Delevoryas, Yale paleo-botanist, considering the moot question of whether plants came from one ancestral group or from several (and decid-ing that it was probably from one—the Chlorophyta—a group of algae), was forced to recognize the now-discarded hypothesis based on the finds Down Under, and referred several times to the "Silurian" plants of Australia!

The simplest vascular plants, Dr. Delevoryas says, were "naked, green, dichotomously constructed plants having sporangia at the tips of some of the slender branches. . . . The naked axes were photosynthetic, and a slender, simple, conducting strand traversed the center of each axis. These plants would have no roots; anchoring and absorbing would have been effected by some of the branch systems." From that beginning could have risen more specialized groups.

In any event, before the Devonian had run a great part of its course, there were club mosses, horsetails, ferns, seed ferns, and other tracheophytes. Because the vascular tissues strengthened the plants, some of those early tracheophytes reached tremendous heights and were very sturdy.

In Devonian forests grew tall "trees" of *Eospermatop-tera,* which had fronds at the top, and were thus named because they were originally thought to be seed ferns, though actually they bore spores. They appeared along with several species of lycopods, which include among their modern de-scendants the ground pines and club mosses. One species had leaves about twelve inches long; another had wider leaves, which were overlapped like scales, and bore cones filled with spores, at the tips of the branches. In that Devonian time, the forests also contained *Callixylon,* with its tall, slender trunk, crown of branches, and pointed fleshy leaves. Below these trees was an undergrowth that included seed ferns, and some true ferns with fronds three feet long.

Then, at the end of the Devonian, came the scale tree, *Lepidodendron* (a name familiar to everyone who has looked at pictures of plant fossils), which might be one hundred feet tall, dividing high up into branches that bifurcated again and again, with a crown of forking branches at the top, and with its lance-shaped leaves arranged spirally on the smaller branches. It persisted into mid-Permian, so that its stems are among the most common fossils from the Carboniferous. Also, it bore cones, some of which carried two kinds of spores; and, in fact, coals of the Carboniferous are sometimes made up almost exclusively of compressed spores of *Lepidodendron* and *Sigillaria* (another tree that grew abundantly, not so tall but sturdier, and sometimes branching). Characteristic leaves of the period were made up of many leaflets placed opposite each other along a midrib or set in whorls at intervals along a stem.

From the Pennsylvanian period of the Carboniferous in this country come vast numbers of various kinds of plant fossils, which were engulfed in the great series of swamps in such places as those now called Pennsylvania, West Virginia, Illinois, and Kansas, where coal eventually formed. Alongside the scale trees grew the *Cordaites* (to which pines are distantly related), which carried heart-shaped seeds on stalks among the leaves; conifers, including *Walchia* (also called *Lebachia*), with short, narrow, pointed leaves; the *Calamites* (horsetails and their relatives, also known as scouring rushes); many seed ferns (pteridosperms), which of course bore seeds, and were ancestral to the conifers but closer to the cycads; and true ferns, which grew in forms like that of the modern royal fern, as trees, and reproduced by spores.

Although great physical changes occurred in the Permian, with continents rising and mountains being built, some of the conditions that had existed in the Carboniferous continued for millions of years, and the whole time is sometimes called the Permo-Carboniferous. The lush lowlands disappeared, and many of the primitive land plants with them, including the lycopod trees, and *Sphenophyllum* and many of the other seed ferns. Some of the true ferns vanished too, though the majority of them persisted. Forests of the time contained *Glossopteris* and its relatives, horsetails, club mosses, cycadophytes, and such conifers as *Walchia* and *Voltzia*. Carboniferous species of seed ferns began to be replaced by other types. Toward the end of the Paleozoic, plants with vascular tissues make up the greater part of the fossil record. Foliage begins to look more like what we think of as *real* leaves. Here, for example, are *Supaia compacta,* with all its leaflets fused into one, along the midrib, but deeply indented; *Cordaites,* bearing a long leaf with smooth edges; and *Glossopteris conspicuus,* having a smooth-edged leaf.

Desert conditions prevailed over a large part of North America at the beginning of the Mesozoic, and much of the plant life that had been abundant during the preceding periods died down. There were fewer algae, fungi, and liverworts, and the center of the stage was left to the tracheophytes—especially the newer forms. There were still a few scale trees; some horsetails, though smaller ones; and certain more modern types of Filicineae (true ferns), including the tree fern *Tempskya,* which is a typical Jurassic and Cretaceous fossil, familiar in all paleobotanical literature. The pteropsids (now a subphylum of the tracheophytes) were now completely dominant—to such an extent, in fact, that (because Cycadales is one of the forms) the Mesozoic is sometimes called the "Age of Cycads."

In the Triassic, two types of gymnosperms—pteridosperms and Cordaitales—still persisted from the Paleozoic, but in smaller numbers; and cycadophytes and conifers became more prevalent. It is known also that some angiosperms were growing during the Triassic, that they became more frequent in the Jurassic, and that they had achieved worldwide distribution by the end of the Cretaceous. Just what their origin was is still uncertain. Some contemporary paleobotanists think their ancestor may have been some fern that grew during the Paleozoic; but others find this inconclusive. They are all waiting for some lucky fossil find that may settle the matter.

The Jurassic was a time of widespread development in the lowlands of forests in which there grew large-sized ferns, modern-looking horsetails, conifers, and ginkgoes. Conditions were being made ready for modern plants, which were to take over at the beginning of the Cenozoic, though their distribution was different from that of today.

By Cretaceous time, in our West, there were a few

conifers and cycads, but 90 per cent of the trees were of the flowering types, such as maples, oaks, elms, poplars, tulip trees, magnolias, willows, and sassafras. Screw pines and palms were common; *Eucalyptus* grew near the Atlantic coast; and redwoods flourished from Alberta to New Jersey. *Metasequoia* (dawn redwood) grew in forests along with birches, beeches, chestnuts, oaks, and sweet gums. To be sure, when the Paleocene epoch came along, there were still, of course, some representatives of almost all the lower phases of plant evolution—as there are today; but time was ripe for the wild efflorescence of the angiosperms. At present, more than 250 families of angiosperms are listed—of which magnolias and buttercups are thought to be the most primitive. Typical of the Paleocene were the maple, viburnum (snowball), katsura, and buckthorn.

Although, of the two basic types of angiosperms—monocotyledons and dicotyledons—the former have never been so plentiful as the latter, palms have been found in such unexpected places as North Dakota. Of the dicotyledons, the person who collects Cenozoic plant fossils may find *Sassafras, Quercus* (oak), *Ficus* (fig), *Platanus* (plane tree), *Sequoia* (redwood), and many other genera. The grasses apparently developed at some time during the late Cretaceous but did not appear as fossils until the early Oligocene. There appearance marked the real start of the mammals.

There has been comparatively little change in North American flora since the Oligocene. Consequently, if the fossil hunter wants to know when (during the past, say, 35 million years) the fossilized object he has found was a live, growing plant, his first procedure must be to identify the stratum in which he found it. That is not always easy, and sometimes the best method is just to ask a geologist. To identify an individual specimen for oneself is sometimes even more difficult. But encyclopedias, handbooks, and other basic texts often have illustrations of plant fossils, and in them there may be advice about specific methods of identification. For example, a handbook called *A Guide to the Common Fossil Plants of West Virginia* gives a key to the "major types of sterile leaf genera" found in the state's coal measures, and provides exact information on how to make use of the key.

In consulting a book that is not recent, the amateur must allow for the fact that there have been radical changes within recent years, in classification, arrangement, and terminology. For example, if a text says Pteridophyta and Spermatophyta, he should make it read Tracheophyta. And in the smaller categories there are numerous pitfalls, even for the experienced paleobotanist. Leaves, or seeds, or cone scales, which undoubtedly looked quite different when they were growing on their own primeval trees, can look distressingly alike in the fossil form. Or bits that belong together may show no apparent relationship to each other. Parts of one plant, separated sometimes, received individual names, and later were found to belong together. That happened to *Cordaites,* and the original names for the parts are still used, making what are known as form genera—the roots, *Amyelon;* casts of pith in the trunks, *Artesia;* and seed-bearing stems, *Cordaianthus.* In a genus of lycopsids, stems were placed in the genus *Lepidodendron;* detached leaves in *Lepidophyllum;* cones in *Lepidostrobus;* and the rootstocks in the genus *Stigmaria!* Thus when different organs of the same plant were first found separated, and only later discovered in close association, they were sometimes assigned to different genera. The foliage of seed ferns, now known as *Alethopteris,* was once called *Medulosa;* and it is now realized that the three-ribbed fruit once known as *Trigonocarpus* grew on *Alethopteris.* Moreover, it must be admitted, not even today are all genera of fossil plants interpreted in the same way by all paleobotanists. With these difficulties, it is perhaps a good thing that plant fossils are so beguilingly handsome.

The fossilized remains of animals—vertebrate or invertebrate—have always been, in most places, easier to find than those of plants; yet, written mention of fossil plants comes from as far back as the thirteenth century, when Albertus Magnus (or Saint Albert the Great, or Albert of Bollstädt) told of finding them. Albert made collections and noted his observations about them in such books as *De vegetabilibus*. Some three centuries later, when Martin Luther came on fossil wood, he concluded that it had been washed away in the Biblical Flood. Actually it was not until there was extensive mining of coal in western Europe that something of the meaning of Carboniferous plant life (found in coal) began to be understood, even by scientists. Most persons, if they thought about it at all, still believed that those plants were the remains of vegetation that had escaped the Deluge.

Credit for being the founder of the science of paleobotany goes to the Frenchman Adolphe T. Brongniart, who, in the nineteenth century, established a classification of fossil plants. Other nineteenth-century paleobotanists include H. Witham of England, who made the first anatomical analysis of ancient plant life; H. R. Goeppert of Germany; Oswald Heer of Switzerland; J. W. Dawson of Canada; and Leo Lesquereux, the Swiss who came to this country in about 1848, founded paleobotany in America, identified untold numbers of fossil plants, and made his name a household word among all paleontologists.

Before he came to the United States, Lesquereux had already won a prize for a treatise on plants in the peat bogs of his own Swiss district, and had also fulfilled a Prussian government commission to explore bogs all over Europe, thereby attracting the attention of Louis Agassiz, himself a Swiss. After Lesquereux arrived here, he first assisted Agassiz, who was then professor of zoology and geology at Harvard, and later went to Columbus, Ohio, to work with the eminent bryologist W. S. Sullivant. Geological surveys of the period contain Lesquereux's analyses of the coal formations in Pennsylvania, Ohio, Illinois, Arkansas, and Kentucky, but his basic fame now rests in large part on what he wrote for the second geological survey of Pennsylvania, published between 1880 and 1884 as *Description of the Coal Flora of the Carboniferous Formation in Pennsylvania and Throughout the United States*. Other great early scientists who followed his lead in this country included, especially, F. H. Knowlton and Edward Wilber Berry.

CHAPTER V

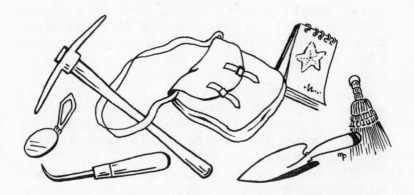

The Finding and Care of Fossils

NOWADAYS, WHEN MORE AND MORE LAYMEN ARE MAKING a hobby of fossil hunting, the scientists themselves are watching for what the amateurs may come across. Moreover, they are relieved and delighted when a nonprofessional knows how to collect properly, and how to take care of his finds. Usually they are glad to give advice, and even mechanical assistance, if the project is important enough.

Obviously, any amateur has the best chance to learn about "digging" if he can go out with professionals. But if that isn't possible—and of course it seldom is—his best bet is either to join some local field trip or to go along with an experienced amateur. If he has an adventurous spirit, it won't be long before he wants to do at least some prospecting by himself. He might well do a little reading and studying too.

*Illustration above shows Tools.

He should remember, first of all, that fossils are of different kinds, created in different ways.

Very commonly, the original material is dissolved, and *replaced* by some such mineral as silica, or possibly quartz. This is what has usually happened to whole skeletons or individual bones of land vertebrates, which are sometimes shiny and often very heavy. This mineralization process seldom occurs in the air, but rather under sediment, or under water.

Fossils may also be created when the cavities around a specimen are filled with some rock-making substance, so that, for example, a shell is protected and not crushed out of shape. In the nest thus made, the shell may persist, or it may eventually disappear.

There we get into the matter of molds and casts—terms often confused by even the well-informed. Most paleontologists say that when a dead object dissolves or decays and leaves a cavity where it lay, that cavity is a *natural mold*. The cavity may be kept by the collector as it is; or he may fill it with something like plaster of Paris to duplicate the surface and shape of the fossil, thus making a *squeeze*, or *cast*. If the shell remains, and nature herself filled the *interior* with something like grains of sand that became cemented, the result is best known as an *interior mold*. The impression left by the *exterior*—as, for example, the beautiful details of the outside of a scallop shell—is an *external mold*.

One common type of fossil is known as an *imprint*. This is really an external mold of some thin object like a leaf, flower or insect, and is often found in Coal Age strata. Or another type of fossil is that of a plant that gradually lost some of its more perishable materials, leaving only a thin layer of carbon. Such a fossil, sometimes found in the clays associated with coal deposits, is called a carbon film.

Remains such as dinosaur footprints, which are technically *impressions*, were made because the mud was just the right consistency to take the impression of the foot and to keep it in shape when the foot was withdrawn. Later the mud dried. Then that depression was covered by more mud or sand, which followed its contours but didn't get mixed up with it. So there, inside the rock, are both a mold and a cast. If the rock is split in just the right place, in just the right way, the top piece shows the cast, the lower one the mold.

The person collecting fossils in sandstones and shales may sometimes come on peculiarly shaped hardened lumps that look like fossils. He will do well to break a few of them open, because in certain localities such lumps (known as *concretions*) have been made by the depositing of concentrated mineral solutions around leaves, seeds, shells, or similar objects; and there the fossils are, inside the concretions. They are especially common in Illinois, Kansas, and Colorado.

In certain parts of the country, the hunter may find fossils lying right on top of the ground. In other places, he will have to do some digging, and often may have to cut his finds out of the rock. What he comes across may be the remains of vertebrates, invertebrates, full-grown plants, or microscopic organisms of some kind. Gathering and preserving each of these types presents its own peculiar problems.

Let's start with vertebrates.

The experienced paleontologist never starts to dig until he sees at least a bit of bone. As Roy Chapman Andrews, one of the most colorful as well as most successful of American explorers, put it, "Never dig for bones unless you see them."

If the place where the amateur is to dig is sandy, he will need very few implements. A long-handled shovel will move large piles or dig into untouched levels. A trowel and scratcher will take care of shallow digging. A sounding rod —a stiff wire about four feet long, with one end twisted to make a handle—is helpful for prodding gently to learn where harder substances may be buried in the soft sand.

If the rock is hard, one should have a geologist's hammer (preferably one with a chisel end), one or two other chisels, of different widths, an awl, and some kind of pick (drift, marsh, or infantry).

Everybody should have a stout knapsack, which can hold some of the tools and various odds and ends. A box or basket is often useful. And everybody should carry a loose-

leaf notebook and a good black pencil (ink may smudge if it
rains), bags of various sizes, and of course, the proper maps.
The searcher should also take along shellac or gum arabic
(and something to mix it in), brushes, a whisk broom, strips
of burlap, wrapping and tissue papers, a couple of pans,
some plaster of Paris, and a jug of water. A steel tape and a
pocket magnifying glass often come in handy.

On newly eroded slopes where rocks are rapidly wearing
away and soil is not accumulating, there will often be fossiliferous material on the surface, though the person who
has not learned to observe closely may not recognize it immediately. Obviously, hunting is made easier if the area is
cut into gullies, ravines, canyons, or escarpments, so that a
cross section of the various strata is visible. Walking along
beside such a cut, a keen-eyed observer may catch a glimpse
of the end of a bone—or perhaps fragments—at any given
level. This is his signal to go ahead, once he has made sure
that what he sees isn't just some old bone a dog has buried.

There is a sad story of a Yale paleontologist who—not
so long ago—rushed off to another part of the state in
response to an excited request that he excavate an odd
skeleton that had just come partly to light on an old farm. A
few minutes after the scientist started to dig he found—
close to the bones—a rusty horseshoe!

A fossil is heavier than a new bone, usually darker and
somewhat mottled, and is likely to crack apart. If it is petrified—that is, if its organic material has been replaced by
minerals—it will break *like a rock,* along cleavage lines at
right angles to the grain. A new bone breaks lengthwise and
may fall into flinders. However, this is not a test to be recom-
mended.

If the searcher comes across fragments of bone, shell,
or petrified wood, his next step should be to follow them
hither and yon until he finds a place where only portions are
sticking out of the rock. There he starts to dig—but slowly
and carefully! If proper tools are not at hand, he should
wait, no matter how impatient he is. Many a fine fossil has
been ruined by haste and impetuousness—not to speak of
ineptitude.

Now, suppose he sees something that looks worthwhile, and has the tools and other essential equipment. The next step is to collect all surface "float"—that is, odd bits lying around loose—and wrap this float tightly in paper, marking each package with a number by which he will identify the particular specimen in it, and indicating whether the package contains pure float or perhaps bits he himself broke. As an extra precaution, he may sift the loose dirt around about and pick out any pieces. In that way he will have taken all possible care not to step on or overlook material that might be important.

By merely looking at certain fossils, anyone can see that they will crumble or break if he is not careful. They may be strengthened with shellac mixed with an equal amount of alcohol, or gum arabic crystals with an equal amount of water, applied with a soft brush. But even those specimens that look and feel as solid as stone should be handled cautiously, for they may be exceedingly brittle. It is unfortunately not too unusual for something like a mastodon tusk that has lain unbroken in the earth for hundreds of thousands of years to smash into a dozen pieces when it is dropped on a concrete floor.

If the dig is at some distance from headquarters, of course the maximum equipment should have been taken along, to be available in case of need. Shellac may be carried in a jar with a screw top if a hole is punched in the lid, a long-handled brush is inserted, and string is wound around the brush handle at the opening.

To unearth an unfragmented specimen, the collector should begin by digging *above* it, never at the side. As it emerges, he cleans it gently with a scratcher, a whisk broom, or a brush. If it looks very strange, or too delicate for him to handle, he stops right there and calls for help. Otherwise, he goes ahead, still cautiously.

If a fossil is large, seems to be something rare, or is fragile, it should be especially well protected before it is moved from the site.

In one of his several books, Dr. Andrews tells of the pains he and his associates took with the mastodon bones (including those of several young ones) they found in Mongolia, in what had once been a bog. After the bog dried up during the Ice Age, the author explains, the surface blew away, and it was still being eroded when he came upon the cache. The bones were badly preserved, impregnated by only a small amount of mineral matter, and so chalky that as soon as a portion of one was exposed the men had to soak it with shellac. That tedious work was continued throughout the six weeks of digging. Also, as soon as an area of shellac was dry, the exposed surface of the bone was covered with Japanese rice paper and gum arabic, which held any loose particles in place. On top of that went strips of burlap soaked in flour paste. When the paste dried, the strips formed a hard shell, like a cast on a broken arm or leg, protective enough to permit the fossil to be turned over and treated in the same fashion on the other side. This whole process of protecting the fossil, known as jacketing, prepared it for boxing, so that it was ready to travel in a truck or on a camel's back. Later, in the laboratory, burlap was easily removed with water.

Even working alone, an amateur may do something very like this. To jacket a large specimen effectively, he should first excavate above and then all around it, exposing as little as possible of the actual surface. It is smart to let the fossil stand with overhanging edges, on enough foundation to make a strong pedestal—preferably one with rounded corners. Next, the specimen's upper surface should be covered with strips of wet paper painted liberally with the shellac or gum arabic, to prevent what is to be next applied from coating the bone.

From burlap, such as that in an old feed sack, one may already have made strips from two to four inches wide and from one to three feet long. The strips should be put into water to soak while the material with which they are to be impregnated is prepared. That may be either plaster of Paris, or flour paste such as the Gobi expedition used. Plaster is better.

If plaster of Paris is used, one should fill a pan half full of water and sprinkle in the plaster until it just begins to show above the surface. The plaster should be permitted to settle, with very little stirring, until it becomes the consistency of thick cream. This process isn't so easy as it sounds, and the amateur might well practice a bit before starting forth on a collecting trip. Presupposing that he *has* been able to mix material of the right consistency on the dig, he should next wring out a strip of burlap, submerge it in the plaster, remove the excess, and wrap the strip over the specimen. He should continue in this way, lapping each strip a little over the preceding one, until the exposed area is covered. A long burlap strip should be wound carefully around the base of the entire fossil, and pulled tight. Then the specimen should dry, for as long as twenty-four hours if possible.

After the drying interval, one should excavate all around the pedestal, well below the level of the cap, and finally under it. Then, very gently, turn the specimen over and remove the excess rock from what was the underside. This side should be soaked with the solution, then permitted to dry. After that, the paper and plaster bandages can be completed so that the entire fossil is jacketed.

A slow-setting plaster is best. If plaster isn't available, flour paste will do (except in frost or rain), though it isn't so firm. If the specimen is large or heavy, the block of protective material should be reinforced with sticks and wire; if it is too large for one person to carry, the sticks may be left to project from the sides, to make carrying poles like those porters grab hold of on safari. If a person ever wants to ship such a specimen by freight, it can go at a special rate, if he marks it "fossils in rock."

So far, so good. But finding and even jacketing is by no means the whole story. No true collecting is complete without careful notes, made on the spot if possible. A record should be made of the condition of the bone, the kind of matrix (surrounding material) it was found in (with a piece perhaps carried away for analysis), the geologic age of the stratum (if known to the collector), any prominent landmarks nearby, and the presence of such things as coal, charcoal, plant stems, or rotted material. The position of the specimen in the matrix may also be important, and a sketch of the way the pieces were scattered will help in piecing them together. Bits of bone should be numbered to correspond with numbers on the sketch. All boxes should be well marked, and the markings entered in a notebook. It is much better to leave material in the field than to take it away without proper notes.

Charles Darwin, who had to make up his own methods when he collected fossils, wrote some specific advice for those who came after him. Trust *nothing* to memory, he said. Put a number on every specimen and every fragment. If a specimen is wrapped in paper, put the number on the paper *and* on what is inside. On the spot, immediately, enter it in a catalogue, giving data on where it was found, and so on. Keep notes simple, and use a separate page for each specimen.

Delicate and tedious cleaning, requiring great skill and special equipment, may be learned best by imitation, though there are numerous treatises. Such cleaning should be carried on in a true (or at least a makeshift) laboratory. An experienced technician may have a motor and dentist's drill, various fine metal tools and soft brushes, special photographic methods, apparatus for making chemical analyses, ultraviolet and infrared light (especially for the investigation of plants), and perhaps the new pneumatic chipper no larger than a fountain pen. The amateur is not likely to have such elaborate equipment.

Certain of the major steps in the cleaning process are, however, within the scope of even the novice, if he works carefully. When he gets back home, he should open any packets, being sure to keep a record of the original field numbers while he is cleaning the fossils as best he can. If some of the bones are broken cleanly, he may stick the parts together with cellulose-acetate cement, which is waterproof and dries quickly. If there are large irregular breaks, or gaps, they may be filled with plaster of Paris, which is also used for molds and casts—and best made under supervision at first. To mend small areas inconspicuously, a dilute solution of gum plaster is helpful. This is made by soaking lumps of gum arabic in hot water until a saturated solution is obtained, diluting the result with three parts water, and stirring it into the plaster. A little ochre may be added to the mixture to add some color. After the substance has set, it can be scraped or modeled to the desired contours, and the whole thing may get a coat or two of shellac. That, too, will penetrate the bone, and if it leaves the surface shiny, the shine may be removed with alcohol or steel wool.

The foregoing suggestions for collecting and preserving apply chiefly to vertebrate fossils, but there are traditional methods of dealing with other fossil remains. And of course, by and large, in most parts of the country it is easier to find plants and shells and other invertebrate remains than animal bones.

In 1955, a new method was devised for collecting and storing fossils found in a soft, breakable matrix. While the overload of earth is in place, certain shales contain a good deal of moisture which is lost rapidly as soon as the shale is exposed to the air; as a result, the shale is likely to break in such a way as to injure any fossil or fossils in it. Dr. Herman F. Becker, paleobotanist, research associate of the New York Botanical Garden, has invented a method he has found effective for transporting blocks of matrix—in thin, transparent plastic bags, preferably colorless, and 8 x 12 or 10 x 15 inches. The matrix should be laid flat on thick newspaper or cardboard, then trimmed while it is moist; the fossils in the trimmed matrix are placed immediately in bags, each containing only a single layer of fossils. The open end of each bag is then folded over and covered with cloth, paper, or cardboard. Four or five bags may be stacked on each other, separated by cushions of folded newspapers, and the specimens will remain in their moist condition for several weeks if necessary. When they reach the laboratory, the bags should be placed singly on tables or shelves, with the mouth of each propped open. If humidity is kept at a minimum, constant gentle ventilation for from ten days to two weeks will dry most of the specimens. As certain ones dry, they should be removed, leaving the others to be subjected longer to the same process.

Transporting and cleaning some invertebrates, such as pelecypods and brachiopods, is comparatively simple, because their shell coverings consist of only two parts, and there are not many problems about keeping those parts together, in proper relation to each other. Creatures covered by a single shell naturally present even less of a problem. But when it comes to arthropods, especially crustaceans, arachnids, and insects, there are so many legs, antennae, sections of exoskeletons, and other parts (some of which may be very tiny and fragile) that the person who attempts to sort out the oddments will need to be a very deft technician as well as a clever sleuth. It is fortunate that such fossils are usually stabilized in the matrix, but despite that helpful circumstance, in many instances it is much better to leave them alone until some experienced person can assist.

Most marine and fresh-water invertebrate fossils are likely to be found in masses, and cleaning them means getting rid of the matrix. If that is very hard stone, and the fossils have been mineralized, the individual specimens may be cleared away by chipping carefully at the stone. Professionals sometimes leach out a fossil by using acid, but that is a very dangerous process and should *never* be attempted except under proper conditions and by someone who knows exactly how to do it; if the leaching is not done properly, the fossil itself may be dissolved along with the stone.

If, as with many mollusks, the body itself has disappeared, leaving a mold of its shape, a perfect cast of the original may be obtained by filling the mold with plaster or latex.

Microfossils are sometimes easy to collect, but isolating them from the material in which they are found and storing them in practical fashion requires a laboratory, a microscope, and a good deal of other specialized equipment. However, if an amateur has just a microscope, he can enjoy himself a good deal by peering at minute fossils—some of which are very beautiful.

Plant remains, such as leaves and fronds, taken from the site in the matrix can later be split carefully along the bedding planes. Such fossils will appear oftenest in sandstones or shales of Pennsylvanian age, though in the Cretaceous of the West the hunter may come on a few cycads and conifers, and many leaf types like those of today. They should always be carried in protective chunks of matrix, cut out at some distance from the specimen. But taking them out of the rock is a very tricky (laboratory) process, usually involving acids, and should never be attempted by the novice.

All in all, in places where there are any fossil bones at all, it is much easier to become a paleozoologist than a paleobotanist. And as a matter of fact, most of the unusual finds by nonprofessionals have been in the field of *vertebrate animals*.

CHAPTER VI

And Now to Hunt Them!

EQUIPPED WITH ESSENTIAL TOOLS AND SUPPOSEDLY having some idea of what a fossil is like, the amateur is ready to set forth.

How shall he know where to look?

In the first place, he should get a popular handbook if one is available. In some states official agencies put out publications that tell where fossils have been found, and are likely to be found. Some of these publications give detailed information about where fossiliferous areas are and how to reach them; others supply only generalized data. Some of them refer to quadrangle maps—of which more anon.

Certain states have no popular publications because they have almost no fossils. In certain other states, though they may be among the best fossil-hunting areas in the country, budgets don't cover the outlay, or early printings are exhausted. Or a state may hesitate to give out informa-

Illustration above shows the Mammoth.

tion because it has had unfortunate experiences with irresponsible amateurs. As one geologist says, "There is always someone who will back up a truck and take everything in sight, and famous areas for fossils have been ruined in that fashion."

Once in a while (and of course in an area where fossils are plentiful) those in authority say that they are *glad* to have anyone hunt in their territory. For instance, a Missouri geologist has written of his state, "The field of exploration . . . is almost limitless, and will not be overcrowded by searchers, regardless of the numbers that succumb to the natural appeal. . . . It is a fascinating and rewarding task for the very many. . . . The State Geological Survey wishes to assist in every way possible but can do little more than coordinate your efforts, record your finds, and give advice in making identification."

Only one (and certainly reasonable) reservation is made: In an educational booklet of 1962, we read: "In the following pages, reference numbers like MGSQV-1010 will be seen frequently. These numbers refer to localities in Missouri from which Pleistocene vertebrates have been reported. Each locality has been assigned, arbitrarily, a number in the series (Missouri Geological Survey Quaternary Vertebrates). These numbers are recorded in the files of the office of the Survey . . . at Rolla, with all available information. . . . In some cases, where scientific investigations are now in progress, the exact location is omitted to prevent interference with these investigations. In such cases . . . qualified investigators may obtain further information by addressing the Director of the Missouri Geological Survey at Rolla."

Now, certainly even without a guidebook, the most inexperienced amateur can guess that there will be no fossils in any place where outcroppings or near-surface rocks are igneous or of a completely metamorphosed type, as in many parts of New England. On the other hand, one must remember that even the proper kinds of rocks do not necessarily contain fossils. Plants and animals lived and died there, but a great many conditions had to be just right for their remains to be preserved, and only a minute proportion of once-living things has been fossilized. That is one of the reasons it is a good idea for the novice to go immediately to someone who knows what may be around.

In almost any part of the country, there are enthusiastic amateurs who know where, in a given region, one is most likely to get results. It is an excellent plan for a person new at the game to become friendly with some of those better-informed hunters. If he has no way of reaching such amateurs, or if (as frequently happens) they guard the identity of their digging grounds as if they were mines full of diamonds, he may have better luck appealing to professionals at universities, geological surveys, or paleontological and other natural history museums. In approaching those authorities, he had better persuade them, first of all, that he is serious and responsible, and will not abuse any privileges. Once they are convinced of that, the chances are that the experts will be agreeable, thoughtful, and generous with all kinds of help.

It cannot be too strongly emphasized that many fossiliferous spots are privately owned, and no one wants unknown diggers running around on his land. Public lands are often protected by law. It is always politic (as well as polite) to get permission from the owner if a person wants to dig on private property, and from the authorities, for public lands. Some places—such as abandoned mines and water-filled quarry holes—are dangerous too, and the hunter should make certain that he knows what he is getting into.

Scattered through the country are museums (see p. 325) where the layman may look at exhibits of fossils, often with identifying labels telling where they were unearthed. These museums and other centers frequently put out publications that will be useful. Occasionally such printed matter is available without charge. If a charge is made, it is usually comparatively small.

The USGS, many state geological surveys, and certain other agencies produce maps indicating what the topography is like in various states or regions, and what sediments were laid down there. Geology books are helpful too. Some of them will show how far the waters moved inland in various

periods—Cambrian, Permian, Cretaceous, for example—
and what layers of sediment one may expect to find more or
less on top of one another in a given area.

Maps based on events of many millions of years ago
show topographical features that existed then but disappeared long before the continents looked as they do at
present. Even for a person untrained in geology, it is not
difficult to form some sort of mental picture of what strata
lie under the surface, and one can refer to atlases and other
maps showing our present mountain ranges, lakes, rivers,
and plains.

This information is the A B C of geology, but it may be
of very little help in locating *specific* places in which to
search for fossils. Moreover, even publications that do give
something about fossils are sometimes not so helpful as the
amateur could wish. Although they *may* be written so
clearly and simply that they can be understood by a person
who doesn't know a *Lepidodendron* from a horseshoe crab,
they may, on the other hand, quite well be couched in language so scientific that the layman will have trouble translat-
ing it. Also, some papers that were practical when they were
published are now so old that the fossils are gone, or the site
has disappeared or is impossible to get to.

By and large, it is easier to find marine fossils than
those of land life, and marine fossils have been preserved
in the most unlikely places, such as the sides and crests of
mountains, like the Rockies, which were formed by folding.
In certain areas of almost any part of the country, there may
be little but shells; in others (though many fewer spots),
almost nothing but plants. Though the bones of vertebrates
are commonplace in a few areas, such as Florida and
Nebraska, in general they are much more difficult to find.

A word of warning to all those who set forth to discover
paleontological secrets hidden in the earth: No matter what
wonderful minerals you may find (how beautiful the agate,
how colorful the semiprecious stones!) don't pay too much
attention to them, or the first thing you know you'll be a
rock-hound as well as a fossil hunter; and in no time flat
you're likely to want to be a lapidary, manipulating all sorts

of cutting and polishing machines. As a matter of fact, it isn't always easy to keep the two interests separate, or even to know whether to classify what you have as a fossil or a stone. Because fossils take on color and texture from the minerals that pervade the rock in which they lie, bones can actually become jewels; bones of Utah dinosaurs have become so beautiful that they are cut and polished to make costume accessories.

In looking for animal fossils, it is a good idea to recall the processes by which they were preserved. The majority of animals that have provided us with fossils were covered closely and completely very soon after they died, so that the bodies did not decay rapidly, and the bones were not destroyed or scattered by wind, water, or predatory creatures. Most often, the body was covered by silt, which later hardened. Occasionally, creatures that met their death in deserts were buried by hot sand. In places like the Rancho La Brea tar pits of Los Angeles animals sank in asphalt. In dinosaur beds, such as those of western Canada, bodies were washed into swamps and very quickly buried. No matter where they were, as time went on, the remains were changed by mineral action. Eventually some of them are exposed to view, either by natural physical disturbances, or through mining, dredging, or other man-made upheavals.

Some potential paleontologists must give up all hope of finding anything near their homes and wait for the opportunity to hunt in other parts of the country. They are lucky if their travels take them to places where spectacular finds have been made and became part of the public record. Those finds are sometimes recorded in books, and local newspapers almost always have stories about them. It is smart, in any event, to take a look at newspaper files, and the back numbers of scientific magazines. Libraries, too, are always helpful places.

Useful maps range all the way from those that tell little more than where the roads, rivers, and towns are to those that pinpoint specific localities, and the serious searcher will need both kinds.

To begin with, for locating general areas, there are the

maps issued by the American Automobile Association and by gasoline companies. For more detailed help, there are topographical sheets compiled by the United States Department of the Army Corps of Engineers and issued by the Department of the Interior, Geological Survey. These may be obtained from the U.S. Geological Survey, Washington, D.C., at a minimal charge. A folder listing and describing these maps and the symbols used on them is obtainable, free, from the same source. They are in several colors, and display contours, railroads, roads, other communication systems, boundaries, and even individual buildings, orchards, and other minutiae. These maps make it possible to locate outcrops within yards.

A detailed geologic map of the United States may be obtained from the same source. It is in four large sheets, scale approximately one inch to forty miles, prepared in 1932, and reissued in 1960. There are, of course, even more detailed geological surveys, but they must be obtained directly from the states or other special sources.

One such kind of guide (published by the USGS) is the quadrangle map. Such maps show a section of a state, ruled in such a way that places on them may be referred to by a set of apparently esoteric symbols. One will find in certain publications—even those intended to guide the amateur— such a notation as this: "N½ NE¼ sec. 33, T. 5 N., R. 9 W." The notation refers to a quadrangle map, and directions will usually tell the reader which map—such as, for example, the "Blanchardville Quadrangle." The technical shorthand is interpreted to mean "North half of the northeast quarter of Section 33, Township 5 North, Range 9 West." If notation was: "NW¼ NW¼ sec. 22, T. 3 N., R. 5 E.," it would mean "Northwest quarter of the northwest quarter of Section 22, Township 3 North, Range 5 East."

For many years, the USGS has been engaged in creating such topographical quadrangle maps, and in recent years has increased its efforts to cover the entire United States, Puerto Rico, and the Virgin Islands. Nevertheless, it is likely to be some time before all this is accomplished.

These quadrangle maps may be of several kinds, with

the unit of survey bounded by parallels of latitude and meridians of longitude. The most usual are: (1) covering 7½ minutes of latitude and longitude, and published on the scale of 1:24,000 (1 inch = 2,000 feet); (2) covering 15 minutes of latitude and longitude, published on the scale of 1:62,500 (1 inch = approximately 1 mile); (3) covering 30 minutes of latitude and longitude, published on the scale of 1:250,000 (1 inch = approximately 2 miles). A few special maps have been published on other scales. All of them (of whatever size) give many other symbols, for such features as roads, railroads, etc.

In certain instances, guides or bulletins for fossil hunters give the symbols for section, township and range, but omit the name of the quadrangle. That omission probably means that there is no large- or medium-scale quadrangle map specifically for that part of the country. For example, in North Dakota, symbols are sometimes given, referring by implication to the Dickinson sheet of 1:250,000 scale, because only about half of the state has been covered by ordinary quadrangle maps. Once in a while, geologists admit, the name of the quadrangle isn't there just because somebody was too lazy to look it up. If, however, the site is otherwise carefully described, the quad name is not always necessary. Indexes to topographic maps, showing what is available for each state, may be obtained free from the USGS, on request.

Very early in our history, a system of "meets and bounds" had grown up in the eastern and northeastern part of our country; but in 1785 Congress authorized a land survey of all territory north and west of the Ohio River, to avoid the complex system that obtained along the Atlantic seaboard. It is much less important to give the quadrangle name for a part of the country covered by the U.S. Land Survey, than it is for the eastern and northeastern part, and in a few areas of old Spanish claims in the southwest. In the Spanish areas, it is important that quadrangles, counties, and parishes (though they have no relation to quadrangles), and all other such pertinent information that is available should be consulted if one wants to establish localities with great accuracy.

Unusually helpful maps may be obtained from the Institute of Geographical Exploration, Harvard University, Cambridge, Massachusetts. These are called Landform Maps, and display features, both in draughtmanship and text, not found on any others. Not only topography but soil types and other surface features are clearly indicated, and identified in the text.

Ideally, of course, the reasonable and practical way to consider *large* areas where fossils may be found would be to think of the whole continent in terms of regions—regions that owe their character to the nature of what went on there in ancient geologic times. What sediments, if any, were laid down? What form of terrain resulted? What type of vegetation grew on the terrain? And, in consequence of all that, what plants and what animals flourished and died there, leaving their remains perhaps in a type of sediment that would help them to become fossils?

The great mountain backbone of the Western Hemisphere, which starts in northern Alaska and reaches to the tip of South America, binds our continent geologically into one entity, and any fossil hunter should think of it in that fashion. The mighty mountain chains, creating for North America what is known as the Cordillera, are confined in Canada to a fairly narrow strip on the west, seen on the map as the Rocky Mountains and the Coast Mountains. In the United States, where the backbone broadens somewhat, the Cordillera includes the Rockies, the Sierra Nevada, the ranges of the Great Basin, and the Coast Ranges. In Mexico, the Sierra Madres of east and west come together not far from Mexico City. One has only to look at a topographical map to realize that the boundaries between the United States and Canada, or the United States and Mexico, are purely arbitrary.

It very soon becomes apparent also that as far as fossils are concerned many of the boundaries between states are equally artificial. No map makers were around in those far-off times when primeval waters swept across the face of the land, and receded, leaving their varied deposits. And no one was thinking of what fossilized flora and fauna were hidden beneath the surface when surveyors set up their theodolites and stretched their chains to determine exactly where lines should be established, let's say, between Colorado and Wyoming, or Oklahoma and Kansas.

Nevertheless, because most Americans are accustomed to thinking in terms of states, we present the ensuing material under state headings.

Succeeding pages discuss conditions in certain of the better known and well-charted areas; and also give some guidance to places about which information is not easily available. Some states are considered briefly because they have almost no fossils. Others receive little space because what information there is, is so scattered or so sternly scientific or so hard to come by that the person who wants to go fossil hunting had better just go to someone who can give him firsthand advice.

In addition to the difficulties that have always existed, there is the saddening and maddening fact that many sites, sometimes prolific ones, disappear overnight with the advent of developers and their bulldozers. Even though the digging may expose fossils that had hitherto lain there unsuspected, chances are very good that they will be at least scattered; often they are smashed to bits. The most passionate pleas of conservationists seldom have much effect on men intent on "progress"; but, fortunately, now and then a hopeful report comes across the nation. In the spring of 1965 the Ohio Bureau of Public Roads and the Ohio State Highway Department agreed to work in collaboration with the Cleveland Museum of Natural History to save Devonian fish fossils from a six-mile stretch in the southwest quadrant of Cuyahoga County (see p. 234). And in August 1966 an even more remarkable case of official and private cooperation occurred when new dinosaur tracks came to light in Connecticut (see p. 114).

One of the gratifying aspects of any good hobby is that the hobbyist who gets lightly involved is likely to become increasingly serious. It is entirely possible that the person who makes use of this book will eventually turn into a real paleontologist, or at least become a collector who wants to know *exactly* what he has found—what type the shell, how old the trilobite, the complete identification of the plant. But we assume at the moment he is a novice, concerned at present chiefly with *finding* something because of its beauty or strangeness, and willing to wait a bit before he gets too technical about it. It will not be long, however, before the collector realizes that, for example, this shell is likely to be this or that; this plant may well be thus and such. There are reference books, such as *The Fossil Book* by Carroll Lane Fenton and Mildred Adams Fenton, which contain thousands of photographs and drawings and can be used easily for identifying many fossils.

What follows does not pretend to be in any sense a complete guide to fossil hunting in the United States. Though it contains resumés of many publications (both popular and scientific), it is not intended to replace them, and they often contain helpful details that naturally could not be included here. A list of certain official publications is included in the Bibliography.

Even if the amateur reads all the books and follows all the advice, it is unlikely that he will find a new species of dinosaur. But you never can tell. Stranger things have happened!

FIFTY

CHAPTERS ON

STATES

ALABAMA

CRETACEOUS ROCKS FORM A SHAPE LIKE THE EYE OF A HOOK AND eye, southward through Tennessee, along the eastern border of Mississippi, in a sweep eastward across Alabama, and up into Georgia. Thus, Cretaceous sediments (plus later, Cenozoic, deposits) form a large portion of the Coastal Plain, which takes up approximately three fifths of the southeast part of the state, falling away from the Cumberland Plateau, which is to the northeast. Much of Alabama is exceedingly fossiliferous, containing all manner of delights for the hunter.

The guide for amateur collectors published by the Geological Survey of Alabama is a most helpful pamphlet. It lists forty invertebrate fossil localities, as of 1963:

ORDOVICIAN

1. Limestone County, Liepers Formation—road cut on north side of county road, 0.5 mile southeast of Scarce Grease, reached by traveling north from Athens on State Highway 99 to Mount Roszell, turning right on road to Scarce Grease (3.3 miles from State 99), turning right at Scarce Grease, and going on 0.5 mile—bryozoans, corals, and brachiopods.

2. Blount County, Chicamauga limestone—road cut on west side of State Highway 75, 3.3 miles north of U.S. 231 and State 75 intersection in Oneonta—bryozoans and brachiopods imbedded in limestone near north end of cut.

3. Shelby County, Athens shale—road cut on south side of State Highway 25, 2.3 miles west of intersection in Calera of State 25 and U.S. 31—graptolites preserved in carbonaceous films in dark gray shales.

MISSISSIPPIAN

1. Colbert County, Gasper Formation—road cut in east side of county road 2.5 miles south of Barton—corals and brachiopods.

2. Colbert County, Gasper Formation—road cuts in west side of U.S. Highway 43, 5.9 miles south of U.S. 72 and 43

intersection in Tuscumbia—corals, bryozoans, brachiopods, and blastoids.

3. Franklin County, Bangor limestone—road cut on west side of U.S. 43, 3.0 miles north of Franklin County courthouse in Russellville—corals and bryozoans.

4. Madison County, Hartsell sandstone—road cuts on Monte Sano mountain along U.S. 431, 4.9 miles east of U.S. 231 and U.S. 431 intersection south of Huntsville—solitary corals, bryozoans, brachiopods.

5. Morgan County, Gasper Formation—east end of road cut through Trinity Mountain, approximately 4.5 miles west of Decatur on State Highway 24—brachiopods.

6. Morgan County, Gasper Formation—road cut on south side of State Highway 36, 1.0 mile west of Lacey's Spring—bryozoans, brachiopods, and blastoids.

7. Blount County, St. Louis Limestone—railroad cuts opposite Blount Springs Railroad station, which is 0.3 mile north of county road between Blount Springs and Hayden—crinoid stems and plates.

8. Jefferson County, Fort Payne chert—road cuts on north and south sides of U.S. 78 East, 0.8 mile west of Starlight Drive-In Theater—corals and brachiopods.

9. Jefferson County, Fort Payne chert—chert pit directly opposite Greenwood Community Center in Greenwood, 3.9 miles west of Parkwood—brachiopods and corals enclosed in chert.

CRETACEOUS

1. Sumter County, Bluffport marl member of Demopolis chalk—road cuts at intersection of State Highway 39 with improved dirt road 0.5 mile north of intersection of State Highway 39 and U.S. 11 (intersection is 6.0 miles northeast of Livingston) —pelecypods.

2. Sumter County, Ripley Formation and Prairie Bluff chalk—four exposures on south side of U.S. 11, 5.0 to 6.0 miles northeast of Livingston—pelecypods and gastropods.

3. Marengo County, Ripley Formation and Prairie Bluff chalk—road cuts on each side of post office in Jefferson—pelecypods, gastropods, and cephalopods.

4. Marengo County, Bluffport marl member of Demopolis

chalk—road cut on west side of State Highway 25, 2.0 miles
northeast of Dayton—a few excellently preserved pelecypods,
though locality is in poor condition.

5. Marengo County, Prairie Bluff chalk—road cuts on each
side of Marengo County Highway 53, 1.0 mile northeast of
Thomaston—pelecypods, gastropods, cephalopods.

6. Montgomery County, Ripley Formation—road cut on
east side of U.S. 331 South, 0.3 mile north of Strata Church of
Christ—pelecypods.

7. Montgomery County, Prairie Bluff chalk—lower end of
road cut on west side of U.S. 331 South, 1.2 miles south of
Strata—pelecypods.

8. Barbour County, Ripley Formation—road cut on west
side of county road south of Batesville, 1.7 miles south of intersection of Batesville–White Oak county road with U.S. 82—
pelecypods.

9. Barbour County, Ripley Formation—road cuts on each
side of county road, 3.9 miles north of intersection with U.S.
Highway 431. Travel north on Highway 431 from Eufaula; turn
off to the left for 3.9 miles at Wheeler's Nursery Road—pelecypods.

10. Russell County, Blufftown Formation—road cuts on
each side of State Highway 165, 2.3 miles south of Holy Trinity
—pelecypods.

11. Russell County, Blufftown Formation—road cut on
State Highway 37, 6.4 miles north of Hurtsboro—pelecypods.

12. Russell County, Eutaw Formation—road cuts on State
Highway 37, 11.1 miles north of Hurtsboro—pelecypods.

13. Dale County, Tuscahoma sand—beneath Alabama
Highway 134 bridge across Hurricane Creek, 0.1 mile west of
intersection of State Highways 123 and 134 (the intersection is
1.2 miles north of Newton)—pelecypods, gastropods, and corals.

PALEOCENE

1. Marengo County, Matthews marl member of Porters
Creek Formation—cuts in logging road 75 yards behind small
store, reached by traveling south from Linden on U.S. 43 for
5.75 miles (store is directly opposite intersection of county road
from Octagon with U.S. 43)—pelecypods.

2. Barbour County, Clayton Formation—railroad cut on Central of Georgia RR, 200 yards north of Alabama Highway 30 in Clayton—pelecypods.

EOCENE

1. Choctaw County, Lisbon Formation—road cuts in hillside above Souwilpa Creek, 4.0 miles south of Gilbertown on Choctaw County Road 17—pelecypods.

2. Choctaw County, Lisbon Formation—road cut on east side of county road FAS 749 (1), 1.2 miles southeast of Johnson's grocery in Barrytown—pelecypods and gastropods.

3. Choctaw County, Yazoo clay—road cut on south side of Choctaw County Highway 12, 0.6 mile east of Isney, which is near the Mississippi state line and west of Silas—solitary corals and a few shark teeth.

4. Clarke County, Bashi marl member of Hatchetigbee Formation—road cut on hillside above south bank of Bashi Creek, about 4.0 miles south of Morvin on east side of State Highway 69—pelecypods and gastropods.

5. Clarke County, Moodys Branch Formation of Yazoo clay —road cut on State Highway 12, 2.6 miles west of Grove Hill— pelecypods.

6. Clarke County, Yazoo clay—road cuts on each side of U.S. 84 between Grove Hill and Gosport 3.0 miles west of Pigeon Creek—pelecypods and echinoids.

7. Monroe County, Gosport sand—road cut on north side of U.S. 84, 2.5 miles west of end of Claiborne-Murphy bridge over Alabama River—pelecypods.

8. Monroe County, Lisbon Formation Gosport sand, and Moodys Branch Formation—Claiborne Bluff on east side of Alabama River, with beds under bridge and along small road to Claiborne Landing—pelecypods, gastropods, and echinoids.

9. Marengo County, Nanafalia Formation—several fossiliferous road cuts on county road between Sweetwater and Half Acre, 3.0 to 5.0 miles northwest of Sweetwater—pelecypods.

10. Marengo County, Nanafalia Formation—road cut at intersection of Half Acre–Sweetwater county road with Marengo County Highway 17, 2.5 miles southeast of Half Acre—pelecypods.

11. Pike County, Nanafalia Formation—erosion gulley on

back side of road on east side of Pike County Highway 3, 0.5 mile north of Henderson—pelecypods.

12. Butler County, Bashi marl member of Hatchetigbee Formation—road cut on east side of U.S. Highway 31, 4.5 miles south of intersection of U.S. 31 and Butler County Highway 106 south of Georgiana—pelecypods and gastropods.

OLIGOCENE

Clarke County, Marianna limestone and Byram Formation —road cut on east side of Clarke County Highway 15, 5.0 miles southeast of intersection at Jackson of Clarke County 15 and U.S. 43—large discoid foraminifers.

THE GUIDEBOOK in which these sites are listed (called *Curious Creatures in Alabama Rocks*) contains a map on which they are indicated in red. A great deal of other useful information is also included. The author gives a chart of geologic time, discusses dating, classification, and nomenclature, gives some hints on collecting procedures, and presents condensed material on the major invertebrate fossil groups, with many drawings. Throughout, specific references are made to what may be expected in Alabama, and why. This pamphlet, which sells at a very nominal price, should be helpful to anyone collecting invertebrate fossils anywhere.

Part of the Cretaceous sediment, especially within the curve of the eye (the so-called Tuscaloosa Formation) has been studied since 1856, and its importance for fossil plants recognized since at least 1919, when a USGS Professional Paper listed a dozen good localities, which had revealed more than one hundred kinds of plants.

A series of lock-and-dam systems built in the Warrior River between Tuscaloosa and Demopolis may have inundated sites at White's Bluff and Sanders Ferry Bluff, and a new dam on the Chatahoochee below Eufaula will cover some of those in that area. However, certain localities good in 1919 may still be available. As given then they were:

Glen Allen—in cut along St. Louis–San Francisco RR about one-quarter mile east of Glen Allen, near northern boundary of Fayette County for about 150 yards on both sides of tracks— thirty-nine species of plants.

Shirley's Mills—about twenty-five miles south of Glen Allen, in southern part of Fayette, where Davis Creek has cut a small valley—ninety-eight species.

Tuscaloosa—immediately around city: (1) two places on University grounds; (2) in railroad cut just east; (3) banks of Black Warrior River in the city; (4) roadside outcrop a few miles southwest.

Cottondale—along public road about 10.0 miles east of Tuscaloosa and 2.0 miles southeast of Cottondale—richly fossiliferous.

Snow Plantation—two outcrops (Upper Ravine; and Catamount Bluff, or Big Gulley) on west bank of Black Warrior, about 9.0 miles southwest of Tuscaloosa—thirty forms.

Sanders Ferry Bluff—in next meander of Black Warrior below Snow Plantation, several miles farther southwest—five species.

White's Bluff—in northeastern part of Greene County, on right bank of Black Warrior River.

Soap Hill and Centerville, Bibb County.

UP TO 1919, the Eutaw Formation had provided fossils from only one locality in Alabama—between 1.5 and 2.0 miles southeast of Havana, in north central Hale County, in extensive gullies—fourteen species, with many detached leaves of sequoia. Other places noted (in the Ripley Formation) are Cowikee Creek, and a spot 7.0 miles north of Eufaula.

To obtain information about specific plant localities accessible now is somewhat difficult. The eastern part of the state, however, is dotted with abandoned coal strip mines, all of which contain plant fossils of the Pennsylvanian. Plants may also be found in shales immediately above and below coal seam outcrops along highways in Jefferson, Shelby, Walker, and Blount counties.

As anywhere else, of course, plants and most invertebrates stayed moderately *in situ;* marine vertebrates could swim, and land vertebrates could stroll around. Consequently, it is never easy to say where the fossils of vertebrates may be found; in any event, they are much less common than their spineless brethren. In Alabama, dramatic vertebrate finds have been made from time to time. At Choctaw Bluff in Greene County, mosasaurs and giant marine turtles have come to light. Fish have been found in Section 10 of Morgan County, and mosasaurs and several varieties of terrestrial reptiles in the Clayton area.

It is probable that Folsom Man roamed that region more than ten thousand years ago. Opening into a mountainside near the Tennessee border is Russell Cave, as big as an auditorium, first investigated in 1953, and a national monument since 1958. Skeletons and remains of fires have been dated as more than nine thousand years old, and by 1958 more than two and a half tons of artifacts had been taken out. These include kinds of tools and implements never before found in the southeastern United States, and resembling those of the far north.

A most exciting find was made in July 1961, when a farmer ploughing his field near Millry in Washington County ran into one of the vertebrae of a *Zeuglodon* or *Basilosaurus*—the early Tertiary whale that ruled the seas of his time. Very remarkably, virtually the whole skeleton was there—118 vertebrae, thirty-eight ribs, and the head, which was six feet long (with five grinding teeth, two premolars and one incisor on each side). The bones were taken to the University of Alabama at Tuscaloosa, where paleontologists set about making an exhibit for the museum. The creature was sixty feet long and is estimated to have weighed 180,000 pounds.

But such whales are old hat to Alabamans. In *Moby-Dick,* published in 1851, Herman Melville wrote that "by far the most wonderful of all cetacean relics was the almost complete vast skeleton of an extinct monster, found in the year 1842, on the plantation of Judge Creagh, in Alabama. The awe-stricken credulous slaves in the vicinity took it for the bones of one of the fallen angels. The Alabama doctors declared it a huge reptile, and bestowed upon it the name of Basilosaurus. But some specimen bones of it being taken across the sea to Owen, the English anatomist, it turned out that this alleged reptile was a whale, though of a departed species. . . . So Owen rechristened the monster Zeuglodon; and in his paper read before the London Geological Society, pronounced it, in substance, "one of the most extraordinary creatures which the mutations of the globe have blotted out of existence."

Melville would certainly be astonished if he could hear that, though scientists of today agree that this Eocene animal was *not* a lizard, they find *Basilosaurus* ("king lizard"—the name given to it by the "Alabama doctors") more acceptable than the *Zeuglodon* of Owen, though the two terms are sometimes used synonymously. These creatures belong to an extinct suborder of the Cetacea, or whales, known as the Archaeoceti.

ALASKA

As geologists at the university of alaska put it, "alaska is a very large state [571,065 square miles], and exceedingly little of it is accessible by road, so that the average fossil-bug would have poor luck up here. However, there are some wonderful outcrops that afford great collecting. These are described mainly in publications of the U.S. Geological Survey, which is virtually the only body doing any publication on Alaska." At least some of those USGS papers are available in any large library.

The landscape of this new state is, of course, the most dramatic in North America, with hundreds of glaciers, many active volcanoes in the Kenai Peninsula and the Alaska Range, interior mountains that have never yet been explored, and extraordinarily complex rock formations created by a geologic history of unimaginable activity and variety. Because of lack of roads or railroads, many areas are so inaccessible that they can be reached only by bush plane. Some are almost impossible to reach by any means. Deep permafrost often makes digging difficult, even for the trained geologist. Distances are so great, exploration so laborious, the record so incomplete, and much of the landscape so inhospitable that specialists are likely to confine themselves to restricted paleontological problems more than is done in many other parts of the country.

Seas covered most of Alaska during Triassic and Jurassic

times, and enormous eruptions poured floods of lava from island and submarine volcanoes. Beginning in mid-Jurassic, earth movements created the shape of the present mountain ranges— all of which except the Brooks Range and those of the Aleutian arc and Alaska Peninsula lie in concentric curves around the Gulf of Alaska. During the Miocene and Pliocene, the land reached something like its present extent, and frequent eruptions continued through the last Ice Age.

Geologists divide the state into four basic regions: the Pacific Mountain system; the Interior and Western Alaska; the Brooks Range; and the Arctic Slope. From the point of view of the amateur fossil hunter, certain areas in the first two are most interesting. General sites of special importance include (1) east side of Frederika Valley, Wrangell Mountains, southeast central Alaska—coaly material with well-preserved leaves; (2) Copper River plateau along Glenn Highway, west of Eureka—fossiliferous Cretaceous sandstone; (3) Cook Inlet (long narrow embayment in south coast; easily accessible)—coal-bearing Tertiary beds, north of Kachemak Bay on west of Inlet, and in lowlands at base of Alaska Range; (4) around Fairbanks, in beds of buried stream valleys—bison, mammoth, mastodon, giant elk, moose, horse, etc.; (5) interior highlands of eastern part: (a) south of Yukon (called Yukon-Tanana by early writers)—most parts easily accessible by automobile on highways (Alaska, Richardson, Steese, Elliott, and Taylor) and by secondary roads and trails, large and small boats, and bush plane; (b) between Yukon and Porcupine rivers, in swampy Yukon flats, and on Canadian border—Cambrian to Tertiary rocks, poorly known geologically, and very complex in many places.

The floras of the state—upper Cretaceous and Tertiary— have been studied intensively, and information is available about numerous fossiliferous localities. The first published reports on Tertiary plants were probably written in 1850. It is, however, only since about 1900 that Cretaceous plants have been collected and recognized. Leo Lesquereux wrote of Alaskan fossil plants from "Cape Lisbourne," and other early paleontologists recorded numerous sites on the Yukon River. Long papers published in the 1930s give more recent information:

CRETACEOUS

In two distinct groups of assemblages, representing distinct geologic horizons, including 235 species, with a predominance of cycads, and coming chiefly from the lowlands. Cretaceous rocks are widely distributed in all major provinces, and notably on the lower Yukon and in southwest Alaska. Lower Cretaceous are found as shales, sandstones, and conglomerates on the Pacific coast and in the Yukon and Kuskokwim valleys; Upper Cretaceous, on most of the Pacific coast, except on the southeast, and in many parts of the Yukon and Kuskokwim valleys as well as in a few places in the north. Localities include:

Alaska Peninsula—hundreds listed; chiefly in (1) Chignik Bay, (2) coal beds on Herendeen Bay, (3) Anchorage Bay.

Upper Yukon—only in banks of Yukon and its tributaries, between Woodchopper Creek and Eagle: (1) near Seventymile River—plants only; (2) Rampart-Tanana district, near Wolverine Mountain.

Lower Yukon—plants and some invertebrates. Hundreds of sites discovered between 1902 and 1908 were chiefly between Melozi and Andreafski, and lower reaches of Koyokuk, in sandstone, conglomerate, and shale—ferns, gymnosperms, and angiosperms, including ginkgo, cycads, algae, *Hepaticae* (many kinds), conifers, sequoia, *Pinus, Ficus,* elm, magnolia, laurel, *Platanus, Ampelopsis,* oak, etc.

TERTIARY

First collected on Unga Island, shores of Cook Inlet, Alaska Peninsula, Aleutian Islands, and in southeast Alaska. Numerous localities were found in 1903 between Eagle City and Awik. More recently, the then-called thallophytes, pteridophytes, and spermatophytes included many *temperate-zone, subtropical,* and *tropical* plants. This flora is identical with the so-called Arctic Miocene (now known to be Eocene) of other areas in what is known as the holarctic region (affected by the Arctic cold), with fifty species not found outside Alaska, and many in the Fort Union region, farther south. Marine deposits are found (1) in the Lituya Bay–Katalla region, south coast; (2) in the Alaska Peninsula region in western Alaska; (3) on the Pribilof Islands;

(4) in the Nome district in Seward Peninsula of northwest; (5) on the coastal plain adjacent to the Arctic Circle.

Terrigenous deposits are found (1) in the Matanuska–Cook Inlet region; (2) on the Alaska Peninsula from Cape Douglas to Pavlov Bay; (3) in the Alaska Range; and (4) in the Yukon Basin. There are other miscellaneous land deposits, with much lava, throughout the state.

General fossiliferous localities are (1) southeastern Alaska; (2) Yakutat–Copper River region; (3) Matanuska–Cook Inlet region; (4) Alaska Peninsula; (5) Lower Yukon–Norton Sound region; (6) northwestern Alaska; (7) Tanana region.

THOUGH THE SEWARD PENINSULA (a remote westward projection of the mainland, with uplands, rugged mountains, and broad basins) is of much interest to paleontologists, there is little access except by air, and by some roads from Nome. The Brooks Range, a glaciated barrier that runs almost across north Alaska to the Arctic, has a backbone of rocks mostly between Silurian and early Cretaceous. It can be reached by bush plane, and there are certain trails through the mountains, but much of the range is unexplored.

The Arctic Slope, with its frozen tundra, is almost totally uninhabited; this huge area is technically divided into the geologically complex foothills near the Brooks Range, and the Coastal Plain beyond. In 1947, in the foothills, in the Utukok River region, a geological survey party found a flint-chipping station, with a Folsom point among the flints. Fossil bones of the mammoth, mastodon, bison, musk ox, and horse are fairly common in the surface muck. Cretaceous rocks are best exposed in bluffs along the Colville River from Umiat downstream to Ocean Point, and fossil shells can be collected at Umiat Mountain and in the next largest bluff downstream. Invertebrate specimens have also been obtained from late Miocene, late Pliocene, and Quaternary beds at Point Barrow, along the Colville River, and in other areas of the plain. USGS papers list more than a dozen localities; however, except for a few, which can occasionally be approached by sea, these localities can be reached only by bush plane.

Five species of Upper Cretaceous pelecypods of the genus

Inoceramus, important as index fossils to Upper Cretaceous rocks of midwestern North America and northern Alaska, have come from several hundred localities in the same area. Late Paleozoic gastropods of thirty-four species (nine of them new) have been collected from Mississippian and Permian rocks in northern Alaska, chiefly in the Brooks Range, at locations identified in the following quadrangle maps: Misheguk Mountain, Noatak, Point Hope, Howard Pass, Killik River, Chandler Lake, Philip Smith Mountains, Demarcation Point, Table Mountain, Sagavanirktok, and Mount Michelson.

The pelecypod *Aucella* (now renamed *Buchnia*) has come from Katmai Bay in the southwest, and from several localities in the northern part of the state. This invertebrate is the only fossil sufficiently widespread and abundant to be used for tracing the boundaries of systems and formations.

Cook Inlet sites, easily accessible from Anchorage, are of great interest to fossil hunters. Jurassic (upper Bajocian) rocks appear at the eastern end of the Talkeetna Mountains (which run almost due north from the upper end of the inlet), in the Tuxedni Bay area, and farther down on the west side of the inlet. There, farthest south, the Iniskin-Chinitna (or simply Iniskin) Peninsula forms a quarter-circle projection between Chinitna and Iniskin bays, facing an opening from the inlet into the Gulf of Alaska. This peninsula and the next northern projection (south of Tuxedni Bay) are sometimes known as the Snug Harbor region; the areas are very similar in geologic composition and are often considered together.

The whole Snug Harbor region is extremely fossiliferous, with many marine invertebrates in the mid- and late-Jurassic sediments. Among characteristic fossils are ammonites, which for many years have been collected from a number of localities.

Sites in the Talkeetnas include those (1) near Boulder Creek, left fork; (2) near the head of Sheep Creek—with many fossils, including especially belemnite fragments, the gastropod *Amberlya,* pelecypods *Oxytoma, Lima, Isocyprina* (?), and *Astarte*; (3) Anchorage, D-2 Quad., on Sheep Creek; (4) ridge west of Sheep Creek that enters main Boulder Creek from north, 3.0 miles above its junction with East Fork.

Sites near Tuxedni Bay are (1) tributary entering Bear

Creek from southeast, 4.75 miles south and 22 degrees west of Fossil Point; (2) about 0.3 mile above mouth of tributary entering Bear Creek from southeast at point 2.5 miles from Tuxedni channel; (3) about 0.5 mile above mouth of same tributary.

On Iniskin Peninsula, ammonites appear at (1) right fork of Cliff Creek, about 2,700 feet above junction with left fork, and 2.5 miles south, 15 degrees west, of Fitz Creek; (2) right fork of Cliff Creek, about 8,000 feet above junction with Fitz Creek, and 2.5 miles south, 15 degrees west, of mouth of Fitz Creek; (3) Cliff Creek, 3.5 miles east of Tonnie Peak, and about 200 feet downstream from a prominent cascade one and a quarter miles above junction with Fitz Creek; (4) right fork of right fork of Cliff Creek, 9,000 feet above junction with Fitz Creek, and 2.5 miles south, 16 degrees west, of mouth of Fitz Creek.

In the general Alaska picture, interesting and varied finds have been recorded from time to time in popular publications. Anthropologists have become excited over discoveries of human bones related to those of Folsom Man, often buried with eoliths and artifacts, and sometimes with bones of Pleistocene animals. These animals, one should remember, lived over into the Recent, to be contemporaneous with man on this continent; in some cases they did not become extinct until historic times.

Mammoth remains have been found on one or another of the Pribilof Islands at least five times since 1836. In 1897, some were found in a volcanic cave on the island of St. Paul—so unlikely a place that some persons think they were planted as a practical joke. In any event, no more were found there until early 1952, when someone came on a mammoth tooth, 9.75 inches long and weighing 3 pounds 11 ounces (partly fossilized but not in matrix). Collections from the Cretaceous have been made south of Kamishak Bay in the Kamishak Hills, between the Kamishak and Douglas rivers, and at Cape Kaguyak on the west side of Shelikof Strait, about seventeen miles north of Kukak Bay. Bits of fossil amber may sometimes be picked up on the beach of Nelson Island in the Bering Sea.

Study of Alaskan fossils emphasizes how completely North America is one land mass, which cannot properly be considered in bits and pieces. For example, the Callovian deposits of the early Jurassic come down through Canada to form a boot-shaped area that takes in part each of Montana, Idaho, North Dakota, Utah, and New Mexico, plus a tiny bit of Colorado and almost all of Wyoming.

A late report from the University of Michigan reveals that after three unsuccessful summers, the university gave up its search for terrestrial vertebrates in Cenozoic deposits.

ARIZONA

NOWHERE IN THE WORLD, IT IS SAID, CAN ONE GET SUCH A picture of the way geological layers have been built up, through many, many millions of years, as in the Grand Canyon of Arizona. This fantastic and tremendous canyon is also the world's most spectacular example of erosion. The great gash begins on a high plateau in northwestern Arizona, at the junction of the Colorado and Little Colorado rivers, and runs for more than two hundred miles, toward the west and south, to Grand Wash Cliffs near the Nevada line. In places it is eighteen miles wide and more than a mile deep, with intricately sculptured chasms, buttes, and smaller canyons within the main one. At the lowest level winds the river, which cut down through the deposits at the time the land was rising, perhaps not more than 6 or 8 million years ago. Actually, the river may have cut down through more than *two* miles of rock, with the top mile having been eroded away. What remains has Permian at the top, and at the bottom the earth's basal rocks that lie below the Archean. Only the Ordovician and Silurian are completely lacking, though other periods are not represented everywhere. The sort of things that were above the Permian of the Grand Canyon before they were eroded away may be seen in Zion and Bryce canyons in Utah.

Here in Arizona, one of the amazing helps to the geologist is that the remaining top layers are stacked neatly one above the other, horizontally, like cards in a pack on the table. Below the

Cambrian, the Proterozoic cards are on end, tilted at a sharp angle. Fossils are found all the way up, though not always in every layer in every place. The earliest jellyfish fossil ever discovered is a cast found in Proterozoic rock in the Grand Canyon in 1938. There are trilobites in the Cambrian, primitive fish in the Devonian, various kinds of shells in many strata, and plants in the Mississippian and Permian. The earliest known evidence of vertebrate life is the footprint of an amphibian or reptile, found in 1915 by Charles Schuchert; since that time many prints have turned up, and may be seen along the trail. During most of the year a museum is open near the village of Grand Canyon. The museum exhibits fossils taken out of the area. And it is still possible for the tourist to pick up fossils for himself.

In the middle of the nineteenth century, rumors of the glories of the Canyon had spread, and in 1869 Maj. John W. Powell paved the way for future scientists and tourists by traveling, with a handful of companions, in three 21-foot wooden boats for 538 miles down that dangerous, uncharted river. Powell got through, after the most hair-raising experiences, but one man was drowned, and three others (too terrified to go on) turned back and were murdered by Indians as they were trying to return to civilization. Powell gave the world its first real idea of what the Grand Canyon was like.

In 1900 the USGS published a report on the petrified forests of Arizona in which a writer spoke with deep concern of the fact that all and sundry were carrying off anything from small chips to mighty logs, and urged that stern measures be taken to preserve the forest wonders. The first petrified forest had been noted as early as 1853, by the Pacific Railroad Exploration Survey, and in 1873 an expedition had been sent from Fort Wingate to collect logs for the Smithsonian Institution. Six years after the 1900 report the Petrified Forest was officially made a national monument.

Though Arizona's strata range from the Precambrian to the Quaternary, most of the official paleontological work has been done in the northern part of the state, around the Grand Canyon, and the department of geology of the University of Arizona admits unhappily that much remains to be done. No complete studies of the fauna of any formations have yet been published; and not only does the Bureau of Mines, which serves as the State Survey, provide no popular guide, but even its (highly specialized) scientific bulletins give the amateur little help in finding fossil localities. In an official publication, one of the University of Arizona's geologists writes of the need for "paleontological and stratigraphic studies of Arizona formations." He says, "The fauna should be studied as a unit, and the study should not be confined to a single mountain range. In addition to this, many faunal groups should be studied as a unit, either separately or in conjunction with larger studies."

He suggests several possible projects such as (in the south) Pennsylvanian and Permian fusulinids, nonmarine Cretaceous shales, Devonian fauna, Cenozoic nonmarine mollusks and ostracods; (in the north) the Cretaceous, older Paleozoic, and Cenozoic rocks. A study of arenaceous foraminifers would also be useful, he says. Certainly here are outlines of a career for young people of Arizona who want to be geologists.

In the general literature about the state, in addition to references to the tracks of Permian amphibians and/or reptiles, several important individual finds are noted: fish near Phoenix; a surprising array of Permian plants on trails leading into the Grand Canyon; a number of Triassic amphibian skulls near Metro Crater; many broken bones of Triassic dicynodonts in a quarry near St. Johns; late Triassic plants (including ferns, club mosses, etc.), many skulls, and armor in the Chinle shales and sandstones of the Painted Desert and in the Petrified Forest. In 1942, mastodon skeletons, still standing upright, were found in a marsh near a salt lake in the San Pedro Valley.

Trilobites and other primitive marine creatures have been found in the shale of one part of Coconino County; and in another, insect wings, plants, and tracks of amphibians and reptiles. The bones of many small rodents, and Pleistocene animals (mastodons, camels, giant sloths, and other mammals) have come from Graham County. Dinosaur tracks and crocodilians have been discovered in the northern part of Navajo County, and a rich cache in the same county gave up skulls and other bones of similar mammals. From the mountains south of Tucson came dinosaur fragments, a *Gorgontosaurus*, fishes, and turtles. A Miocene camel and another, larger camel were found on the flank of the mountains in Yuma County.

For the enthusiastic fossil-hound, hunting in Arizona may be especially exciting just because the whole state has *not* been carefully charted and subjected to scientific investigation. The amateur has a good chance to make a real strike!

ARKANSAS

THERE ARE NO CAMBRIAN EXPOSURES IN ARKANSAS, BUT OUT-croppings of all ages from the Ordovician through the Eocene are found, in many cases containing fossils. However, even in the Eocene, almost all the fossils are invertebrate.

The Arkansas Geological and Conservation Commission recommends eighteen sites:

1. Bradford, Jackson County—in Midway (Eocene) lime-stone along U.S. 67 and Missouri Pacific RR—*Ostrea, Turritella* (a prosobranch), and echinoderms.

2. Forrest City, St. Francis County, 300 feet downstream from bridge over Little Crow Creek on State Road 1—in Jackson (Eocene) shell marl—large *Ostrea* numerous.

3. Alexander, Pulaski County, Limerock Dairy, 0.5 mile off U.S. 67, 9.0 miles from Little Rock city limits—in Midway lime-stone along Fourche Creek—brachiopods, echinoderms, *Ostrea, Turritella.*

4. Arkadelphia, Clark County, junction of State Roads 26 and 51, 5.0 miles west of Arkadelphia—in exposures of Creta-ceous Nacatoch, Saratoga, and Marlbrook—*Exogyra, Ostrea, Turritella, Belemnitella* (a cephalopod), and others.

5. Saratoga, Hempstead County, State Road 55, 12.0 miles north of Fulton—in Saratoga and Marlbrook (Cretaceous)—fossils similar to those near Arkadelphia, and fish teeth.

6. "Acorn Cut," Washington County, on San Francisco

RR, 2.0 miles north of Brentwood, 0.5 mile south of U.S.
71—in Brentwood (Pennsylvanian) limestone—*Pentremites*
(blastoids), *Spirifer* and *Composita* (brachiopods), and other
invertebrates.

7. West Fork, Washington County, along U.S. 71, prominent bluffs paralleling highway for 3.0 miles south of West
Fork—in Pitkin (Mississippian) and Hale (Pennsylvanian)
limestone—*Archimedes* (bryozoans), numerous types of brachiopods, and many other invertebrates.

8. Fayetteville, Washington County, west end of Mount
Sequoyah—in Hale and Brentwood limestone—forms similar to
those listed under West Fork.

9. Fayetteville, State Road 45, near northeastern Fayetteville city limits in Brentwood—forms similar to those listed
under West Fork.

10. Habberton, Washington County, along county road and
White River, 2.5 miles north of State Road 45—in exposures
near base of Fayetteville (Mississippian) shale and Boone (Mississippian) limestone—many invertebrates.

11. Johnson, Washington County, abandoned quarry 1.0
mile west of Johnson—in Boone limestones and chert.

12. Morrow, Washington County, along county road, south
from several Mississippian and Pennsylvanian exposures, only
two of which are fossiliferous here.

13. Summers, Washington County, State Road 59, 1.0 mile
north of Summers—in Fayetteville limestone.

14. Caddo Gap, Montgomery County, on State Road 8, in
highway and railroad cuts 1.0 mile south of gap—in shaly parts
of exposures of novaculite (Devonian)—sporangites and conodonts.

15. Cushman, Independence County, 3.0 miles west of
Cushman on Penters Bluff road—in Ordovician limestone and
shale and Silurian limestone—many forms.

16. East Lafferty Creek, Independence County, at ford 4.0
miles west of Cushman on Penters Bluff road—in Ordovician
limestone exposure.

17. Batesville, Independence County, junction State Roads
11 and 25, 2.0 miles south of Batesville—in Mississippian sandstone.

18. Moorefield, Independence County, State Road 69, in small creeks 2.0 to 3.0 miles east of Batesville—in Mississippian limestone—many forms.

CALIFORNIA

CALIFORNIA IS A WONDERFUL PLACE TO COLLECT FOSSILS. EVERY kind of rock, from the earliest known to the most recent, is represented somewhere in the state. In many places the rocks contain fossils, and several localities are among the best known anywhere for certain kinds.

Geologists outline the stratigraphic record according to geomorphic (natural) provinces: Eel River valley (Upper Jurassic through Upper Pleistocene); Redding region (Devonian through Quaternary); Warner Range (Tertiary); north side of Mount Diablo (Upper Cretaceous through Pliocene); Copperopolis Quadrangle (upper Paleozoic through Quaternary); western Santa Lucia Range (pre-Jurassic, probably through Pliocene); west side of San Joaquin Valley (Upper Jurassic through Lower Pliocene); Los Angeles basin (Jurassic through Pleistocene); Nopah and Resting Springs Mountains (Precambrian through lower Pennsylvanian); southwestern San Diego County (Triassic or Jurassic through Pleistocene).

Reliable authorities give important invertebrate collecting localities in various parts of the state, including:

CAMBRIAN (Lower)
San Bernardino County, about 200 yards west of rock quarry in first south-opening canyon at south end of Marble Mountains—in greenish-gray shale—trilobites of at least two genera.

MISSISSIPPIAN
San Bernardino County, on Kokoweef Peak, Marble Mountains—in Montecristo limestone—silicified corals and brachiopods.

PENNSYLVANIAN

San Bernardino County, on Striped Mountain, in Bird Spring Formation—silicified corals and brachiopods.

CRETACEOUS

Butte County, on northwest side of Big Chico Creek, in cliff of hard sandstone, reached by short trail going a few hundred yards upstream from old corral at end of road at northeast corner of Bidwell Park. This is an old and famous locality, where fossils are found in hard pod-shaped concretions. The same formation is exposed for about six miles to the northeast along the creek. Much of this is private road, and in summer there is a fire hazard.

EOCENE-MIOCENE

Kings County, on Reef Ridge, in Avenal sandstone (Eocene), reached by side road off Highway 33, branching southwestward just before Avenal. A Miocene locality in McLure shale nearby.

MIOCENE (Middle)

Los Angeles County, in cut on old Topango Canyon Road, 2.4 miles below Calabasas—in sandstone and siltstone—moderately well-preserved invertebrate marine fauna, with a diversity of gastropods and pelecypods.

PLIOCENE (Late)

Humboldt County, many localities in Scotia-Eureka area, including bluff along east bank of Eel River, just north of Scotia, and in river bank near bridge—in Wildcat Series of shale, siltstone, and sandstone beds—moderately well-preserved shells of marine invertebrate fauna.

EVEN THE PERSON who isn't a fossil-hound is likely to have heard or read a good deal about the Rancho La Brea tar pits. There, in the heart of Los Angeles, from the tar into which they had fallen somewhere up to a million years ago, the remains of hundreds of thousands of animals were unearthed between 1906 and 1916, leaving incredible numbers still there.

Of course amateurs cannot poke around in the Rancho La Brea tar pits, but there are other places that produce extraordinary numbers and varieties of vertebrates, invertebrates, and plants. For example, the Ventura basin contains a deposit nearly two miles thick—one of the best sources known for Pleistocene marine invertebrates.

Well-known authorities give lists of localities for vertebrates, invertebrates, and plants, in the San Francisco Bay country. Vertebrate localities there include:

PLIOCENE (Early)

1. Berkeley Hills, near Lafayette, south of Saint Mary's College, in foothills south of Mount Diablo, in hills on edge of San Joaquin Valley west of Tracy, and along Stanislaus drainage in the Sierran foothills—scattered fragments (horse teeth, tusks of young mastodont, camel limbs and foot bones, part of lower jaw of oreodont).

2. Famous Black Hawk Ranch quarry on south side of Mount Diablo. Finds here have included a rabbit the size of a cottontail, a primitive ground squirrel, a small gray fox, a ring-tailed cat, a mustelid, part of a lizard's jaw, two teeth of a raccoonlike animal, mastodonts (very common), horses (particularly the three-toed *Hipparion forcei*), camels of at least three species, peccaries, oreodonts, big cats like mountain lions, perhaps saber-tooths, cranes, small beaver, and hyenoid dogs (two kinds).

PLIOCENE (Middle)

1. Mulholland quarry, near Saint Mary's College—bones of ground sloth, bear-dog, small rodents, large and small camels, two kinds of horses, rhinoceros, pronghorned antelopes, mastodonts (and their tracks on steep bank), flamingo (found by a small boy, in a road cut), almost no carnivores.

2. Near Rodeo on south side of San Pablo Bay—in tuff—bones of horse, abundant teeth of pronghorn, rhinoceros, and a few bones of other mammals.

PLIOCENE (Late)

Near Pittsburg, and in Willow Pass north of Mount Diablo —in conglomerate—giant tortoise, and the first of many modern types of mammals.

PLEISTOCENE (Early)

Since 1942, excellent remains have come from Irvington gravel pits and from the Black Hawk Ranch assemblage, making the best early Pleistocene fauna from the Pacific Coast and

Rocky Mountain states—deer, elk, musk-ox-like creatures, camels, a very peculiar pronghorn, true horses, many small rodents, and carnivores such as saber-tooth, dire wolf, and primitive coyote.

PLEISTOCENE (Late)

Characteristic types are found almost everywhere. Some of the best come from Lone Tree Point near Rodeo, the vicinity of Mussel Rock, southwest of San Francisco, and Livermore Valley. Mammoth teeth and part of a bison jaw were dredged out of the Bay.

THE BAY AREA has vast assemblages of invertebrates, with mollusks and echinoids most abundant. The Department of Natural Resources cites:

JURASSIC

Radiolaria in many localities. Particularly good are Stow Lake and an adjacent hill in Golden Gate Park.

CRETACEOUS (Middle)

Fossil pearl oyster, from area 1.5 miles south, 10 degrees west of old settlement of Carnegie, San Joaquin County; ammonites, from about three-fourths mile south of old settlement.

CRETACEOUS (Upper)

Characteristic types in Western Pacific RR cut near Altamont, Alameda County; ammonites in railroad cut between Altamont and Greenway; uncoiled ammonites in creek south of aqueduct tunnel in Arroyo del Valle, Alameda County, on east side of same valley in SE¼ sec. 11, T. 4 S., R. 2 E., M.D., and on top of ridge near road between Marsh Creek and Briones Valley, Contra Costa County; other invertebrates under bridge on State Highway 1, about one mile north of Gualala, Mendocino County, in sea cliff about two miles north of Gualala, and on hillside north of highway about a half mile west of Muir Station, Contra Costa County.

EOCENE (Middle)

There are several thousand feet of Eocene sediment in the Mount Diablo area, with gastropods, pelecypods, and corals abundant at Muir Station, near highway, in banks of stream under railroad trestle; in the banks of the railroad cut just east

of Muir Station and on the hillside just northeast of the highway intersection solitary corals are quite abundant; there are
also a few corals north of Mount Diablo, 2.0 to 2.5 miles northeast of Clayton, about 100 feet above long-ago-mined seam of
coal.

OLIGOCENE

One of the best localities is about a half mile southwest of
the town of Walnut Creek, in south side of creek bed about 100
yards east of Oakland-Antioch RR bridge; but this site is almost
inaccessible because of recent building.

MIOCENE

There are several well-known localities, with great abundance of fossils. Some of the best are: (Middle) about 1.5 miles
southwest of Stanford University, under bridge where Alpine
Drive crosses Los Trancos Creek just above its junction with San
Francisquito Creek, Santa Clara County, numerous acorn barnacles; (Upper) Kirker Pass, 1.5 miles northeast of Clayton,
Contra Costa County, where one type of oyster grew to eighteen
inches; one easily accessible locality, first described in 1856, and
known as the "Pecten Beds," along the shore of San Pablo
Bay, just west of the town of Rodeo and a little south of Lone
Tree Point, where there is a profusion of small scallops; in the
town of Rodeo at intersection of Third Street and Pinole Av-
nue—sand dollars; (lower part of Upper) quarry opposite Devil's
Slide, at sharp turn in road about 2.0 miles from gate to south
entrance of Mount Diablo Park, contains oysters and scallops;
farther along this road, just opposite the ranger's station, are
many gastropods; at Haggin Creek, about 200 feet below bridge,
1.0 mile east of Penn Grove, Sonoma County, are small nonmarine pelecypods and gastropods.

PLIOCENE (Upper)

Some of the most prolific localities are: Along Seven Mile
Beach south of outlet to Lake Merced in San Francisco—sand
dollars; in bluffs between Pillar Point and a spot about 1.0 mile
south of outlet of Lake Merced—pelecypods and gastropods; in
cliffs south of Halfmoon Bay, San Mateo County, in beds along
roadside where highway crosses various ravines and in cliffs
south of the mouth of San Gregorio Creek—pelecypods and gastropods; in quarry about 1.0 mile west of Millbrae, San Mateo

County, and in bluffs at Bolinas Bay, Marin County—ark shells; about one half mile north of Freestone, 200 feet east of trestle in stream, and also in other localities in Sonoma County— variety of marine fossils.

PLEISTOCENE

On raised beaches at several localities along coast—oysters, and hardshell and spiny cockles; in cliffs along northeastern shore of Tomales Bay, about 0.5 mile from ocean, and on point on east side of bay, east of Inverness Yacht Club; oysters, hardshell cockles, and spiny cockles.

PLANT FOSSILS ARE FOUND in many areas of the state. Near San Francisco is one of most continuous known sequences of Pliocene floras, and there are also many plants from the Pleistocene. The most ancient plant fossils were collected many years ago near Tesla, Alameda County. Recently discovered material includes leaves of the fan palm, magnolia, avocado, sebestena, and huanchal. There are fragments of plants and a few pieces of petrified driftwood. In Oligocene gold-bearing gravels in Trinity County are leaves, fruit, and wood; a few leaves have been found near Boulder Creek in Santa Cruz County; and oak and other leaves have come from the western border of the Mojave Desert, but not from the San Francisco Bay area.

In the Bay area, plants transitional between Miocene and Pliocene are found from San Pablo Bay east to Pittsburg and southward to Altamont Pass and Corral Hollow; these include swamp cypress, tupelo, sycamore, willow, alder, cherry, poplar, chumico, magnolia, elm, live oak, sumac, mountain mahogany, bush poppy, flannel bush, desert sweet, Catalina ironwood, Christmas berry, California lilac, coffee berry, dogwood, manzanita. The Petrified Forest on the road from Santa Rosa to Calistoga is one of the best examples in the world of an ancient forest; it contains enormous sequoia, fir, spruce, Douglas fir, hemlock, wax myrtle, red alder, chinquapin, tan oak, pepperwood, rhododendron, and huckleberry. On the east side of Santa Clara Valley is a similar flora, including incense cedar, and other trees such as elder and madrone (*Arbutus*), Pleistocene flora are found all over the Bay area. In the Tomales region—twelve species of modern trees; from near San Bruno—such specimens as a Doug-

las fir log six feet in diameter, with seeds and needles; at Carpin-
taria—coast redwood in its southernmost habitat.

Some of the specific San Francisco Bay region localities
where fossil diatoms may be found are (1) on east side of
Mount Diablo, in Eocene—especially well exposed in Markley
Canyon, where diatoms are beautifully preserved; (2) a few
slightly elevated spots of pure diatomite around the Bay, with
one on the south side of San Pablo Point, where there is a
saddle-shaped brackish-water form; (3) north of the Bay in
certain fresh-water beds, with one of the best known at Mark
West Springs, 8.0 miles southwest of Healdsburg, Sonoma
County. There are also many deposits in Lake County, especially
near Kelseyville.

AMONG DISCOVERIES of great scientific interest has been that by
University of California scientists of two new genera of mosasaurs, in the hills bordering the western side of the San Joaquin
Valley—*Kolposaurus bennisoni* (unearthed in 1926 and 1937,
and *Kolposaurus tuckeri* (in 1937). Scientists found these specimens of special interest in relation to mosasaur material brought
to light between 1938 and 1940 by expeditions sent out by the
California Institute of Technology to a Cretaceous area north
of Coalinga. Dramatic finds in other parts of the state have gone
down in the history of paleontology. For example, more than
2,300 species of Tertiary insects have been recovered from tar
deposits.

The most complete skeleton yet found of a Miocene sirenian
—a dugongid called *Halianassa*—was collected in 1963 by Samuel Welles of the University of California at Berkeley.

Museums pay more and more attention to fossils and allied
exhibits. There is to be a new paleontological museum near La
Brea, and the science portion of the Los Angeles County Museum is now called the Los Angeles County Museum of Natural
History.

As this book goes to press, California paleontologists are
completing the reconstruction of an aquatic mammal that was
discovered on October 2, 1964, during excavations on the
campus of Stanford University. The creature, which they named
Paleoparadoxia, nine feet long and not unlike a sea lion, is

estimated to have lived 14 million years ago, as it belongs to the order Desmotylia, an extinct group of mammals that ranged from late Oligocene to late Miocene. The almost complete fossil, containing 175 of a possible 200 bones, is the first of its kind discovered in North America, and only the second to be identified anywhere in the world. Knowing the age of the rock in which this skeleton was found makes it possible to date rocks in which fragmental remains of *Paleoparadoxia* have been found from time to time—rocks that are common along the border of the north Pacific. The old shoreline where *Paleoparadoxia* fell is now inland, and about two hundred feet above the present shoreline.

Charles A. Repenning, a specialist in vertebrate paleontology with the United States Geological Survey, and now at Menlo Park in charge of reconstruction of the skeleton, says that it may well be one of the more significant discoveries on the North American continent. Other paleontologists agree with him, and are very excited about the find.

Dr. Repenning theorizes that this particular creature met a violent death. Apparently it fell from a cliff into the water, broke its back legs, and crippled and unable to swim was attacked by a school of sharks. A good number of sharks' teeth have been found during the preparation, and it is probable that the missing pieces of bone were carried off by the predators.

When the study of the specimen is completed, it will be transferred to the Museum of Paleontology at the University of California, with which Dr. Repenning is also associated.

COLORADO

Although colorado is thought of as a rocky mountain state, almost 40 per cent of it is in the Great Plains, where its rolling grasslands are punctuated by occasional mesas and buttes. At the west, the open land ends abruptly where the southern Rockies (trending nearly north and south) rise sharply to high above the level of the plains. The easternmost of the complex group of mountain chains is the Front Range, which makes a belt about forty miles wide, continuing at the south in the pendant of the comparatively low Wet Mountains.

Because of its dramatic history of uplifting, eroding, uplifting again, folding, faulting, and other geologic gyrations, Colorado shows rocks of all ages, from the unfossiliferous gneisses and schists of many of the mountain cores to those laid down in the Recent. Fossils may be found in almost any part of the state, though some systems are more richly fossiliferous than others.

Geologic maps are helpful, as always, in showing where rocks of various ages appear on the surface. Ordovician crops out predominantly west of the Front Range, near Salida and Glenwood Springs, on the White River plateau, in the Sawatch and Mosquito Ranges, and in the San Juan Mountains. There are few good fossil localities for the Carboniferous, and though there are some for the Permian, they don't compare with those in Texas and Kansas. Jurassic appears in the foothills west of Denver as well as in many other localities; and Cretaceous all along the Front Range, and in other areas.

In general, one may look for Precambrian—nonfossiliferous—deposits in the largest exposures in the Front Range and the Wet and Sangre de Cristo mountains.

Paleozoic deposits are:

CAMBRIAN and LOWER ORDOVICIAN
Along flanks of major ranges of the central part of the state, and in Glenwood Canyon in the northwestern—marine.

MIDDLE and UPPER ORDOVICIAN
In a narrow, semicontinuous belt in the central mountainous area.

LATER PALEOZOIC
Around borders of all but a few of the ranges, though few fossils. Some Mississippian megafossils have come from North Fork-Crow Creek, and near the Wyoming border, north of Boxelder Creek, and as far south as Cache la Poudre River near Bellevue.

MESOZOIC IS FOUND on the flanks of nearly all present basins

except San Luis Valley, with especially extensive outcrops in the
Great Plains, on Uncompahgre Plateau, and in the northwest
and southwest.

TRIASSIC and JURASSIC

In a wedge, thinning toward the east, deposited on a shelf
sloping westward toward the geosyncline that has its eastern
flank in western Utah. These deposits alternate between marine
and nonmarine (red sandstone), with the Triassic predominat-
ing. One of the most obvious outcrops is in the Garden of the
Gods, in Colorado Springs.

CRETACEOUS

Deposits rich in fossil shells and coal. Clastic beds, 12,000
feet thick, dominate in the northwestern area, where they are
preserved in structural basins. Nearly a quarter of the state is
underlain by Cretaceous and Tertiary coal; the most important
deposits are on the east flank of the Front Range, on the south
and east flanks of the Washakie Basin, on the northeast and
south flanks of the Piceance Basin, on the north edge of San
Juan Basin, in the Raton-Huerfano Basin, and in North Park.
Pierre shale and Niobrara sediments are particularly rich in
fossils.

CENOZOIC

All of continental origin (some bearing coal)—is found in
basins bordering ranges that began in the Cretaceous to look as
they do now. There are especially large exposures in the northern two thirds of the state's Great Plains; in the trend of intermontane parks; in the northern part of the San Juan Basin; and
in the northwestern part of the state. Alluvial material was
deposited along major streams, and glacial in the high mountains. Eocene appears especially in the south-central, east-
central, and northwestern parts of the state. Pleistocene gravels
are found on the mesas.

THERE IS A WONDERFUL CONTINUITY, unusually complete (from
Archean to Pleistocene) around Colorado Springs, which gives a
key to sedimentary rocks along the whole front of the Rockies,
from New Mexico to Montana. Strata often stand vertically, and
it is possible to cross the *edges* of some 10,000 feet of deposits.
Without too much difficulty, any observant person can pick up

fossils in the Colorado Springs area. When finds were recorded in 1906, they included a mastodon tooth near Colorado City; parts of a mosasaur from the Jurassic, found a quarter mile south of the Garden of the Gods; invertebrates of many thousand species—from ever younger geologic ages as hunters progressed toward the east from the foothills of the mountains; several invertebrate species from red sandstone above the granite in Ute Pass, and from Manitou (now Williams) Canyon, just upstream from the narrows; Cretaceous shells, in gray limestone, from the face of a cliff just west of the Standard Mill; clams and coiled cephalopods in Pierre shale in bed of Monument Creek; leaves like those of the willow in fine sandstones near the base of cliff at Austin's Bluff; ferns and other leaves in abandoned tunnel-like openings across river east of Pikeview.

One of the great collecting grounds in North America for insects and plants is at Florissant; where the rock consists of volcanic ash, coarser volcanic debris, and gravel and shale of Oligocene age, which lie in places to a thickness of 300 feet. More than a thousand species of insects have been found in those beds; 150 species of plants, including types of sequoias seventeen and a half feet in diameter; and fossils of many mammals. Because much of the state is underlain by coal deposits (chiefly Cretaceous), Cretaceous plants may be found in many places, but Florissant is so remarkable that in 1965 it was suggested it be made a federal preserve.

A comparatively small but important region for fossils is the Denver foothills, between Boulder and the town of Morrison in Jefferson County, which is south and slightly west of Denver; the area is less than four miles wide, and makes the western rim of the Denver Basin. It has Precambrian rocks, and then everything from Carboniferous to Eocene, tilted to make a region of hogbacks in which most of the formations appear at the surface. It contains the Table Mountains (lava-capped mesas of the area around the town of Golden), with Ralston Dike to the north, and Green Mountain to the south. Beginning with the earliest, the fossil picture, much simplified, is:

CARBONIFEROUS
In Lyons Formation (usually making east wall of Red

Rocks), and in Fountain (brown to red sandstone)—very few fossils.

PERMIAN

Lykins Formation—in deep red sandy clays with light gray spots, and sometimes in limestone or gypsum—a few fossils.

JURASSIC

Morrison Formation, on lower west slope of Dakota hogback—in sandstone and some limestone, and in delicately tinted gray, green, or maroon shales—reptile bones, poor plant fossils, and some fresh-water gastropods.

Same formation, in districts of Canon (pronounced Canyon) City and Morrison—good dinosaur material.

Digging in the Morrison Formation in Colorado and Wyoming in 1877, three men found dinosaurs at the same time, and several hundred have come from that rock alone.

CRETACEOUS

Dakota (makes prominent hogback somewhat east of Red Rocks)—in massive light-colored sandstones separated by clays —some fish scales, leaf impressions.

Benton (usually very dark clay-shales with thin patches of white)—marine reptiles in some localities, marine invertebrates common here and there.

Niobrara (much limestone, often chalky), in ridge near foot of slope of main hogback—fossils similar to those of Pierre shale, with some sharks' teeth.

Pierre (dark shales with some limy material and sandstone, seen at some distance to east of prominent hogback, and weathered flat)—clamlike bivalves, straight-chambered cephalopods, small oysters, and numerous iron concretions, some with shells.

Fox Hills (yellowish sands and shales, best exposed north of Denver)—marine mollusks.

Laramie (sandstones, shales, and lignite)—abundant plant material, chiefly leaves of deciduous trees, ferns, and palms; oysters and a few mollusks.

EOCENE

Denver and Arapahoe formations—in soft sandstones, grits and clays, well exposed on slopes of Table Mountain, at Golden, and in several localities nearer Denver, such as hills west of

Overland Park—impressions of leaves of palms; ferns and characteristic trees and shrubs; petrified wood; a few scattered bones
of mammals and reptiles.

SOME OF THE MOST SPECTACULAR fossil finds of all time have
been made in other parts of Colorado—especially around Canon
City. There, about 1890, Charles D. Walcott and others found
the oldest known vertebrate remains, dating from mid-Ordovi-
cian times. These came from the gray and reddish shallow-water
sandstone formation directly above the Precambrian rocks,
where the first finds had been small bits of bony plates (which
turned out to be broken parts of the dermal plates of ostracoderms—the most primitive of fishlike forms, with backbones,
but jawless, related to lampreys and hagfish). With the ostracoderms were trilobites, sponges, ostracods, gastropods, pelecypods,
articulate brachiopods, conodonts, and worm borings. *Stegosaurus*, a late Jurassic dinosaur now in the Denver Museum of
Natural History, is from Garden Park (the Cope-Marsh collecting
locality [see p. 294]) near Canon City, an area long known for
its dinosaur remains.

Other exciting finds that have been made in Colorado
through the years include:

TRIASSIC
In valley of the Colorado River—tracks of reptiles and a
few amphibians; near Fall Creek Post Office, in the upper
Dolores Formation—leaves.

CRETACEOUS
In Pierre shale—mound-shaped bioherms, some about fifteen inches in diameter. Duckbilled dinosaur bones have come
from some areas, and several small types were discovered in
1925 in the eastern part of the state. Tracks were found in a
hogback west of Denver, and on the Purgatory River, thirty
miles from La Junta. Also from the eastern part of the state
came the fossil of a very small mammal, probably close to the
ancestry of all placental mammals. From the Front Range, particularly in the famous Niobrara Formation (which occurs in
numerous other states), come finds as diverse as dinosaurs and
the pelecypod *Ostrea congesta*. A plesiosaur sixty to seventy feet

long, now in the Denver Museum, is from Baca County in south-eastern Colorado.

Plesiosaurs have been known in England since 1821. In 1811, at the age of twelve, a girl named Mary Anning, looking for fossil sea shells to sell, came on the Cenozoic "fish-lizard" which came to be known as an ichthyosaur. Ten years later, she found the first plesiosaur—the incredible creature that has been compared to a turtle with a snake running through it. And in 1828 she unearthed the first flying reptile to be found in England.

PALEOCENE

Early Paleocene turtles are being unearthed in the Denver Formation on South Table Mountain near Golden. Two were found in 1960 by Malcolm McKenna of the American Museum of Natural History, and others were found in 1961 by Peter Robinson, curator of the University of Colorado Museum at Boulder.

EOCENE

From the Gardner-Walsenbury Formation of the south-central part of the state, a block of *Eohippus* skeletons was unearthed in 1955 by an American Museum of Natural History expedition. From the northwest part came the skull of a large uintathere and a smaller skeleton; and titanotheres of the early hornless type, something like small rhinoceroses.

OLIGOCENE

In about 1920, after it had been discovered that the Oligocene formations of South Dakota's White River Badlands extended southward and westward into adjoining states, the Denver Museum made a very rich strike. Dozens of skulls and articulated skeletons—including those of titanotheres, "giant pigs," and rhinoceroses—were found. Among specific finds, from a quarry in Weld County, which is very fossiliferous, is a slab of rhinoceros bones in the matrix. At Florissant and elsewhere were abundant insects, including beetles.

MIOCENE

During the mid-1960s Peter Robinson has been working on Miocene vertebrates in Middle Park, slightly northwest and not far from Denver. There, he reported in 1964, he had already found the skull of a moderately large camel. He also discovered a new microfaunal locality in the park—making seven known ones altogether.

PLIOCENE

Various kinds of rhinoceroses, giant pigs, and other mammals.

PLEISTOCENE

All sorts of characteristic mammals.

Whether they are from Colorado or not, the Denver Museum shows the most usual mammalian forms, arranged as part of its series of chronological exhibits. Among the several elephant creatures is *Archidiskodon*, closely related to "Archie" of the University of Nebraska (see p. 190), which is not only one of the largest and best preserved specimens of the mighty mammoth but notable because the unfortunate beast had been hit by a spear point. Among recent Colorado finds are a mammoth tooth and tusk unearthed in the spring of 1963 by a road crew working near Limon in Lincoln County, near the Kansas border.

IN THE SUMMER OF 1961 Colorado made headlines with stories about a tremendous find of fossils in Douglas County, south of Denver. Beginning in June scientists from the Smithsonian, with a staff of collegiate helpers, dug up a waterhole "graveyard" where cattle still drink and where fossils were buried in comparatively shallow mud. It had become evident that there were masses of bones there when one of the owners of the grazing land began to dredge out a better watering place. By way of Denver paleontologists, word was sent to Washington, and (through funds from the National Science Foundation) the Smithsonian sent a group of experts. In the lowest layer were bones of the Columbian mammoth, and higher were bison, horses, and camels. By the end of the 1961 summer, 341 fossil bones, packed in thirteen huge cases, had been shipped to the National Museum.

CONNECTICUT

CONNECTICUT IS WORLD FAMOUS FOR ITS TRIASSIC DINOSAUR tracks, but produces very few other fossils except an occasional incomplete skeleton of a dinosaur, usually comparatively small, and a number of plants and fishes—all from the Triassic. The tracks—some of huge reptiles, others no bigger than as if made by birds—may be found in red sandstone all up and down the Connecticut Valley. Often, when a road crew is blasting or bulldozing, a block of sandstone will fall apart, showing the prints —positive on one half and negative on the other.

The Connecticut Valley is part of the Newark System, which extends across Massachusetts and Connecticut, in general following the depression left by the Connecticut River. This Triassic depression is bounded on either side by rocks that are at least as old as the Paleozoic. During "Newark Time" the area was a flatland; the hills of the Great Fault Scarp were on the east, and on the west the area merged into a somewhat similar flatland in New Jersey and southern New York. A great accumulation of gravels, sands, and clays was laid down, interbedded with lava sheets.

At an early date, the valley had such expert paleontologists as Professor Othniel C. Marsh of Yale and Professor Edward Hitchcock of Amherst. Professor Hitchcock wrote in 1822 about the flora, and in 1848 about tracks.

Plant finds have been made in Connecticut at Newgate Prison, Southbury, Middletown, Suffield, Southington, Durham, Bristol, Middlefield, Tariffville, and Portland, but only in shales close to trap ridges. These finds have included conifers, cycads, ferns, and rushes.

Invertebrates, including two known species of mollusks, and one insect, have been found near Middletown. Trails of arthropods and mollusks have been found in a few localities in Connecticut (more in Massachusetts).

Vertebrate finds include the actual osseous remains of fish and reptiles; and tracks of reptiles and probably amphibians.

Fish fossils have come from two levels: the lower at Durham, Bluff Head, Higby, Berlin, Southington, and possibly Southbury; and the upper at Durham, Westfield, South Bloomfield, North Bloomfield, Rocky Hill, Lake Saltonstall, and Middlefield. Six genera and probably thirteen species have been found.

Skeletal reptile finds, which have been made at East Windsor, Ellington, Simsbury, New Haven, and Manchester, have supplied three genera and five species of dinosaurs, one species of phytosaur, and two species of pseudosuchians. Although the first dinosaur was found in South Windsor in 1818, by far the most notable locality for finds is Manchester, where the important specimens from which types have received their names were found of *Ammosaurus major, Yaleosaurus* (or *Anchisaurus colurus*), and *Anchisaurus solus*. All are now in the Peabody Museum at Yale. The first of these was found in a quarry a mile north of Buckland Station, in 1884, by the owner of a quarry, Charles O. Wolcott; but before its importance was recognized, the rock containing the skull and forequarters had been built into the abutments of a bridge over Bigelow Brook, South Manchester. When the block containing the hindquarters was taken out of the quarry, Prof. Marsh was notified, and Yale got the specimen. *Yaleosaurus* was found in the same layer, in a large block of sandstone, some twenty feet farther north, where part of it had been showing for a long time. *Anchisaurus solus*, of which nearly all was recovered, was found at the same time as *Yaleosaurus*, in two small blocks. In 1894, also in Manchester, one rib of a fourth specimen was found. From Simsbury came the type specimen of *Clepsysaurus*, received by Yale in 1888. The Peabody Museum also has the impression of the dorsal armor plates of *Stegomus arcuatus* Marsh from a quarry in Fair Haven (New Haven) near the Perry Street Bridge over the Quinnipiac River.

Reptilian tracks have been found at Suffield near Enfield Bridge, Portland, Middletown, Middlefield, Higby, Berlin, North Branford (Sugar Loaf Tunnel). At least seven genera, thirteen species, and one subspecies have been recovered. Where footprints of dinosaurs are concerned, conditions in Connecticut and Massachusetts are so similar that the states are often considered one locality. In 1858 Hitchcock of Amherst listed thirty-eight quarries where they could be found, and not many additional localities were discovered after that date—until the mid-sixties.

On August 23, 1966, a young man named Edward Mc-Carthy, working for a contractor, was running a bulldozer, digging the foundation for a state highway department laboratory on a slope in Rocky Hill, a dozen miles from Hartford. As he turned over the red Triassic sandstone, lifting it from the hard gray mudstone beneath, he saw both positive and negative impressions of three-toed feet and thought they might be those of dinosaurs. Then and there he stopped the bulldozing and consulted a neighbor who knew more about fossils than he did. Before night a reporter had been to the site, and the news was on the radio. Early the next morning the public was already trooping to Rocky Hill to see the tracks, and perhaps to dig some up.

Then ensued several days of great excitement. The governor and various commissioners were notified; the state geologist, the director of the Children's Museum of West Hartford, and specialists from nearby colleges and universities, including Dr. John H. Ostrom of Yale, gathered around; a fence was built quickly to keep out the acquisitive; twenty-four-hour guards were stationed; and everyone got very excited about preserving the site.

Nobody knows how many dinosaurs had once milled around in that area, but there were probably several, and certainly two, because some tracks are large and some small. Ninety-five per cent of them were identified as *Eubrontes* (the name for a track, not a reptile), closest to footprints made by the primitive, rather small, carnivorous bipedal dinosaur *Coelophysis*. The largest tracks indicate a stride of 52½ inches—presupposing a creature perhaps eight or nine feet tall.

In addition to containing no one knows how many tracks, the Rocky Hill area is of especial interest to geologists for two other reasons. Across it runs a fault, where the layers were tilted, and skewed approximately 90 degrees. And there are not only ripple marks made by the wind or water but impressions of raindrops that fell on a day some 200 million years ago! The value for education in the earth sciences, teachers say, can scarcely be overestimated.

The fact that the public knew something about fossils had astonishing immediate results. The governor decided that seven and a half acres should become a state park, with twenty thousand feet in the center cleared to show the tracks and the fault—making what will be one of the best dinosaur parks in the country. The nearby Rocky Hill Veterans' Hospital gave another piece of land to the state highway department for its laboratory. And, even more remarkable as an example of cooperation, the state, with public approval, paid $23,000 to the contractor for excavating already done, and continued to pay $1,000 a day for further work.

A week or two after the Rocky Hill finds, it developed that Homer Scott of West Hartford, a well-informed amateur paleontologist, a year before had discovered *more* tracks—in Newington, only a few miles from Rocky Hill. He told reporters that there were at least fifteen varieties there, which he believed were 3 to 5 million years older than those Edward McCarthy discovered, and that he himself had already taken four hundred tracks out of the small site.

For Connecticut, all this makes what has been called "the find of the century."

DELAWARE

A LARGE PORTION OF DELAWARE IS COVERED BY PLEISTOCENE sediments, and the only good collecting locality is along the Chesapeake and Delaware Canal, where Upper Cretaceous rocks are exposed. This can be reached only at low tide; tides for Reedy Point, printed daily in Wilmington and Philadelphia papers, give approximate hours for the canal.

A glance at the map will show that Delaware looks like a section of Maryland, cut out very arbitrarily, and that it is closely related to New Jersey on the other side. There is a strong correlation between Delaware's deposits and those of these adjacent states.

In the Chesapeake and Delaware Canal, the Cretaceous formations are known as the Merchantville and Wenonah of the Matawan Group (present below the zone of the pelecypod *Exogyra cancellata*), and the Mount Laurel–Navesink and Red Bank of the Monmouth Group. Somewhat different groupings and terminology have been applied to the sediments in Maryland and New Jersey, but similar fossils will be found wherever the Cretaceous appears in these states.

Along the canal, which connects Chesapeake Bay with the Delaware River, and was originally built between 1824 and 1829, the outcrop is sixteen miles long. In 1922 the U.S. government took over ownership from private interests, and the government has since deepened and widened the canal. Geological work was begun there in 1952, and numerous species were collected during an intensive search in 1954.

The so-called Deep Cut in the canal has been written about since at least 1829; in 1845 Sir Charles Lyell, the great English geologist, made reference to the Cretaceous of New Jersey and adjacent areas, and reports and analyses have been appearing periodically ever since, with geologists agreeing or disagreeing about the formations and offering new evidence to support their conclusions. Both marine and nonmarine Upper Cretaceous formations have been found in New Castle County, through which the canal cuts, and they are unconformably overlain by Pleistocene sands, gravels, and clays.

The most extensive invertebrate faunas of the Merchantville Formation come from the north spoil bank (Station A) 2,500 feet east of Summit Bridge, yielding annelids, pelecypods, gastropods, and cephalopods, and especially abundant claws of the crustacean *Callianassa mortoni* from east of the Pennsylvania railroad bridge. This formation may be seen from 2,400 feet east of Bethel, Maryland, at navigation light 39, for 4.2 miles to a spot 1800 feet east of that bridge, where it passes below sea level. The soil of the Merchantville grades from coarse silt, which is dark blue to black, to fine sand with considerable silt and clay; the lower sand is dark greenish, whereas the top layer is gray, except from navigation light 39 to a spot about

2,900 feet west of Summit Bridge, where the upper two feet are orange. The thickest section (about forty feet) is near the overhead cable, approximately a mile and a half west of Summit Bridge.

As for the Wenonah Formation—it is rust-brown and gray sand, containing numerous cylindrical tubes that have been called *Halymenites major* Lesquereux, and the exact nature of which is not known. Wherever the Wenonah appears along the Chesapeake and Delaware Canal, it overlies the Merchantville conformably, and grades into it. The Wenonah may be seen from a point 2,100 feet east of Summit Bridge, in the south bank, eastward to navigation light 20.

The Mount Laurel–Navesink, lower formation of the Monmouth Group, changes gradually downward from fine dark greenish-brown sand with numerous rust spots, to a dark green to black silt. Though the Mount Laurel sand and the Navesink silt are considered separately in New Jersey, they are treated as one unit in Delaware, seen in the canal from 1,000 feet east of Summit Bridge in the south bank for a distance of 4.7 miles (occasionally interrupted) to a spot 1.5 miles east of St. Georges, where the top is two feet above sea level. At station 3 it is eleven feet thick. There seem to be three different assemblages: (1) at railroad bridge—poorly preserved specimens; (2) at station 3 —fauna suggests an oyster reef; (3) (probably youngest) at Biggs farm (station 6) on the south bank, about a mile east of where highway 13 crosses at St. George. The most extensive of the formation's fauna has been collected at the third site, where numerous specimens have been found of several species of pelecypods, and the rapidly swimming cephalopod *Belemnitella americana*.

Red Bank, a ferruginous red sand, marine in origin, makes its appearance in the canal 2,600 feet east of Summit Bridge, on the south bank, and can be traced along both banks, with few interruptions, to the railroad bridge. East of the railroad bridge, it has been cut down by erosion, but it appears again 1.5 miles east of St. Georges, in the south bank, conformably overlying the Mount Laurel–Navesink Formation. It contains very few fossils, of few species.

The finds made at the Biggs farm (though few) are considered so important that they are the subject of a separate Delaware Geological Survey paper, published early in 1963.

This report, by Horace G. Richards and Earl Shapiro, was carried out under the auspices of the Academy of Natural Sciences in Philadelphia. Field and laboratory work by Earl Shapiro, the junior author, was made possible by the Jessup Fund of the academy.

The outcrop at the Biggs farm, which was exposed by erosion not long before 1963, contains an unusually rich Upper Cretaceous fauna. When the report was published, some 111 species of mollusks, representing seventy-two genera, had been identified, along with Coelenterata, Porifera, Annelida, Brachiopoda, and Crustacea. A few fragmentary vertebrate remains had also been found. Five species of invertebrates are described as new, and there are fifty-four new records for Delaware.

"The preservation of this material," say the authors, "suggests that the animals lived on a sandy bottom in water between 50 and 100 feet in depth, possibly near the mouth of a bay. . . . It is believed that the fauna of this locality lies near the Matawan-Monmouth boundary, perhaps in the lower part of the Monmouth group."

Preservation is of three types, with the most common that of the internal cast, where the original shell material is weathered away. Next common is the replacement of the original shell by a dark phosphatic mineral. Least common is preservation of the original shell.

Though preservation is generally poorer than that of material from North Carolina, Tennessee, Mississippi, and Texas, it is better than for that of New Jersey.

FLORIDA

THE SOIL OF FLORIDA IS PACKED WITH FOSSILS.

Pleistocene deposits are said to be the richest in the entire world for vertebrates, especially mammals. During the Pleistocene, more animals of more different kinds moved up and down and across what is now Florida than at any one time elsewhere on this continent.

In addition, the state is famous for its Thomas Farm Quarry, richest site in eastern North America for Miocene land mammals. And from the various other deposits have come (and are still coming) the bones of innumerable creatures that lived and died between the Eocene and the Recent.

There are no surface deposits earlier than the Eocene, because it was not until that epoch that the avid waters receded, after several partial or complete inundations, to leave the geological surface of our southernmost state much as it now exists.

Time was, and not so long ago, when in any fossiliferous area a person could find a fossil lying at his feet. With the rash of high rises and smothering concrete, such unsought finds are less frequent; but whenever and wherever a fossil is found, it is likely to be in an excellent state of preservation.

The reasons for this are inherent in the character of the land. The basic rock is covered by sedimentary limestone, and that material continued to be deposited up through the Ice Ages.

At least as early as the Cretaceous, the peninsula was much wider than it is today; now a good deal of the western portion is submerged, so that the Gulf flows across a continental shelf 100 miles or more wide. While successive inundations continued to deposit sediments, dramatic happenings helped to create the peninsula as we now know it.

Beginning in the Cretaceous and continuing through the Oligocene, the Atlantic and the Gulf met between the northern portion and the mainland in what is called the Suwannee Straits. In the Early Miocene, mountains rose in the Straits, filling the gap, and two high areas were created farther south: the Ocala Uplift and the Chattahoochee Arch. When streams flowed down from the mainland, eventually covering almost the entire plateau with clastic sediments, those uplifts remained uncovered. Thus they still have outcrops full of the calcium carbonates that had previously characterized all land south of the Straits.

Coral reefs were building up in the keys, and the surface of the peninsula became increasingly level. Today, the highest point in the state is only about 350 feet above the sea.

A limestone bedrock accounts for the unique physical features of what now lies beneath the surface. Ground waters
moved through the limestone, creating a honeycomb of caves,
underground rivers and sinkholes. The fact that limestone is
alkaline contributes largely to the extraordinary preservation of
the fossils. Limestone's reaction with bone is almost neutral; so
the limestone filled the cavities in the fast-disintegrating soft
tissues and even replaced some of the bony material itself. Any
animals falling into the limy water were quickly preserved. Thus,
streams and sinkholes are likely places to find animal fossils.

In a locality like the Reddick site near Ocala, water pene-
trating joints in the limestone produced an underground stream
that created a cave when the water fell below the level of the
cavity. Cave-dwelling species such as bats left their remains on
the floor, and roosting owls regurgitated pellets and skeletons
onto it. The level of the cave's floor thus rose, until it was more
than half way to the roof. Then, under heavy rainfall, the roof
began to collapse and to form what is known as a karst trap,
with an opening to the air at the top.

Inevitably, large animals fell into the trap, and their fossilized skeletons filled the cave higher and higher. Eventually,
water filled the karst trap and it became a pond, in the depths
of which everything was kept in excellent condition. Sometimes
water also came up as a spring, to fill the sinkhole.

All sorts of once-living creatures are in the traps, along
with shells and vegetation. Some sinkholes contain human bones.

Courageous scientists go down into the traps to bring up
whatever they can of the fossilized material that has lain there
untouched while life on the surface appeared and disappeared,
or developed according to its strange evolutionary patterns.

Despite the compelling fascination of mysterious depths, amateurs are warned to stay away from these death traps and to confine their searching to beaches, upturned earth, or shallow water.

Remarkable treasures have come up from Little Salt Springs
and Warm Mineral Springs, water-filled traps below Venice, just
off the Tamiami Trail. Among them was a human skull thought
to be 10,000 years old, and therefore the oldest human fossil
found thus far in the eastern United States.

Geologically speaking, the Florida peninsula is split lengthwise by an imaginary line, with Pleistocene of two ages on the

east, and a crazy quilt of Pleistocene and earlier epochs on the west. Largely because of fossil finds, geologists frequently revise their thinking about certain areas. As this book goes to press, the Pleistocene end of the peninsula is said to be interrupted by both Late Miocene and Oligocene. Pleistocene of the same age runs in a narrow strip along the Atlantic coast to St. John's County, bounding a broad area of what used to be identified as Recent and is now called Late Pleistocene terrace deposits. More terrace deposits appear in the southern part of the Panhandle, which also has Eocene; Oligocene; Early, Middle and Late Miocene; and Early Pliocene.

The largest outcrop of Eocene is near the Ocala Uplift, where it is bordered on the east by Miocene. Early and Middle Miocene spread out from Tampa Bay, embracing an area of Middle Pliocene. Early Pliocene stretches out from Charlotte Harbor and curves around the top of Lake Okeechobee. All this makes an Eocene-to-Pleistocene grab bag from which almost anything can emerge—and frequently does.

EOCENE

None of the bones of *Eohippus*, earliest known ancestor of the modern horse, have been unearthed in Florida, though later mutations are astonishingly represented in subsequent deposits. Florida's Eocene (marine) deposits (Ocala limestone) are notable chiefly for invertebrate forms, especially shells, with which it is often packed; but remains of the cetaceans *Basilosaurus* and *Pontogenous*, sirenians and several types of sharks have been found in it.

OLIGOCENE

It used to be believed that the peninsula was under water during the Oligocene; but late finds in a tiny solution cavity near Gainesville, labeled the 1–75 fauna, prove that it was not. 1–75 fossils make up the oldest extensive Cenozoic terrestrial vertebrate fauna in eastern North America.

MIOCENE

The Miocene Thomas Farm Quarry was discovered in 1931, when a farmer plowing a field turned up what he thought were bones from an Indian graveyard. After the significance of the site was realized, the land was bought for the University of Florida, and no member of the general public may dig there without written permission from the head of the geology department.

Among notable fossils found in the quarry are several species of horse; a huge, doglike, carnivorous bear; a single species of pig creature; two species of camel; and a very rare distant relative of the camel that had a pair of cowlike horns on the back of its head and a long forked horn near the tip of its nose.

In 1963, a new Late Miocene locality was discovered near Ashville, just south of the Georgia line, and another (probably Late) one near Ocala. A third important discovery was that of an apparently Early Miocene vertebrate locality north of Brooksville, Hernando County, yielding alligators, canids, tapirs, rhinoceratids and oreodonts.

There is also a new Miocene site near Buda, Alachua County, and scattered Miocene sites in Alachua, Gilchrist, Marion, Leon and Gadsden. In that epoch, it is postulated, those areas were above sea level, whereas the ones away from the central ridge were still submerged.

PLIOCENE

A dozen Pliocene sites are known between Georgia and Tampa Bay, with the most exciting one being the Bone Valley in Polk County, where phosphate is mined. Though huge power shovels destroy many of the fossils, searchers still find remarkable things. Terrestrial and marine remains come from depositional environments that are most complex—now mixed with Miocene and Pleistocene—and believed to have originated in the mouths of rivers when the sea was 80 to 120 feet below its present level. Found there are rays, sharks, dugongs, porpoises, whales, seals, crocodilians, amphibians, turtles and various birds, along with terrestrial fossils that include many types of elephant creatures, horses of at least six genera, camelids, tapirs, deer, peccaries, and such carnivores as fierce bears, stabbing cats and ferocious canids. Three horn cores identified a very rare antelope that had three horns sticking straight out above each eye.

In the phosphate, there is also a certain amount of wood, and one hunter dragged out a log that weighed 1800 pounds.

Outside the phosphate district, especially fossiliferous Pliocene vertebrate sites have been uncovered at the McGehee Farm in Alachua County and Mixon's Bone Bed in Levy.

PLEISTOCENE

Because so many millions of animals fled into Florida before the encroaching ice, by far the greatest number of vertebrate fossils are Pleistocene. Because deposits of that age lie atop others in large areas, they are most easily accessible. Because multitudes of creatures fell into karst traps and streams, magnificent collections of beautifully preserved bones come from still or running water. On beaches, the lucky hunter is rewarded by sharks' teeth, parts of other cartilaginous fishes and bony ones, and occasional land animal remains.

The following is a partial list of the multitudinous Pleistocene sites: *rivers*—Chipola, Aucilla, Itchetucknee, Santa Fe, Waccasassa, Withlacoochee, Oklawaha, Peace; *springs*—Wakulla, Rock, Hornsby; Sabertooth Cave; *others*—Haile, Arredondo, Payne's Prairie, Williston and Devil's Den, Reddick, Kendrick, Coleman 11A, Seminole Field, Bradenton, Sarasota, North Port Charlotte, Pool Branch, Melbourne, Sebastian Canal, Vero, North Havana Road, Joshua Creek, Punta Gorda, west of Jupiter Inlet, Nichol's Hammock, and Palm Beach County, where (among other treasures) an entire skeleton of a mastodon was found and later set up in a museum.

During the Wisconsin Ice Age, the sea level rose and fell drastically, periodically covering large areas. Much of the land was probably a moist savanna, with great forests here and there sustaining every kind of animal from mouse to mammoth.

There were mighty herds of grazing and browsing herbivores, which by then had evolved into their most developed forms: *Mammut americanum* and *Mammuthus floridanus* (elephant creatures) that were twice as tall at the shoulders as a man; the even bigger giant sloth, *Eremotherium*, which might be more than 20 feet long and could weigh as much as 12,000 pounds; the huge, armadillo-like glyptodont, which sometimes had spikes in its tail; *Equus*, the modern horse; and bison; as well as deer, antelope, and numerous other small running creatures.

A horde of fierce predators fed on them. Wolves ran in great packs. There were fearsome lions. One horror was a ferocious short-faced bear. Saber-toothed cats slashed and tore with their curving, knifelike fangs.

There on the sands of Florida they lived and fought, slew their enemies or were themselves slain; and their bones were often buried where they fell, remaining to tell us something of their fate. At some time during the Recent, almost all of them became extinct. No one knows why, though one school of thought insists that man himself had a part in their extinction. He certainly hunted the mammoth and mastodon.

INVERTEBRATES

Though Florida's best-known fossils are of vertebrates, its sands have revealed an incredible wealth of fossil shells and a (comparatively) few other invertebrates. There are some corals —from Ocala limestone, usually as casts and molds; and a few years ago beautiful Miocene agate-lined coral geodes, almost unique to Tampa Bay, were abundant. In spoil banks there are also barnacles, one or two species of Bryozoa, a few worm casts, starfishes, sea urchins, sand dollars, and many kinds of Foraminifera. Vegetation is less common, but some leaf impressions are found, and wood occasionally comes to light.

Fossils of the myriad once-living things may be found here and there in private collections and in small museums all over Florida. But the most impressive display is, of course, at the Florida State Museum, which opened in the fall of 1970 on the campus at Gainesville, and devotes a quarter of its space to fossils. It is the largest natural history museum south of the Smithsonian, and is said to be one of the ten top natural history museums in the United States.

GEORGIA

GEOLOGICALLY, GEORGIA IS ROUGHLY DIVIDED INTO THREE regions, which are called the Crystalline Area (covering 30 per cent of the state above the middle), the Paleozoic Area (a small rectangle in the northwest corner), and the Coastal Plain (the whole lower part, taking up more than half the state). Within that framework, the geology is very diverse, and actually a high percentage of the geologic column crops out somewhere. The Crystalline Area contains the oldest rocks, consisting of metamorphosed sediments and intrusive granites from Precambrian to late Paleozoic—making it of great interest to the mineralogist, but of slight value to the paleontologist. The Paleozoic Area runs from the Lower Cambrian to the Pottsville Formation, and apparently has no important fossils. It is the Coastal Plain that interests the fossil hunter.

Surface rocks of that plain range from the Upper Cretaceous in the center of the state (known as the Upper Coastal Plain), to Pleistocene and Recent along the Atlantic, with a thick Tertiary section in between. The Georgia Department of Mines, Mining and Geology prints information about collecting localities on the plain, listing fossils according to geologic ages—in rocks from Paleocene through Miocene:

PALEOCENE and EOCENE

Deposits run in a thin strip diagonally southwest across the middle of the state, from Richmond County on the east. The Clayton Formation, originally called Eocene, is now considered Paleocene. It has produced echinoid spines and other obscure forms—from Fort Gaines, Clay County, on both sides of the Chattahoochee River to a point seven miles above town; molluscan casts—from two quarries and a cave along Route 27, nine miles north of Cuthbert, Randolph County; a few forams—from road cut on Route 49, about a mile south of Andersonville, Sumter County.

The Eocene is in valleys and lowlands between Fort Gaines and Americus. A few mollusk fragments have been found at Fort Gaines; pectens and oysters—in ditch at foot of hill along Route 50, 4.6 miles west of Cuthbert; oysters and echinoids—on south side of McBean Creek, at Richmond-Burke county line; corals, bryozoa, and mollusks—at Keg Creek, 6.0 miles northwest of Sandersville, Washington County; extensive microfauna—in Sumter County, at Danville Bluff, west side of Flint River, about a mile above the mouth of Pennahatchie Creek; a few plants—near Grovestown, Columbia County, and south of Macon, Bibb County.

OLIGOCENE

Extensive outcrops occur in wishbone shape following south edge of Paleocene-Eocene as far as Laurens County, with small areas in Jenkins and Screven counties. Typical fossils include various corals, thirteen varieties of pelecypods, and

eleven of gastropods. Among the fossiliferous sites are Wyley
Landing, south of Bainbridge and 3.0 miles above the mouth of
Spring Creek; Hale's Landing, 6.25 miles southwest of Bain-
bridge; Forest Falls Sink, 6.5 miles north of Whigham; quarry
south of Beaverdam Creek, about six miles north northeast of
Sylvania; Red Bluff, 6.0 miles north of Bainbridge; State Route
257, about a mile and a half south of Oakfield; Route 341, south
of Clinchfield; Route 280 between the town of Plains and the
Webster County line; Spring Mill branch, 4.5 miles north of
Millen.

MIOCENE

Outcrops in something more than half that portion of the
state southeast of Oligocene deposits. A few fossils (chiefly
gastropods and pelecypods) have been found on the Savannah
River in Forest Falls Sink and at Porter's Landing; and at
Doctortown, Wayne County, on the west side of the Altamaha
River, especially near the base of concrete surface water observa-
tion shelter.

A special NSF In-Service booklet tells where fossils may be
found in northwest Georgia, near Shorter College, Rome:

Cephalopods—ball field (next to avenue of pines) across
road from main plant of General Electric Corporation. Also
brachiopods and a few molds of tree-fern bark.

Crinoids—pieces (usually broken stems) all around Rome,
in Floyd and adjacent counties; heads at Youngblood farm,
about 1.5 miles from Armuchee School on Piney Road, and on
Kirton farm in Hall's (sometimes called Paul's) Valley.

Bryozoa—lacelike traces in many places; "Archimedes'
screws" and plainer types on road banks between Rome and
Summerville and on side road beyond Storey home near Floyd
County line.

Trilobites—several whole and many parts on Benton (formerly Spann) farm, 1.0 mile west of Cedar Creek Church, near
Livingston.

Blastoids—great abundance in clay fields and roads on
Youngblood farm, with crinoid stems, some fluted brachiopods,
and bryozoa nets; large blastoids were found in 1961 on the
Kirton farm, near the Floyd County–Alabama line.

Brachiopods—many shapes and sizes in most of northwest

Georgia, and abundant at General Electric plant. An additional type on Youngblood farm; and still another on Floyd Spring Road; large bed of big specimens in ravine about a mile beyond Berry School gates, on east side of highway, and plentiful specimens in whole area.

Corals—two types of cut variety about two and a half inches long on General Electric land, sticking out of clay on erosion gullies; good specimens on Kirton farm in Hall's Valley.

Plant Prints—from Lookout Mountain, Pennsylvanian coal beds, in shale, especially in Durham mines.

Gastropods—on Kirton farm, Hall's Valley, along with crinoid heads and stems, cup corals, large blastoids, and brachiopods.

AMONG THE CHIEF LOCATIONS for Cretaceous plant fossils have been McBride's Ford, about eleven miles southeast of Columbus, in Chattahoochee County, just above ford on Upatoi Creek—a few plants, poorly preserved; Chimney Bluff, on the left bank of the Chattahoochee River, twenty-two miles below Columbus—especially large foliage-bearing twigs and detached leaves of *Araucaria bladenensis*; and a site 6.0 miles east of Buena Vista, on Central of Georgia RR, 1.5 miles northeast of Byron, and Broken Arrow Bend.

A new Pleistocene locality was discovered in the fall of 1963 by Warren Moore and his family, who found fossil bones and mollusks in a limestone quarry at Ladds, Bartow County, in northwest Georgia. These finds were reported to Shorter College, and subsequent collecting is being done under the auspices of the college, in collaboration with the Smithsonian Institution. Although all sorts of enthusiasts have participated, the most active have been Mr. and Mrs. Moore and other public school teachers, members of the Shorter faculty, and students and friends of the college.

Fossils occur in small fissures exposed in a remnant pinnacle of limestone at the southerly end of Quarry Mountain (Ladd Mountain), in red cave earth. Collecting thus far has yielded some forty species of vertebrates, including a new kind of large chipmunk, christened *Tamias aristus,* and closely related to another species already known from Georgia.

HAWAII

BECAUSE OF THE VOLCANIC ORIGIN OF THE ISLANDS, THERE ARE very few fossils in our beautiful fiftieth state. Bits of plant material have been found in the volcanic deposits of Oahu, and a few marine organisms, chiefly mollusks and coral, have come to light in the coastal sediments. The B. P. Bishop Museum in Honolulu has carried on archeological explorations, but little searching has been done specifically for fossils, and most of what has been written about the few discovered is out of print. If anyone who finds himself in Hawaii wants to search for fossils, he may best go to the museum and ask for directions.

IDAHO

THERE ARE NO POPULAR GUIDES TO FOSSIL HUNTING IN THIS state, but through the courtesy of the department of geology and geography of the University of Idaho and the department of geology of Idaho State College, we are able to suggest localities where fossils are likely to be found. Fossiliferous formations range through the geologic column from Cambrian to Pleistocene, with only a few periods missing. Almost any outcrop of Paleozoic or Mesozoic rocks will yield invertebrate fossils, often prolifically, and such outcrops may be located on any geologic map of the state.

PRECAMBRIAN
Worm trails in argillites in Blackrock Canyon south of Pocatello.

CAMBRIAN
From south end of Pend Oreille Lake—trilobites and primitive brachiopods; Middle Cambrian in outcrops immediately east

of Mink Creek Road, just inside north boundary of Caribou
National Forest (T. 7 S., R. 35 E., Pocatello Quad.)—trilobites,
brachiopods, and gastropods in abundance.

ORDOVICIAN

Graptolites in abundance in road cuts in vicinity of Sun
Valley.

CARBONIFEROUS

Marine faunas (especially colonial and solitary tetracorals,
tabulate corals, and brachiopods) in limestone outcrops in hills
near Mackay and Arco.

PERMIAN

From beds in southeastern corner of state—spiny brachiopods, corals, crinoids, and fusulinid forams.

CRETACEOUS

From continental beds in southeastern part of state—
petrified wood, with the extinct fern *Tempskya* the most interesting.

TERTIARY

Sediments exposed in cliffs along Snake River in vicinity of
Bruneau contain considerable number and variety of vertebrate,
invertebrate, and plant fossils; in Salmon area—Oligocene
floras of leaf imprints; along west-central border of state (Pay-
ette and Boise area)—Miocene floras in form of leaf imprints
locally common; in northern panhandle (near Moscow and
Coeur d'Alene)—famous Latah flora; in road cuts in vicinity of
Weiser—Pliocene leaf imprints.

PLEISTOCENE

Mammals are abundantly represented by preserved skeletal
remains along the shores of American Falls Lake, a short distance west of Pocatello; finds have included mammoths, camels,
bison, saber-tooths, giant sloths, and short-faced bears; also
many mollusks. (The State University asks that any finds in
quantity from the area be reported at once to the university's
museum in Pocatello.)

A 1938 PAPER lists some of the discoveries on the Snake River
plain, not far from Boise. It seems probable that the hunter may
have luck in the same area, if he can reach the sites:

East of King Hill—bones of mammoths and extinct bison

from Recent deposits; locally, in small flood plains—Pleistocene elephantines, sloths, camels, and bison.

Between King Hill and Blackfoot—in Hagerman Lake beds, near mouth of Salmon Falls, in diatomite twenty feet thick, above tuff—well-fossilized mammals and numerous fresh-water shells of upper Pliocene.

Riverside Ferry cone—in tuff (in Banbury volcanics)—recently fossilized camel bone.

Base of Centennial Mountains along lacustrine (lake) and fluviatile (river) rocks—Pliocene fossils.

Bluffs along Snake River near town of Hagerman: Elmer Cook, a farmer, found rich deposits, from which Dr. Harold T. Stearns took several hundred pounds of upper Pliocene bones. In 1928 Dr. Stearns sent a representative collection to the National Museum. Later, parties from the Smithsonian, under J. W. Gidley and N. H. Boss, dug in a quarry on a hill in NW¼ sec. 16, T. 7 S., R. 13 E., and about thirty feet below the top, found a large number of skulls, lower jaws, and some articulated vertebral sections of a horse (intermediate between *Pliohippus* and true *Equus*), now known as *Plesippus shoshenensis*. The site, which was probably a drinking hole, also yielded remains of frogs, fish, beavers, swamp turtles, and other water-loving animals, with leaves, coarse grass, and small pieces of wood. From the same vicinity have come remains of mastodons, peccaries, camels, sloths, cats, otters, hares, aquatic birds, and a rodent of the muskrat type.

King Hill Canal, about five miles upstream from King Hill, in highly fossiliferous sandstone—invertebrates, including fresh-water clams.

Center of sec. 15, T. 4 S., R. 32 E.—a log of redwood, and several bones and teeth of an elephantine—probably late Pleistocene. Occasional tree molds are found on the Snake River plain here.

Acequia gravel pit, SE¼ sec. 7, T. 9 S., R. 25 E.—many bones, including large part of an elephant skull, with tusks; upper part of skull of a new species of bison, with horn cores of fifty-inch spread; horn cores and part of skull of a musk ox.

Near Rupert—*Elephas imperator*.

Minidoka Dam—*Equus idahoensis*.

Snake River, just above old town of American Falls—*Bison alleni.*

Pit on shore of American Falls Reservoir, 6.0 miles northeast of Aberdeen—elephants, horses, and bison, but mostly fragments.

Pit 4.0 miles above Aberdeen—complete mammoth skeleton exposed in American Falls Lake beds on ledge of lava, sec. 10, T. 8 S., R. 30 E.

Older alluvium along Snake River—many bones now in State Historical Society exhibit at Boise, which includes *Elephas columbi, Elephas imperator,* etc.

In younger alluvium—sand, silt, and water-worn gravel, all appearing very recent—there are two sites:

1. At foot of American Falls, on the east side of the river, in sand pocket in spring pool—several skeletons of mammoths found in 1904. One tusk is fifteen feet long and fifteen inches in diameter at the base. Some of the bones discovered in 1904 are in Boise, at the state capitol; about five hundred pounds were shipped to the University of Iowa; and one tooth of *Elephas columbi* was sent to the Smithsonian. This tooth came from beneath fifty feet of lava. *E. imperator* came from NW¼ sec. 10, T. 10 S., R. 18 E., near Twin Falls.

2. In NW¼ sec. 4, T. 10 S., R. 18 E., near Twin Falls— from quicksand—many bones, including skulls, of extinct bison, and teeth, leg, and thigh bones of elephantines considered to be *Mammut americanum.*

AN UNSPECIALIZED IDAHO GUIDE speaks of some of these finds, and emphasizes petrified trees (very unusual in Idaho) in walls of basalt on Santa Creek, 6.0 miles north of Emida; the trees were found because the ends of carbonized logs could be seen in lava near the water's edge. These trees, it is deduced, were remains of an immense Miocene forest, which grew when perhaps 200,000 square miles of our Northwest were deeply covered by lava. Very minute structures are sometimes preserved in the wood. The trees are oak, redwood, beech, and cypress—none of which now grows in or near the forest site.

ILLINOIS

WHEN IT COMES TO FOSSILS OF PLANTS AND INSECTS, ILLINOIS has some of the most remarkable deposits in the entire world. No collecting areas are more famous than the beds along Mazon Creek in the northeastern part of the state. In all, some 130 kinds of insects have been identified from that area, including dragonflies, roaches, damselflies, and numerous forms not found in modern times. Also, from the same site came the first true scorpion, and many primitive spiders. The state is equally famed for the remains of Pennsylvanian plants, which are also found along Mazon Creek, as well as in various other areas. Moreover, insects and plants make up only a small portion of the state's fossils.

Among the spectacular Mazon Creek finds are the only specimen known of a salamanderlike branchiosaur; a small amphibian (*Amphibamus grandiceps,* Cope), which may point the way to the ancestry of the frogs; a nearly complete coelacanth; and primitive vertebrates (found in nodules), with the soft parts preserved. All of these are from the Pennsylvanian.

Fossils are so common in Illinois that, as an Illinois Geological Survey guide says, they can be found "in the gravel or crushed stone of your driveway or in stone walls and foundations." They may be seen "in counter tops in restaurants, utility marble in public buildings, in stone sidewalks in several . . . cities, or in riprap along the shores of Lake Michigan . . . and major rivers." They may also be seen in tributaries of the major rivers—the Mississippi, Illinois, Ohio, and Wabash.

In age, they range most plentifully from the Ordovician and Silurian through the Pennsylvanian. Because most of the Mesozoic and Cenozoic rocks, except the Pleistocene, have been eroded out, Illinois vertebrate fossils come from either the Paleozoic or the Pleistocene. From the former come some fish teeth and scales and a few small reptiles and amphibians; from the latter, mammoths, mastodons, and many still-extant forms.

Plant fossils are widespread, and their remains are found in various forms: whole plants (sometimes in stony nodules), parts of plants, casts, molds, and compressions (pressed carbonized remains). (See Chapter IV). These include scale- and seal-trees, scouring rushes, *Sphenophyllum,* ferns, seed ferns, *Cordaites,* and fruiting bodies not possible to assign to particular plants. They are found in any place where Pennsylvanian rocks are exposed (almost the entire state), and especially on Mazon Creek, in Grundy and Will counties. Sites there, four to six miles northeast of Morris, were the first to be well known, more than a century ago. Great numbers of fossils have been discovered since 1920, when coal stripping began. Strip mines where specimens may be found are mostly between Braidwood and Wilmington, and in Bureau, Knox, Mercer, Warren, Fulton, McDonough, Vermilion, Lawrence, Saline, Pope, Johnson, Perry, and Jackson counties.

The best place to look for plants is in certain shales directly over coal beds, where they often are in ironstone concretions or on bedding planes. Plants are rarely found in the black slaty shale in which there are marine fossils. Except for Mazon Creek, the most likely places are spoil heaps from shaft mines. Some specific spots are: along Mill Creek, about one mile northeast of Pleasant View; three miles north of Pleasant View, and a quarter of a mile northwest of Onion School; bluff of Kerton Creek, about three and a half miles north and a quarter mile west of Bluff City; along middle branch of Copperas Creek, six miles west of Glasford; old mine dump and ravines along Edwards River, northeast of Aledo; about three miles southwest of Alexis, in gully about a third of a mile southeast of Center School; along Court Creek in East Galesbury; near DeLong, in mines southeast of Victoria; south end of Kankakee River bridge along county line; southwest of Harrisburg, northwest of Eddyville; south tributary of east branch of Cedar Creek, about six and a half miles south of Stonefort; near Du Quoin and Murphysboro; northwest of Mount Vernon; near Grayville; in Friendsville area, near Berryville and Calhoun ("coal balls"). Finds have also been made southeast of Franklin, at Neelys, and at a number of places in the south and west parts of Rock Island County.

If a person is fossil hunting in this state for animal remains, invertebrate or vertebrate, he must arm himself with a very good geological map on which at least the major stratigraphical groups, if not the formations, are shown, because the surface outcropping is highly complex. Thus armed, he may seek for such fossils as follows:

Foraminifers—calcareous type very common in Salem limestone, in bluffs of Mississippi River along McAdams highway northwest of Alton and in bluffs of Monroe and Randolph counties. Forams have been found also near Anna and Jonesboro in the southern part of the state. Fusulinids are plentiful in rocks of the Pennsylvanian.

Sponges—"sunflower coral" sponge common in Ordovician of north central and northwest Illinois; *Hindia* in Silurian of Chicago region.

Corals—found often in limestone, where sometimes they make up a large part of the rock. Also in shale and sandstone.

Bryozoa—very common in Mississippian, throughout state.

Brachiopods—found in almost any part of the state, but especially common and well preserved in Mississippian limestone in bluffs on Mississippi and Ohio rivers.

Marine worm jaws—oldest are in Ordovician sediments, but most common in Silurian of northeast.

Gastropods—common in Ordovician and Pennsylvanian; those of Pleistocene found abundantly along bluffs of major rivers.

Cephalopods—straight and coiled in several varieties, in Pennsylvanian.

Pelecypods—especially clams, common in Pennsylvanian of central Illinois and in some Ordovician limestones in the northern and western parts of the state.

Crinoids—in limestone cliffs along Mississippi River between Alton and Burlington.

Blastoids—most common in river bluffs and banks of streams in Randolph County and in the southern part of state, near the Ohio River.

Cystoids—most are from quarries in Silurian rocks of the Chicago region and from the bluffs of the Mississippi, in northwest Illinois.

Graptolites—most common in the Ordovician of northern Illinois.

Conodonts—in bedrock formations throughout the state.

Trilobites—several good collecting localities in northeast, and one in the west-central part of state.

Ostracods—frequent, but usually microscopic.

Insects—nearly all from the Mazon Creek–Braidwood area, in ironstone nodules with plant fossils; but there are very few complete specimens. The insects are of kinds that would live in woodland near low seashore, and often have no modern counterparts.

Horseshoe crabs—relatively few—all from Mazon Creek area and of Pennsylvanian.

AMONG FOSSILIFEROUS OUTCROPS along the Illinois side of the Mississippi, in Calhoun County, are, especially, those of the Chester series near Red Bud, where one may pick up brachiopods, "Archimedes' screws," corals, crinoids, blastoids, and similar invertebrates; and the limestone quarries near Grafton, which yield trilobite casts and molds. Especially handsome pieces of coral may sometimes be found in a gravel bar near Dallas City.

INDIANA

INDIANA IS A HAPPY HUNTING GROUND FOR THE ENTHUSIAST— one of the best collecting places in the world. In nearly every bit of the bedrock, and beneath the loose material on the surface, some kind of fossils can be found. Most specimens are marine, though there are abundant plant fossils in the coal-bearing strata of the western and southwestern parts of the state. The earliest strata are Ordovician, chiefly in a strip in the southeast corner. Then there is a large area of Silurian, north and west of the Ordovician and in the northwest corner. A mixture of Mississippian and Devonian is exposed in the north, and in a narrow strip diagonally across the center with Devonian along one side of it, and Mississippian along the other. Mississippian takes up a large part of the center and also appears in the northeast corner. Pennsylvanian makes a long triangle along the west border. All these deposits are connected with those of Michigan on the north, Illinois on the west, Kentucky on the south, and Ohio on the east. As always, the most fossiliferous deposits are in exposures along roads, railroads, hillsides, and streams and in such excavations as quarries. The best localities are in the southeastern part of the state, in the vicinity of Madison, Vevay, Versailles, Rising Sun, and Batesville.

In popular pamphlets, the Geological Survey recommends many locations, often giving more specific directions than we do here. These are:

1. Bluffs at Madison—long cuts along State Highway 7, just northwest of Madison—spectacular abundance of Ordovician marine forms.

2. Ruins of Tunnel Mill, old quarry, and nearby Muscatatuck State Park, 0.3 mile south of junction of Highways 3 and 7 —fine crinoids, and other invertebrates.—Vernon Quad.

3. Road cuts along Highway 56, 3.0 miles south of Rising Sun—remarkable for Ordovician bryozoans of many forms. —Aberdeen Quad.

4. Between Guilford and Weisburg, along Cleveland, Cincinnati, Chicago and St. Louis RR, a stretch of nine miles from which tons of fossils have been taken, and many may still be found, especially easily in cut on right side of Highway 48 as it goes up bluff just west of Lawrenceburg—all sorts of Ordovician specimens, including rare trilobites.—Lawrenceburg Quad.

5. Old cut, 3.0 miles west of Peppertown, on Highway 229, in W½ sec. 17, T. 11 N., R. 12 E.—Ordovician.—Metamora Quad.

6. Quarry northeast of Highway 46 at southwest edge of Hartsville, Bartholomew County (NE¼ sec. 2, T. 9 N., R. 7 E.) —good Silurian specimens in gray-blue shale between lime-

stones. (Also the same types in gray-blue shale in southeastern Shelby County.)

7. Near Liberty, on small stream running into Silver Creek—excellent Ordovician corals, brachiopods, and bryozoans.

8. Around Richmond, almost everywhere, and especially along Elkhorn Creek, 4.0 miles south of Richmond, between Liberty Pike and Highway 227—Ordovician fossils.

9. Erie Stone Company quarry near Huntington—Silurian fossils fairly well preserved including brachiopods, and chain and honeycomb corals.—Huntington Quad.

10. Stuntz-Yeoman Company quarry west of Delphia, 0.8 mile northwest of junction of Highways 25 and 39—in Silurian coral reef with numerous fossiliferous exposures—rare trilobites and cephalopods.

11. France Stone Company quarry, 2.0 miles east of Logansport, on north side of U.S. 25—Silurian and Devonian fossils.—Logansport Quad.

12. Abandoned Midwest Rock Products Corporation quarry 1.0 mile southwest of Spencer, and west of Highway 67—few but good Mississippian brachiopods, corals, and tiny ostracods. —Spencer Quad.

13. Stobo lens near Bloomington, reached by crossing Stephens Creek, 6.0 miles east of Bloomington, and going 0.3 mile farther, where lens is exposed on north side of road and along eastern of two secondary roads to the north—stems of Mississippian crinoids.—Unionville Quad.

14. Abandoned quarry and dump, 1.5 miles southwest of New Ross, Montgomery County, reached by taking road past cemetery and going 0.5 mile on first road leading west—crinoid stems and some heads. Permission required.—New Ross Quad.

15. Abandoned Silverville quarry—in massive limestone and rubble, and in ledges at west end—Mississippian fossils.— Oolitic Quad.

16. Abandoned Seymour Gravel Company quarry, reached by road straight from Medora, to T-junction, 3.0 miles west, on old road—Mississippian marine forms.—Medora Quad.

17. In Salem limestone where Chicago, Indianapolis and

Louisville RR cuts through Spergen Hill in Washington County —famous dwarf-sized marine fossils.—Salem Quad.

18. Old Cleveland quarry (NW¼ sec. 20, T. 7 N., R. I. W.) reached from Harrodsburg (just west of Highway 37), by going 1.0 mile north on secondary road—fossiliferous Salem limestone.—Clear Creek Quad.

19. Exposed bank of Ohio River, at southwest edge of Jeffersonville, along Riverside Drive at Pennsylvania RR bridge, and downstream near Dam No. 41—Devonian corals.—New Albany Quad.

20. In green shale 1.0 mile north of Carwood—small corals, brachiopods, crinoids, bryozoans, cephalopods, etc., of Mississippian.—Speed Quad.

21. Abandoned Lutgring and Sons quarry near Branchville, 2.0 miles east of Highway 37, and reached by going 0.6 mile on road east of village and 0.1 mile north—one of best places in state for Mississippian marine fossils.—Branchville Quad.

22. Abandoned coal pits near Buffaloville, especially 0.25 mile north and 0.6 mile west of village, on either side of road—fine Pennsylvanian specimens, including brachiopods and ostracods.

23. Warren County, on dumps of abandoned Quality Coal Company mine, 3.0 miles north of center of Boonville, on Highway 61, and west on secondary road to about two miles west of highway—many plant fossils; also, within a mile or two of the line between Scalesville and Yankeetown, going through Boonville—many old pits with marine fossils.—Boonville Quad.

24. Bluff at West Franklin, on Ohio River, along dead end road just east of town—brachiopods and gastropods, also found near Evansville in ledges on east side of U.S. 460.

25. White Ash Mine dump, 2.0 miles west of Wheatland, just west of mine buildings and north of U.S. 150 and B & O RR—Carbonaceous plants.—Wheatland Quad.

26. Maumee Chieftain Mine dumps, 1.0 mile south of Youngstown on U.S. 41, then 2.0 miles east on secondary road, onto haulage road and along right fork for 0.4 mile farther—concretions with imprints of ferns and other plants. Permission required. In same area, on either side of Highway 159, north of Blackhawk—brachiopods, crinoids, etc.; and 2.8 miles south-

west of Petersburg on Highway 57, in old strip mine where road curves sharply to right—concretions.—Lewis Quad.

27. Above coal from Old Min Win mine, reached by going 2.5 miles northeast of Petersburg on Highway 57, Lick Creek School and church, and along old mine road—brachiopods, crinoid stems, gastropods, and pelecypods. Also in many strip mines north of Highway 257—Sandy Hook Quad.

28. Abandoned strip mine reached by going 1.5 miles south of Highway 48, on road one and a half blocks west of Chicago, Milwaukee, St. Paul and Pacific RR, in Jasonville, turning west from intersection, crossing railroad spur, and proceeding 0.4 mile—Pennsylvanian fossils, some turned to pyrite.—Jasonville Quad.

29. Along line between Owen and Clay counties, especially Commodore mine near small lake (SE¼ sec. 2, T. 9 N., R. 6 W.) —Pennsylvanian corals, brachiopods, and microfossils.—Coal City Quad.

30. Small outcrop on Highway 63, 4.3 miles south of West Lebanon, along Wabash River, across bridge and near second bridge, then 0.3 mile farther, on west valley of small stream— many Pennsylvanian specimens, including microfossils.

31. Banks of Wabash, especially in shale pit of Porter-Herron Brick Company, 1.0 mile northeast of Attica, south of secondary road and near Wabash Railroad tracks—Mississippian.

32. Marl pits of northern counties—Pleistocene gastropods, pelecypods, and ostracods.

COLLECTING SITES according to geologic age include:

ORDOVICIAN
1. NW¼ SW¼ sec. 9, T. 4 N., R. 11 E., about six miles northeast of Madison, on road paralleling south side of Jefferson Lake.

2. Riley Creek, Pennsylvania RR cuts, and exposures on Highway 7, NW¼ SE¼ sec. 34, T. 4 N., R. 10 E.—classic locality.

3. Road cuts on U.S. 50, between eastern part of Versailles and Laughery Creek.

4. Wilson's Fork Section, 2.0 miles south and 0.5 mile west of Cross Plains, a short distance northwest of Highway 62, NE¼ NW¼ sec. 5, T. 5 N., R. 12 E.—many fossils from nearby hillsides.

SILURIAN

Vail Stone Company quarry, 0.35 mile east of Sandusky, from south face, NW¼ NE¼ sec. 12, T. 3 N., R. 9 E.

DEVONIAN

1. T. J. Atkins and Company quarry, 1.0 mile northeast of Claysburg, W¼ Grant 10, Clark Military Survey.

2. Louisville Cement Company quarry, 1.0 mile northeast of Speed, Grant 132 and southwest part of Grant 131—corals and brachiopods.

3. Scott County Stone Company quarry, approximately two miles south of Blocher, NE¼ NW¼ sec. 20. T. 3 N., R. 8 E.—solitary corals, but difficult to extract.

4. Meshberger Stone Company quarry, about two miles northeast of Elizabethtown, NE¼ sec. 6, T. 8 N., R. 7 E.—stromatoporoids, brachiopods, and corals from upper forty-eight feet.

MISSISSIPPIAN

1. Mulzer Brothers quarry, about two miles north of junction of Highways 145 and 64, SW¼ NE¼ sec. 10, T. 2 S., R. 2 W.—great variety of fossils, well preserved.

2. Ray's Cave section, about 2,000 feet northeast of village of Ridgeport on Highway 54, NW¼ NE¼ sec. 13, T. 7 N., R. 4 W.—large crinoid stems, etc.

3. Road cut about five and a half miles east of Bloomington, on Highway 46, SW¼ NE¼ sec. 4, T. 8 N., R. 1 E.—abundant crinoid stems.

As RESULT OF a state field project in 1953–54, 146 species of sixty-eight genera of fossil plants have been found at ninety-three collecting sites in southwestern Indiana, revealing that fossil plants are much more ubiquitous and important in Indiana than had been supposed, though the first paleobotanical collecting was done there in 1843 by David Dale Owen, at that time state geologist for Indiana. Plant macrofossils are valuable in correlating individual coal seams. Collecting sites include:

1. Abandoned Dixie Bee Mine, 0.5 mile south of Pimento—petrifactions and casts of *Lepidophloios, Lepidodendron,* and *Lepidostrobus.*

2. Spoil banks of abandoned strip and drift mines, 3.0 miles east of Farmersburg—ironstone nodules containing *Asterophyllites, Sphenophyllum, Asterotheca,* and *Syringodendron.*

3. Abandoned strip mine of Long and Price Coal Company, near intersection of Routes 48 and 157—beautifully preserved in ironstone concretions, such plants as *Calamites, Annularia, Asterophyllites, Dorycordaites, Palaeostachya, Calamostachys, Samaropsis, Holcospermum,* and *Zeilleria.*

4. Dumps of White Ash Mine, about two miles west of Wheatland on U.S. 50—variety of well-preserved compressions of *Sigillaria, Sphenophyllum, Alethopteris,* and *Neuropteris.*

5. Abandoned strip mine about one and a half miles northwest of Burns City—ironstone nodules containing *Lepidodendron, Lepidophyllum, Calamites,* and *Artisia.*

6. Abandoned strip mine on Highway 57, about 2.0 miles north of Glezen—concretions in shales, containing numerous species of *Neuropteris, Alethopteris, Asterotheca,* and *Cyclopteris.*

7. Along Raben's Branch, about a mile and a half southwest of St. Wendell—many compressions of *Calamites, Neuropteris, Sphenophyllum,* and *Bowmanites.*

NOTE: See section on West Virginia for explanation of meaning of plant fossil genera given above. Some of them indicate what are known as "form genera."

IOWA

ORDINARILY RARE FOSSILS—OF VARIOUS KINDS OF ECHINODERMS, which include the crinoids (sea lilies) and starfish—have been found in Iowa, especially in several limestone quarries near Le Grand. From the Mississippian limestone of these quar-

ries, which are no longer in operation, at least forty species of
echinoderms have been unearthed. Other fossils from the state
come from the Cambrian and ensuing periods, up to the Mississippian.

The Le Grand quarries (about one mile north of where State
Highway 30 enters the west city limits of Le Grand) have been
noted for their remarkable contents ever since crinoids were
first found in the area in 1858 by W. James Hall, New York
State geologist, who was responsible for dramatic finds in many
fields. In one of the quarries especially, the fossils had retained
their shapes and details in amazing fashion.

One of the most remarkable discoveries was made in 1930
by B. H. Bean, an amateur who began to collect in the 1890s, and
became an authority on the mid-Mississippian life of Iowa. One
block of limestone, which he seized as it was being quarried,
contained 183 starfish—a type of marine life very rarely found
in a fossil state. Nowadays, starfish are not easy to find even
in that area.

Many of the books in which there has been information
about Iowa fossils are now out of print, but are sometimes available in public and school libraries. The state's geological survey
helpfully lists some of the better known fossil-collecting areas:

1. Rockford Brick and Tile Company pit, 0.5 mile south and
0.5 mile west of Rockford, Floyd County, on County Road D—
abundance of well-preserved brachiopods, gastropods, and corals, especially in yellowish shales over blue-gray beds.

2. Bird Hill, near center of north line of sec. 24, T. 95 N.,
R. 19 W., Cerro Gordo County, and about 3.5 miles west and 0.5
mile south of the Rockford plant—same fauna as at Rockford.

3. Elgin-Clermont area, Fayette County, along new highway between Clermont and Elgin, in dry stream bed bordering
County Road Y, east of Clermont, and in high road cuts along
Turkey River southeast of Elgin—large trilobites (usually fragments), and both straight and coiled cephalopods.

4. Gray Station, Dubuque County, on Illinois Central RR,
about 8.0 miles west of Dubuque on Highway 20, and about 1.5
miles north of Highway 20, on a county road—very abundant
straight cephalopods.

5. Mill Creek at Bellevue, Jackson County, about 1,000 feet upstream from highway bridge, in thin dark shale of stream bed—"depauperate fauna" (phosphatic fossils about a twelfth natural size). Careful search is required.

6. Le Grand Quarries (see foregoing)—finest crinoids in the world.

7. Gilmore City area, Pocahontas County, just northwest of Gilmore City, in several quarries—corals and crinoids, though (as with those found at Le Grand) much work is required to prepare them for study or display.

8. Quasqueton area, Buchanan County, in talus along bluff south of Wapsipinicon River and 2.0 miles west of Quasqueton —abundance of horn corals.

9. Near Burlington, Denmark, and Augusta in southeast Iowa, in Mississippian rock—large brachiopods, fish teeth, crinoids, and blastoids.

10. Vinton Limestone Products quarry, northeast of Vinton, in southeast corner sec. 10, T. 85 N., R. 10 W., Benton County— brachiopods (spirifers and *Atrypa*), and colonial coral *Hexagonaria,* often called "bird's-eye marble."

11. Near Lake McBride spillway, about ten miles north of Iowa City—brachiopods and corals.

12. Red Oak–Stennett area, quarries in Montgomery County—in dark brown to black chert—many small white *Triticites* fusulinids (foraminifera).

13. Plum Creek, 1.0 mile east and 1.0 mile north of Thurman (NE¼ NW¼ NW¼ sec. 31, T. 70 N., R. 42 W.), Fremont County—good plant fossils.

14. Westerville Section (SW¼ NW¼ sec. 13, T. 75 N., R. 26 W.), Madison County—in limestone—abundance of brachiopods (*Chonetes* and *Crurithyris*).

KANSAS

SOME OF THE MOST REMARKABLE AND DRAMATIC FOSSILS FOUND in the United States have come from Kansas, which is especially noted for its portion of the Niobrara Formation of Cretaceous chalk, occurring in the western part of the state, and for other surface exposures of the same age, in the central part.

The fossil record begins with a few specimens from the Cambrian, and continues up through the Pleistocene, often from rich deposits; and scientists journey from all over the world to see collections in the geology museum at Fort Hays State College, where many astonishing and some unique exhibits are on view. Among the most famous specimens are the Cretaceous fish-within-a-fish; the best-preserved and most complete skeleton known of the short-necked plesiosaur *Trinacromerum;* and the skeleton of another Cretaceous sea reptile, *Platecarpus.* Also to be seen are fossils of invertebrates, birds, land reptiles, aquatic reptiles such as sea turtles and crocodiles, other fishes, and many Pleistocene mammals.

Among specific important finds that have been made in Kansas from various ages are:

PENNSYLVANIAN

In late shales near Garnett, Anderson County—parts of a dozen reptiles; on Wakarusa Creek at Dightman Crossing, Douglas County—tracks of the gigantic amphibian *Wakaruso-pus gigas,* which weighed several hundred pounds and had a third eye in the top of its head; in two localities in Douglas County, paleoniscid skulls with the soft parts preserved.

PERMIAN

From Wellington shales near Elmo, Dickinson County— more than ten thousand species of insects, making one of the best representations known, and including ancestors of cicadas and leafhoppers, and many modern types such as bees, ants, and wasps, which appeared then for the first time; near Garnett— land plants, including true conifers.

CRETACEOUS

From Ellsworth County—one of the most famous localities in the world for fossil plants (discovered in 1865 by Judge E. P. West)—hundreds of ironstone concretions found over a period of many years by Charles H. Sternberg, each specimen containing a leaf, identified and described by Leo Lesquereux. From the Smoky Hill River and its drainage—a sea turtle now in the

Denver (Colorado) Museum of Natural History, the skull and jaw of a mosasaur now in the American Museum of Natural History, a great flying reptile, *Pteranodon*, with a wing span of twenty-five feet, and also such reptiles as *Elasmosaurus*, forty feet long but with a twenty-foot neck, a primitive toothed bird known as *Hesperornis*, which was flightless and a diver, and *Ichthyornis*, which looked much like a modern tern but had small teeth. Found also were a number of fish, and such invertebrates as crinoids. *Ichthyornis* was found by Marsh, and some of the other very strange creatures were found either by him or by Cope (see Wyoming).

PLEISTOCENE

From rock exposures in Western Kansas—mastodons, mammoths, camels, bison, horses, peccaries, and many other mammals.

EARLY IN 1962 scientific magazines reported the discovery of two new insect beds (geologically the oldest and youngest) in the Wellington Formation, where it crops out in Kansas and Oklahoma. Six such beds are now known, occurring at intervals of about a hundred feet. The oldest is in Sumner County (called Wellington XVIII, in the NW NE sec. 23, T. 34 S., R. 2 E.), appearing north and east of the Kansas Turnpike. Another section is known in Cowley County, 4.5 miles east of Wellington XVIII, and stratigraphically below it. The youngest of the insect deposits is in Kay County, Oklahoma (Wellington XIV, SE NW sec. 20, T. 29 N., R. 2 W.). The discovery of these new beds gives geologists an opportunity to do some very elaborate reasoning about the relationships of the beds to each other and of the insects to associated fossil clam and shrimp beds.

Labyrinthodonts (a type of early amphibian) have come, from time to time, from the coal measures on this continent, but their remains seem to be very scanty everywhere. The earliest reported find was in 1850, from a coal mine in Nova Scotia—an incomplete skull that was sent to London; and the vertebrae of a typical labyrinthodont were found in 1863, also in Nova Scotia. Except for a few footprints found in the Pennsylvania coal measures in 1849, the fragment of a skull found (by Cope) in 1875, and a tooth found near Louisville, Kentucky, in 1897, no

other traces were uncovered in the nineteenth century. Therefore, when part of the skull, the left maxilla, fourteen teeth, and
a mandible of a new genus, *Erpetosuchus*, of a new species,
Erpetosuchus kansensis, came to light in Kansas early in the
twentieth century, it was the sixth unearthing on this continent.
Unfortunately, the exact location where the find was made is
unknown. It was included in the Hambach Collection in the
National Museum, and when some bright-eyed paleontologist
spotted it, it bore a label saying that it had come from Washington County, Kansas. That seemed odd to the specialists, for
there are no coal measures in the Washington County area. The
mystery is still unsolved.

The Ross Quarry, near Ottawa, Kansas, has produced excellent fossils, including trilobites. Ammonites, gastropods,
sharks' teeth, and other fossils representative of primitive marine
life have come from the Blue Hills of Mitchell County.

Kansas does not put out any general popular guide to fossil
localities, but a fairly recent but out of print publication about
its rock column does indicate where, in general, various sediments were deposited. This publication deals with subsurface as
well as surface deposits and is therefore not necessarily helpful
to the amateur, because he is interested chiefly in surface exposures. However, the soil of the state is so richly fossiliferous
in many areas that any intelligent search is likely to be rewarded.

Precambrian rocks, more or less deeply buried, underlie all
of Kansas, and every geologic period up through the Recent is
represented by strata deposited above—sometimes distributed
by the sea, sometimes by streams, wind, or glaciers; but except
for a small area of Mississippian in Cherokee County, rocks
earlier than the Pennsylvanian do not crop out on the surface.
Strata laid down by the sea are very often rich in the sort of life
one might expect; nonmarine deposits may contain remains of
land plants or traces of fresh-water life, or of air-breathing
animals.

Deposits known to contain fossils include:

PENNSYLVANIAN
One of the most important of outcropping strata; occurs in

the far eastern part of the state, reaching a north-south line starting west of Chautauqua County, next to the Permian, and containing varied land plants and many marine invertebrates. Rocks of the age are divided into a bewildering number of series, groups, formations, and members—almost all of which are fossiliferous. Deposits are made up chiefly of limestones and shales, with some sandstones. Localities that have provided collections include Anderson County, where amphibians, fishes, a scorpion, marine invertebrates, and well-preserved plants, including the rare *Walchia,* have been found in shales; Franklin County, where nautiloid cephalopods have been found in limestone; and Montgomery and southern Labette counties, where there are plentiful plant fossils in the shales near coal beds.

PERMIAN

Predominantly marine; outcrops across the state from Washington, Marshall, Nemaha, and Brown counties on the Nebraskan border to Meade, Clark, Comanche, Barber, Harper, Sumner, and Cowley counties on the Oklahoma line—often red beds. Fossils are chiefly in certain members of older, Wolf-campion series.

CHASE GROUP / Herrington limestone—siliceous and calcareous geodes and concretions, with mollusks locally abundant.

Paddock shale—pelecypods locally abundant in northern and central outcrops.

Winfield limestone, Cresswell member—limestone and shale—echinoid spines and other fossils plentiful in lower part.

Matfield shale: Blue Springs member—fossils in limestones and gray shales in southern part of outcrop area; Kinney member—fossiliferous gray shales between limestone layers; Wymore member—fossiliferous in lower part of deposit, southern part of state.

COUNCIL GROVE GROUP / Bader limestone: Middleburg member—fossiliferous in lower part; Eiss member—fossiliferous in shaly portion.

Beattie limestone, Florena shale member—highly fossiliferous, with brachiopod *Chonotes* abundant throughout, greater variety in southern Kansas than in northern, with numerous species of pelecypods, brachiopods, and well-preserved small trilobites locally common.

Eskridge shale—ostracods, mollusks and algae.

Grenola limestone: Neva member—upper parts in southern Kansas have crust of small brachiopods, and basal limestone has either algae or mollusks; Burr member—ostracods in upper parts, and mollusks and others in lower; Sallyards member—molluscans throughout and other fossils locally.

Red Eagle limestone in southern part of the state: (Bennett shale member—abundant brachiopods; Glenrock limestone member—fusulinids.

Johnson shale, Hughes and Americus members—profusion of fusulinids and brachiopods.

ADMIRE GROUP / Falls City limestone in central and northern areas—mollusks, some bryozoans and brachiopods.

TRIASSIC and JURASSIC

Small area in southern Morton County—varicolored shales and red sandstone.

CRETACEOUS

Mostly marine, Pierre shale in northwestern part of the state; Niobrara chalk—belt trending generally northeast-southwest, from north-central to western; Carlile shale—northwestern and western—large septarian concretions in upper part; Dakota clay, shale, siltstone, and sandstone, plus carbonaceous material—north-central and western—plant fossils and land vertebrates; Kiowa shale—south across central Kansas, and a few places in southwestern—abundant molluscan fauna; Cheyenne sandstone—same areas—plant remains.

TERTIARY

The Pliocene Ogallala Formation is spread widely over the western third of the state, and a few places in the central, with the Ash Hollow middle member occurring most widely. This formation, of gravel, sand, silt, limestone (locally "algal"), volcanic ash, opaline sandstone, and clay, crops out over almost the entire surface from Meade County to Decatur County, and westward, from there, as well as irregularly across the next two north-south strips of counties toward the east.

QUATERNARY

All nonmarine; glacial, fluvial, or aeolian. Forms surface materials over approximately half the state, with glacial only in the northeast, and stream-laid and wind-borne generally in the western half and in the valleys of the eastern.

THERE ARE THREE KANSAS STATE MUSEUMS, all on the campus of Fort Hays Kansas State College: one for natural history, one for history and prehistory, and the third for geology and paleontology. They are reached by U.S. 40 or U.S. 183, and Interstate 70 passes one mile north.

As might be expected, spectacular finds continue in Kansas, and the Fort Hays museums are constantly adding to their collections, with especially exciting exhibits for the hall of geology and paleontology. In the summer of 1966 that hall acquired various Niobrara fishes, and scientists were preparing a mount with the well-preserved skull and lower jaws of an *Ichthydectes*. Added also has been an excellent specimen of the Cretaceous shark *Isurus*, found by George Sternberg (curator emeritus) and his party in the lower part of the Smoky Hill chalk, ten miles north of Hays, on the Saline River. Included in that find were 205 vertebrae, about ninety teeth articulated in the jaws, and much fossilized cartilage. Other recent additions to the museum are a *Pachyrizodus*—a large fish (this specimen was found lower than is usual in the Greenhorn); large mammoth material, including several leg bones as large as those of *Archidiskodon* (see p. 190), and skull (of another, exceedingly large mammoth) with very good teeth, from a sandpit forty miles north of Hays; and the Cretaceous pterosaur *Nyetosaurus*—one of the most complete and well-articulated skeletons ever to come from the Smoky Hill chalk. David Bardack of the museum has written a paper giving the exact localities where fossil fish have been found in the state.

KENTUCKY

KENTUCKY WAS KNOWN FOR ITS FOSSILS BACK IN THE DAYS when the general public scarcely knew there were such things.

The state is noted also for containing the greatest and most celebrated Paleozoic reef in this part of the world (at Ohio Falls near Louisville), and as having contributed the biggest and most impressive collection of Pleistocene and semi-Recent mammalian fossils ever dug up anywhere in this country—not excluding Rancho La Brea.

One of the largest caches for Pleistocene animals was at Big Bone Lick, on Big Bone Creek, which comes into the Ohio River at some distance above the Ohio Falls. Perhaps LaSalle saw the lick in the seventeenth century, but though the bones must have been exposed and bleaching in the sun, the sight seems to have made no impression on him. Then, in 1765, Col. George Croghan, who was based at Fort Pitt, made a collection of bones; and a few years later Capt. Harry Gordon gathered together a lot of fossils and sent them to Paris, to Benjamin Franklin and the Comte de Buffon. Excitement over the early finds at Big Bone Lick was behind much of the enthusiasm for later fossil hunting all over the United States. Toward the end of the eighteenth century, tremendous numbers of bones were taken out of that spot where all sorts of Pleistocene animals had gone for salt, for untold thousands of years. In the early and middle nineteenth century scientists wrote innumerable papers about the fossils, and great biologists such as Lesquereux worked at the lick, finding invertebrates and paleobotanical specimens as well as vertebrates.

Almost all the strata of the state's geologic column are sedimentary and were laid down by water. There are no Permian deposits, and the Cambrian are almost unknown. The principal deposits are Ordovician, Silurian, Devonian, and Carboniferous, and there is a gap between Pennsylvanian and Pleistocene, except for brief periods during the Cretaceous and Eocene.

Despite its distinguished paleontological history, and the fact that there are many fossils, of many kinds, still hidden in its Paleozoic and Pleistocene deposits, Kentucky is one of the states where the novice who wants to hunt will do well to look at exhibits in natural history museums and to get whatever help he can from museums, colleges, and the geological survey. Guidebooks for amateurs are hard to come by, and to search out appropriate material from scientific publications requires much

background knowledge. A classic symposium of articles published in 1931 is out of print. The information that follows
comes in large part from those articles:

ORDOVICIAN

Some portions of the three formations are richly fossiliferous
in places; others contain few fossils, and most of those found
are invertebrate. Some localities accessible in 1931 were: Elk
Lick Falls, about twelve miles east of Lexington; in various
quarries and road and railroad cuts in the Lexington area; along
the road from Duncan Station to Glen Creek (southwest of
Frankfort); and in Harrison and Garrard counties.

SILURIAN

Sediments, which came in from the north Atlantic and the
Gulf, and are best shown in the west-central Nelson and Marion
counties, are distributed along what is called the Cincinnati Anticline, which goes north into Ohio, and connects at the south
with a similar elevation in Tennessee. Often, fossils will be
found in other parts of the Anticline, but not in Kentucky. In
the state itself, brachiopods predominate in most places, and
there are many bryozoans. In certain strata there are gastropods,
pelecypods, cephalopods, crinoids, trilobites, and many corals—
usually locally distributed.

DEVONIAN

There are no fishes, and other fossils of the period are
found only here and there.

MISSISSIPPIAN

Large numbers of fossils appear in some localities where
there are thin limestone layers; one of the best of such sites is at
Buttonmould Knob, twelve miles south of Louisville—rich in
bryozoans and corals. In some places conodonts and many species of crinoids are also found.

PENNSYLVANIAN

Up to 1931, no skeletal remains or other evidences of vertebrates had been found, though they were expected. A number of
good invertebrate beds were known, but were hard to trace.
Brachiopods, pelecypods, gastropods, cephalopods, anthozoans
(corals and their relations), echinoids, bryozoans, and crustacea had been found.

CRETACEOUS

Though extensive collections have been made from the Cretaceous in Alabama, Tennessee, and Georgia, it offers poor pickings in Kentucky.

TERTIARY

There are good fossil plant localities in Graves and Ballard counties; and from McCracken County, three miles south of Paducah, near the old Paducah-Mayfield road, have come beautifully preserved fish scales, and casts of marine mollusks. The Holly Springs clay abounds in leaf impressions, with a few fruits, cones, flower petals, and stem fragments. Good collecting localities exist, or have existed in clay pits in Ballard County and in clay pits south of Boaz and in other areas in Graves County; at Chickasaw Bluff and at a site a mile south of Hickman, in Fulton County. At Wickliffe, Ballard County, one man, E. W. Berry, long ago found twenty-seven new fossil plants. From near Columbus, Lesquereux identified eleven plants, and Berry, scores more. According to early reports, no fossil fauna had been found in western Kentucky, except the wing of a termite, discovered 2.5 miles south of Columbus.

PLIOCENE-PLEISTOCENE

Invertebrates—many in Fayette County.

Vertebrates: Thomas Jefferson himself found, at Big Bone Lick, and near Henderson, a ground sloth, which he named *Megalonyx jeffersoni*. This animal was very abundant in many parts of the state, and there were smaller sloths at Big Bone Lick and Bone Lick. In the eastern part of Kentucky, beaver as big as black bears swam in the streams. Tapirs were found at McConnell's Run, Scott City, and Yarnellton Station in Fayette County, and there were horses. Many of the even-toed ungulates were discovered at Big Bone Lick and at Crooked Creek in Rockcastle County; elk at the lick in Wayne County; caribou, moose, stag moose, musk oxen, and bison at Big Bone. The bear was the only carnivore in the area, except perhaps a fox. But there were many elephant creatures, including the woolly mammoth *Elephas primigenius*, at Big Bone and Blue Lick Springs; *Elephas columbi* at Big Bone; and the mastodon *Mammut americanum*, at Blue Lick and in the eastern coalfield.

THOMAS JEFFERSON not only collected fossils as a hobby, but encouraged others. He commissioned William Clark of the Lewis and Clark Expedition to excavate at Big Bone and bring to him the bones he found there—especially those of bison and elephantlike creatures. At the White House, the President studied the bones, with the help of Caspar Wistar of Philadelphia, author of the first American textbook on anatomy, and the man for whom wistaria was named.

LOUISIANA

IN LOUISIANA THERE ARE VERY FEW FOSSILS, AND AS THIS BOOK goes to press there is only one known locality where abundant fossils are readily available and where geologists do not mind having amateurs hunt. This is Creola Bluff at Montgomery Landing on the Red River, where the fossiliferous area is exposed on the left (east) bank. The sediment is Moodys Branch marl, basal unit of the Upper Eocene Jacksonian Formation, and in it nearly fifty varieties of mollusks are to be found.

This site at Montgomery Landing (the most famous fossiliferous locality in the state) was noted as early as 1816, and as the Louisiana Geological Survey puts it, "has been described, figured and sectioned many times since." The main Moodys Branch deposit is easily recognized by the concentration of glauconite and sand and the large numbers of macrofossils.

MAINE

LIKE MANY PARTS OF NEW ENGLAND, MAINE OFFERS FEW FOSsils. Silurian marine specimens are found occasionally in interbedded sediments in lava and ash in those areas of the state adjacent to New Brunswick; Ordovician graptolites have come to light one hundred miles north of Lake Memphremagog; but it is only now and then that anything worth saving is picked up.

MARYLAND

ONE OF THE MOST SIGNIFICANT COLLECTIONS OF FOSSIL PLEISTO-cene mammals—not even excluding that from Rancho La Brea —was made in Maryland after 1912, in a cave in Allegany County, about four miles west of Cumberland. Specimens are in the Smithsonian's collection.

The cave was found when workmen excavated for a rail-road cut, and a good deal of fossil material was destroyed before it was recognized. Dr. J. W. Gidley, a paleontologist who died in 1931, wrote various papers about it, and from 1912 to 1915 con-ducted much field work there. This work was later continued by others, including his son, who in 1938 completed that most important report. Scientists were and are particularly excited about what has been deduced from Cumberland Cave because, except for the remarkable deposits in Florida, the great finds in Kentucky, and those from the California tar pits, a large portion of all knowledge about what mammals were roaming North America in Pleistocene times has come from occasional finds in caves of the limestone areas. Discoveries in such caves have usually been made incidentally by anthropologists, and very little systematic geological and paleontological exploration was undertaken before 1912.

The opening that led to this gratifying cache is exposed at the base of an escarpment of Devonian limestone about seventy-five feet high, where the strata have been tilted upright. At one time there was an opening on the crest of the hill; this opening undoubtedly served as a trap for unwary animals, which fell through and never got out.

Limestone is a peculiarly good preservative for bones, which in this instance were for the most part much broken but showed no sign of having been worn by water. Up to 1938 approximately fifty kinds of specimens had been taken out—many of them of extinct species or even extinct genera, but with certain of them closely related to living forms. Some are much like those now living near the cave; very strangely, others are like those of the far north, while certain others resemble those of an equally far southern region. How they came to be in the same spot is difficult to explain, the authors of the report say, unless they were buried at different times.

Among those mammals that might have come from the north are wolverine, lemming, long-tailed shrew, fisher, mink, red squirrel, muskrat, porcupine, jumping mouse, pika (a small rabbitlike animal), hare, and elk. From the south, perhaps, came some bats, peccaries, a tapir, and a crocodile. The whole fauna seems to suggest a wooded habitat, with plenty of moisture. There are very few remains of any animal larger than a black bear; and, amazingly, many typical forms such as the sabertooth, sloth, camel, elephant, bison, and musk ox are not included. However, in addition to the typically northern and southern forms, there are at least a few bones each of the intermediate belt; these include specimens representative of a horse, a coyote, a badger, bears of several kinds, otter, a pumalike creature, beaver, and other (smaller) rodents, a mastodon, and deer. The deposit seems to be approximately middle Pleistocene.

Although it is not easy to find popular references to them, there are of course many other kinds of fossils in Maryland. The presence of outcrops of Paleocene sediments in Prince Georges County, which lies near Washington, was first established in 1952, and the sediments are called the Brightseat Formation. Paleocene ostracods are found there, in outcrops seven hundred miles north of outcrops of the same age in Alabama and five hundred miles from the nearest ones in Georgia. Ten species of ostracods in five localities in the Brightseat had been identified by early 1954. Among other Maryland fossils are Cretaceous sauropods, the giant shark *Carcharodon polygurus,* and fragmentary crocodiles and birds. Invertebrates are similar to those of Delaware.

As of 1966, Carnegie Museum (Pittsburgh) experts were busily engaged in collecting invertebrate fossils from Scientists' Point on Chesapeake Bay. And from Cumberland Cave comes what is possibly a new type of *Peromyscus,* a rodent.

MASSACHUSETTS

AS HAS BEEN SAID BEFORE, CONDITIONS IN MASSACHUSETTS duplicate those in Connecticut. The Bay Colony also lies in the Connecticut Valley—in the 108-mile-long Triassic depression that has its northern extremity at Northfield. Its rocks are of the Newark System, and its fossilized life is, of course, almost entirely Triassic.

Localities where plant fossils have been found include South Hadley, Deerfield, Greenfield, Mount Holyoke, Mount Tom, Gill, Turners Falls, Westfield, Sunderland, and Montague.

Invertebrate impressions and trails have been found in and near Turners Falls; trails, from Lily Pond in Gill.

As for the vertebrates—fish have come from Turners Falls, Sunderland, and Chicopee Falls. Skeletal material from reptiles has been found at Greenfield, South Hadley, Belchertown, Springfield, and Longmeadow. Reptile tracks have come from the north bank of the Connecticut River, nearly opposite the mouth of Millers River; from Lily Pond and a nearby orchard, Gill; from the ferry near Turners Falls; from canal, quarry, and other spots in and near Montague; from Greenfield and Mount Holyoke; from Moody's Corner, the stream near Pliny Moody's, Dickinson's Quarry, and other spots in South Hadley; from Mount Tom, east and west; from Holyoke and Holyoke Dam; from Chicopee, near Cabotville; from Chicopee Falls; from the Springfield water shops locality; and from the Longmeadow locality.

Outside of the Triassic in New England, New Jersey, and Pennsylvania, fossil footprints are found in only a few places. Sir Charles Lyell, who traveled widely on this continent in 1841 and 1848, was much impressed by the collection of Prof. Edward Hitchcock of Amherst, and by the huge dinosaur prints (of *Eubrontes giganteus*) he saw at Smith's Ferry near Northampton. (See Connecticut.) He deduced erroneously that the Triassic valley was a great tidal estuary.

Tracks come to light frequently. More have appeared in South Hadley and Holyoke recently, coming to light as the layers of shale were pulled off. So many tracks have been discovered that some of them are being sold to the public. This is a far cry from what happened in 1800, when Pliny Moody of South Hadley ploughed up a flagstone, saw tracks, and decided that they had been made by "Noah's raven."

MICHIGAN

ALTHOUGH MICHIGAN IS FAR FROM BEING AS WONDERFUL A hunting ground as Illinois, the fossils found in the two states are of much the same ages—Precambrian through Pennsylvanian, and then Pleistocene, with a gap from the beginning of the Mesozoic through the whole Tertiary. Types of fossils found include:

PRECAMBRIAN
Blue-green algae in a conglomerate formation of mid-Keweenawan age, on Lake Superior shore between Copper Harbor and Eagle Harbor.

CAMBRIAN
A few trilobites, which are more plentiful in later Paleozoic rocks; a few brachiopods; gastropods (found through the Mississippian); a few cephalopods.

ORDOVICIAN
Numerous brachiopods (found also, though less frequently, in the later Devonian sediments in Delta County, and the Mississippian sediments in Huron County); many cephalopods (one straight one, more than fifteen feet long, has been called the largest "shellfish" of all time); crinoids; a few blastoids; and on

Black River, ostracoderms similar to those of Canon City, Colorado.

SILURIAN

Tabulate corals and tetracorals, all of extinct types (continuing through Devonian). There are special concentrations (some seventy feet thick) near Engadine, Trout Lake, and Gould City.

DEVONIAN

Many crinoids, plus bryozoa, corals, and a few plants. Finds have included remains of what was (probably) the now extinct *Callixylon* tree. Devonian fossils provide the best collecting in Michigan.

PENNSYLVANIAN

Many plants, including ferns, club-moss trees, horsetails.

PLEISTOCENE

Mastodon, woolly mammoth, and other animals of period are found occasionally in unconsolidated glacial deposits.

MICHIGAN IS ON THE BORDER of the Canadian Shield, core of the North American continent, and the Great Lakes region is built up on a base of granitic rocks of the Archean. The rim of that granitic basin may be seen in the Huron Mountains of Marquette County. Results of Huronian convulsive earth movements and volcanic activity are visible in the northern peninsula; results of the explosive volcanism and quiet lava flow of the Keweenawan age can be seen in Gogebic, Houghton, Keweenaw, and Ontonagon counties. During the Paleozoic, when the state was periodically inundated, Cambrian seas brought sediments that can be seen in Alger, Baraga, Chippewa, Dickinson, Houghton, Iron, Luce, Marquette, and Ontonagon counties. Ordovician sediments are seen in Chippewa, Delta, Houghton, Menominee, and Schoolcraft counties; Silurian, in Chippewa, Delta, Mackinac, Monroe, and Schoolcraft; Devonian, in Alpena, Charlevoix, Cheboygan, Emmet, Monroe, Presque Isle, and Wayne; Mississippian, in Alpena, Antrim, Arenac, Branch, Calhoun, Cheboygan, Eaton, Grand Traverse, Hillsdale, Huron, Iosco, Jackson, Kent, Ogemaw, Ottawa, Presque Isle, St. Joseph, Sanilac, and Tuscola; Pennsylvanian, in Arenac, Genesee, Ingham, Ionia, Jackson, Saginaw, and Shiawassee.

After the Paleozoic, the seas never again reached Michigan and, though a thin layer of red sands and gypsum was blown over the Pennsylvanian, that layer has not been found at the surface. The state is carved into highlands in the western part of the northern peninsula and the northern and southern parts of the southern peninsula. A great river system ran through the lowlands in the area now occupied by the Great Lakes.

Those lakes are products of the so-called Ice Age, when an icecap moved south to cover the land as far as the Ohio and Missouri rivers. Though it advanced and retreated four times, the last glaciation (Wisconsin) was the most important for Michigan. The Great Lakes were formed during the final retreat of the ice, which melted slowly, making readvances and retreats. In general, as the main ice front advanced, it scooped out three lobes: Lake Michigan, Saginaw Bay, and Lake Erie. After much backing and filling, changing of outlines, and other geologic activity, during many thousands of years, the weight of ice was lifted from the northern section of the state, the land was gradually uplifted and tilted, and the lakes took on their modern form.

Because Michigan is not truly fossiliferous, many Michigan paleontologists do much of their collecting in nearby Canada and Ohio.

MINNESOTA

ON A BASE OF LAVA THROWN OUT FROM VOLCANOES IN ARCHEAN times, stratum after stratum of sediments was deposited in Minnesota, up through the time of that Pleistocene glaciation when the Great Lakes were formed. Many of the earlier strata are buried deep, but their edges may be seen in some places along rivers and streams in the southern part of the state.

Minnesota, lying in almost the exact center of the continent, is level or gently rolling over most of its surface, with almost no parts, except the northeast and southwest corners, rising above 1,500 feet, and the Giant's Range extending from above Birch Lake in eastern St. Louis County southwestward to a few miles north of Grand Rapids. Strata range all the way from the Keewatin (oldest of the Archeozoic) up to the Recent, with (according to today's reckoning) no Silurian, a gap between the Middle or Upper Devonian and the Cretaceous, and no Tertiary.

The following information is from official publications, which say that rocks of the various ages (sometimes fossiliferous) appear in the following places:

UPPER CAMBRIAN

St. Croixian Series in exposures along the St. Croix Valley; mainly sandstones interbedded with siltstones and shales; in four formations:

1. Dresbach—valley of St. Croix, along upper portions of Mississippi bluffs from Minnesota City southward, and up Root River valley as far as Hokah; several kinds of trilobites, brachiopods, pelecypods, pteropods, cystoids, and worm trails may be found at Taylor's Falls and along Mississippi near Winona.

2. Franconia—well exposed along Mississippi River bluffs from Frontenac southeastward, where several kinds of marine invertebrates, worm trails, and burrows may be found.

3. St. Lawrence—widely distributed and easily recognized along St. Croix and Mississippi, with excellent outcrops in Fairy Glen at Stillwater, and La Grange Mountain (Barn Bluff), in Red Wing—contain trilobites and graptolites.

4. Jordan Sandstone—conspicuous light-colored rock, high on bluffs; uncovered in quarries near Jordan in Scott County, and in areas of river valleys and along tributary streams; there is an especially fossiliferous patch in Boom Hollow along St. Croix River at Stillwater.

Special early Paleozoic localities: Interstate Park—by U.S. Highway 8 to beyond Taylor's Falls, on Basil Street and at Curtain Falls Trail; Afton (in a coulee south of town), 6.4 miles on State Highway 95, below where it crosses U.S. 12.

ORDOVICIAN

Mostly mud-compacted shales and limestones; graded almost inconspicuously from Cambrian along bluffs of Mississippi, more abruptly in Minnesota Valley. Oneta dolomite is found in outcrops along the Minnesota Valley and the St. Croix and Mississippi rivers; Root Valley sandstone, in Winona, Fillmore, and Houston counties; Shakopee dolomite, overlying Root Valley. St. Peter sandstone is found in steep bluffs of the Minnesota (formerly St. Peter) River where it joins the Mississippi at Fort Snelling, and is conspicuously exposed in flanks of mesalike hills and in valley walls from Northfield eastward to the Mississippi River, and along the valley of the Cannon River. Platteville limestone occurs above St. Peter, more or less continuously in walls of the Mississippi gorge below St. Anthony's Falls in Minneapolis to the Robert Street Bridge in St. Paul (these deposits contain corals, graptolites, and other marine invertebrates); it is also found on both sides of the Minnesota for a short distance above its mouth, and in quarries near the Twin Cities. Decorah shales are found in many bluffs, precipitous and castellated, along creeks and canyons in Fillmore and Olmsted counties, in a pit of the Twin City Brick Company below Cherokee Park in St. Paul, and in walls of the Mississippi gorge; these shales contain brachiopods, bryozoans, and trilobites. Galena limestone is found above Decorah, where "sunflower" sponges are fairly common in walls and on ledges of quarries. The Maquoketa Formation, which is of limestone and shale, is well exposed in walls of a quarry a short distance southeast of Clinton Falls and along highway paralleling railroad east of Spring Valley, and also in walls of Mystery Cave, near Spring Valley; deposits at these sites contain abundant fossils, including crinoids and marine plants. The formation is also found in: quarry on State Highway 43, 1.5 miles north of Mabel; railroad overpass on State Highway 44, 3.2 miles west of Spring Grove; Myrah Quarry, 1.0 mile southeast of center of Spring Grove; quarries and higher roadside exposures on west side of Canfield Creek northwest of Greenleafton (NW¼ sec. 35, T. 102 N., R. 12 W.); a cave on private road leading west off County Road 11, not far from junction of County roads 11 and 20; old quarries and road cuts on County Road E, 1.5 miles west of Fountain (many species); site half mile north on Fillmore County State Aid Road 7 (east edge of SE¼ sec. 21, T. 105 N., R. 12 W.), 0.5 mile north of its junction with State Highway 30; Rochester

South Quarry, just off U.S. 52, 2.5 miles northwest of cemetery in Marion, and 4.2 miles southeast of junction with U.S. 14 at Southeast edge of Rochester; quarry and cuts along metal-surfaced road that begins at U.S. 52 on south edge of Cannon Falls, going southeastward toward White Rock.

Lower Ordovician cephalopods, gastropods, and trilobites are found from Garden City to Chaska, in deposits reaching from river level (at Hastings) to tops of bluffs (from Red Wing to farther south). Characteristic forms of later Ordovician, plus other, less usual, ones come from many places, but especially below Cherokee Park. One cephalopod, in the museum of the University of Minnesota, is more than five feet long, and there have been specimens fifteen feet long.

DEVONIAN

(Late—all limestones and dolomites) in the Cedar Valley Formation, exposed for only a few miles west of Cedar Valley in the southwestern corner of Fillmore County, in about three quarters of Mower County, and a small corner of southeastern Freeborn County, brachiopods, corals, and a few fish fragments may be found, but no complete fish fossils.

CRETACEOUS

Very variable, with most-uniform exposures in west-central and southwestern counties, under thick glacial drifts. Fossils are found at Springfield, along Cottonwood River south of New Ulm, and in Lyon and Redwood counties; highly fossiliferous areas in the Mesabi Range contain pelecypods and gastropods; well-exposed specimens in iron ore pits near Coleraine have marine fossils, with many oysters and ammonites. Big Stone County has fish teeth and bones; no dinosaur bones or tracks, but some gastroliths. Rich plant remains—including those of pomegranates, laurels, tulip trees, giant redwoods, willows, poplars, and primitive evergreens—may be found along the Minnesota River above Mankato, along the Cottonwood River, near Springfield, and in compact beds near New Ulm.

PLEISTOCENE

Sediments deposited by Nebraskan, Kansan, Illinoian, and Wisconsin Ice Ages, with advances of stages and substages of the last going sometimes across Minnesota, and into Iowa and Wisconsin, leaving, in glacial drift, elk, reindeer, bison, musk

Students collecting fossils in Illinois (Courtesy Illinois State Geological Survey)

In laboratories behind the scenes at the AMNH, skilled technicians mount a skeleton of the *Styracosaurus parski* type of dinosaur, which had a neck frill, a beak, and three horns (Courtesy American Museum of Natural History)

Technicians of the Division of Vertebrate Paleontology prepare for exhibit the skeleton of a large Cretaceous sea turtle, *Protostega gigas* (Courtesy Smithsonian Institution)

TOP: Field preparation on the site of discovery in the Niobrara Smoky Hill chalk of the world-famous giant Cretaceous fish, *Portheus molossus,* with the smaller fish, *Gillicus arcuatus,* in its abdominal cavity. At far left is George F. Sternberg, noted field vertebrate paleontologist, who also prepared the specimen for exhibit. (Courtesy Fort Hays State College Museum, Hays, Kansas)

BOTTOM: *Portheus molossus,* with its meal, *Gillicus arcuatus,* exhibited in the museum (Courtesy Fort Hays State College Museum, Hays, Kansas)

Here in the AMNH are the mounted skeletons of a brontosaur (left) and an *Allosaurus*. They stand on a platform made in part of tracks of a carnivorous dinosaur stalking a herbivorous one. The tracks were taken out of early Cretaceous rock near Glen Rose, Texas, by Dr. Barnum Brown. (Courtesy American Museum of Natural History)

A lower Cambrian trilobite, *Wanneria walcottana*, found one half mile south of East Petersburg, Pennsylvania. This is one of many trilobites identified by Charles D. Walcott, great authority on Cambrian life. (Courtesy Smithsonian Institution)

Niobrara Cretaceous pelecypod, *Inoceramus,* which measures thirty-five by thirty-four inches, now exhibited in the
Fort Hays Museum. It was collected and prepared for exhi-
bition by George F. Sternberg. (Courtesy Fort Hays College
Museum, Hays, Kansas)

Largest fossil reptile skull and jaw thus far collected in Kansas.
This skull of *Brachauchenis,* largest of the short-necked plesiosaurs,
is more than sixty inches long. It was found in the Greenhorn
Cretaceous of the western part of the state by George F. Sternberg.
(Courtesy Fort Hays College Museum, Hays, Kansas)

Edward A. McCarthy of West Hartford, Connecticut, shows slabs containing casts of Triassic dinosaur tracks from the site he discovered in August, 1966, in Rocky Hill, Connecticut. (Hartford *Times* Photo)

ox, mastodon, woolly mammoth, and many smaller mammals such as beaver, badger, skunk, rabbit, and several tiny rodents. It is not hard to find elk skulls and antlers; and bison are exceedingly common, sometimes found in "bison-bone beds," even under thick peat, such as at Sagamore Iron Mine at Riverton, and one in Itasca State Park, plus vegetable matter in old lake beds—logs, branches, leaves, and mosses.

MINNESOTA HAS MADE a significant contribution to North American anthropology. In 1931, a crew building roads near Pelican Rapids found the skeleton of a primitive Mongoloid woman, nine feet down in a laminated glacial lake, where she must have drowned about 22,000 years ago. Because her sex was misinterpreted at first, she became known as the "Minnesota Man." A more recent human fossil, the Browns Valley Man, is estimated to be 12,000 years old.

In the late nineteenth century, when Leo Lesquereux, Charles Schuchert, and others wrote about the state, an irregular strip in the southeast corner, chiefly in Goodhue, Olmsted, and Fillmore counties, was thought to be Silurian, and was discussed accordingly. Lesquereux told of more than two hundred species of Cretaceous flora, identified up to that time as including one *Equisetum,* six ferns, six cycads, ten conifers, three monocotyledons, and 175 dicotyledons. In the fact that the dicotyledons appeared to have sprung to life fully developed, with no gradual changes from any species found in earlier rocks, the great botanist saw evidence of a mysterious occurrence in the middle Cretaceous such as occurred at no other time in geologic history.

Sites for sponges, graptolites, and corals then noted were: 6.0 miles south of Cannon Falls; Kenyon; Minneota; Fountain; near Marion; Stewartville; near Spring Valley; Minneapolis; Oxford Mills; Preston; St. Paul; a quarry 2.0 miles west of Granger; near Caledonia; and other places in Goodhue, Olmsted, and Fillmore counties. Bryozoans came from limestones in St. Paul, Cannon Falls, Minneapolis, Lanesboro, Fountain, Preston, Oxford Mills, and other places. Brachiopods could be found in great variety and abundance, well preserved, in the immediate vicinity of St. Paul and Minneapolis; in Wanamingo;

in Oxford Mills; in and near Fountain; in and near Rochester; in Section 6 of Fremont (Winona County); 2.0 miles west of Granger; on the north branch of the Zumbro River at upper bridge, near Kenyon; in and near Wykoff; in Chatfield; in quarries at Mantorville and Weisbach's Dam near Spring Valley; in Aspelund; in Hader; on Bear Creek, just south of Hamilton; 3.0 miles south of Spring Valley; in Old Concord; near Lanesboro; in St. Charles; in Warsaw; in Eyota; and near Caledonia.

MISSISSIPPI

SOUTHERN MISSISSIPPI LIES IN WHAT IS KNOWN AS THE GULF Coastal Plain of the United States, and the northern part extends into a portion of that plain called the Mississippi Embayment. Under the plain are ancient rocks (Paleozoic and pre-Paleozoic), and then formations ranging from Cretaceous to the present. On the west, north, and east borders of the embayment are outcrops of the Paleozoic.

Upper Cretaceous deposits, all in the plain and the embayment, make a belt up to fifty miles wide east and west, and 160 miles north and south. Its formations are the Tuscaloosa; Eutaw; Selma Chalk (with its partial equivalents, Coffee Sand and Ripley); and Prairie Bluff Chalk and its equivalent, Owl Creek. Investigating the Cretaceous has been particularly important, because of the search for oil which has resulted in the location of significant sites. The state's geological survey gives fossiliferous localities in the various formations, from which invertebrates, occasional sharks' teeth, and a very few plants have been taken. Though the sites were located before 1940, many of them are still accessible. Official bulletins give directions.

TUSCALOOSA / In upper part of sand, clay, gravel, and lignite at Maxey's old mill site, northeast of Fulton—fossil leaves.

EUTAW / In upper part of fine glauconitic sand in Tombigbee massive—cephalopods and pelecypods, plus a few sharks' teeth. Similar deposits in the following counties:

Lowndes—Plymouth Bluff, right bank of Tombigbee River, four to five miles northwest of Columbus, in four beds; bluff a few hundred yards from railroad bridge at Columbus; 7.0 miles east-southeast of Columbus.

Clay—Barton's Bluff, Tombigbee River, 10.5 miles northwest of Columbus; Vinton Bluff on river, 12.5 miles northwest of Columbus.

Monroe—bluff on Tombigbee River below railroad bridge at Aberdeen; Blue Bluff, about 3.0 miles above Aberdeen; 1.0 mile west of old Cotton Gin Port, 4.0 miles west of Amory, on eastward-facing slope of river.

Prentiss—one-quarter mile west of Marietta on Baldwyn Road; near Hare's old mill site on Big Brown Creek, 9.0 miles east of Booneville; northeastern-facing slope of Young's Creek valley, 7.5 miles southeast of Booneville.

SELMA CHALK / Fine, more or less argillaceous and sandy limestone—many oysters, a few forams, many coccolithophores (flagellate algae), and various mollusk forms. Characteristic fossils come from following counties:

Kemper—northward-facing slope of hill 0.25 mile north of T-road intersection, 4.0 miles northeast by east of Scooba; old U.S. 45 on hill south of Wahalak Creek, about 6.0 miles north of Scooba.

Noxubee—U.S. 45, on northward-facing slope of Running Water Creek valley, 4.5 and 4.75 miles south of Noxubee River Bridge at Macon; Louisville road, about 2.0 miles from Macon; cut of Mobile and Ohio RR, 3.0 miles south of Macon; plantation of T. W. Brane, 2.5 miles south of Macon; bluff on left side of Noxubee River, one-quarter mile below highway bridge at Macon; Cranford Bridge road, 3.0 miles northwest of Macon; site one-quarter mile east of house on old Allen Gavin place.

Clay—State Highway 10, near west end of bridge over Line Creek, 1.0 mile east of Cedar Bluff; bald spots near West Point—

Houston road, 2.0 miles southeast of Caradine store; near same road, one-quarter mile south of store; State Highway 25, 2.0 miles west of Tibbee Station; bank of Sakatonchee River just below bridge of State Highway 10, 3.5 miles west of West Point; same road, 2.0 miles west of West Point; abandoned pit of West Point Brick, Tile and Lumber Company, just north of West Point; gullies on Terrell farm, 2.0 miles east of West Point.

Chickasaw—bald spot about two miles east by north of McCondy; 2.0, 3.0, and 4.5 miles west of Okolona, on Houston road; Pontotoc road, 2.5 miles northwest of Okolona; bed of dry stream branch near crossing of Houston road, 0.5 mile west of Okolona; bald spot on west edge of Okolona; bald spots, 1.0 mile northeast of Okolona.

Lee—gullies south of the Troy road, eight or nine miles west of Shannon; bald spots and gullies on westward-facing slope of Tishomingo Creek valley, one-quarter mile west of Bethany; beds of Coonewar Creek at crossing of State Highway 6, about 5.75 miles west by south of business center of Tupelo; State Highway 6, 3.0 and 3.5 miles west of Tupelo; Chesterville road, 1.5 and 3.25 miles west of Tupelo; U.S. 45, 1.0 mile west by north of Saltillo; bald spot on Blair Road, 2.0 miles west of Guntown; cut on Mobile and Ohio RR just north of station at Guntown; washes in field east of Tupelo-Verona road, 2.5 miles south of Tupelo; banks of small branch tributary of Long Creek, 0.5 mile east of Mooreville on U.S. 78.

Pontotoc—gullies on westward-facing slope north of State Highway 6, 6.0 miles west of Tupelo.

Union—bed of Bridge Creek, just below bridge on section-line road.

Prentiss—bald spots near public road, 1.0 mile west of Blackland; bald spots and gullies near Ripley road, 3.5 miles northwest of Booneville; bald spots near public road, 0.5 mile east of Blackland; bald spots near Geeville road, 1.5 miles southwest of Booneville; above and below track level in cut of M & O RR south of station at Booneville.

Alcorn—"Bald Knob" on Joseph Reynolds place, 3.0 miles west of Corinth; cut on Southern RR, 2.75 miles northwest of Corinth; cut on Southern RR, 1.25 miles southeast of Wenasoga; cut on M & O RR, 3.0 miles south of Corinth; cut on

Southern RR, 3.0 miles southeast of Corinth; Stevenson's cut on Illinois Central RR, 2.5 miles southeast of Corinth.

Monroe—gullies on Erskine Miller farm west of road at Black Oak Grove Church, seven (?) miles northeast of Okolona; foot of eastward-facing slope of Old Town Creek Valley on Okolona road, about four miles southwest of Nettleton; bank of drainage ditch on south side of State Highway 8, 1.0 mile east of Gibson; westward-facing slope of a branch valley of Mattubby Creek, 9.5 miles west by south of Amory; southwestward-facing slope of a branch valley of same creek (near NW cor., NE¼ sec. 2, T. 14 S., R. 6 E.); 1.0 mile west of site of old Cotton Gin Port, 4.0 miles west of Amory, on eastward-facing slope of Tombigbee River valley.

Lowndes—western end of Union Bluff on right bank of Tombigbee; northward-facing slope of Ellis Creek valley at J. H. Sparks farm, and on Columbus-Pickensville road; gullies near abandoned public road for 0.25 mile south of Plymouth Bluff, 4.0 to 5.0 miles northwest of Columbus; Plymouth Bluff, right bank of Tombigbee, 4.0 to 5.0 miles northwest of Columbus.

Itawamba—U.S. 78, about 2.0 miles east of Mooreville; Mantachie road, 5.0 miles northeast of Mooreville; gullies on north side of U.S. 78, west edge of Dorsey.

COFFEE SAND / Finely cross-bedded; characterized by glauconite, thin laminae of clay, powdered plant fragments, and macerated pieces of lignite. Contains coelenterates, mollusks, scaphopods, gastropods, cephalopods, and a few sharks' teeth. Found in the following counties:

Lee—abandoned cut of Tupelo-Fulton road on westward-facing slope of Old Town Creek valley, 1.5 miles east of Tupelo; cut on U.S. 45, on northward-facing slope of Kings Creek valley, 0.5 mile south of St. Louis–San Francisco RR, on west edge of Tupelo; road cut on northward-facing slope of Mantachie Creek valley, 2.0 miles due west of Ratliff.

Prentiss—bluff on small branch of Boyer Creek, 0.75 mile south of Booneville; road cut on northeastward-facing slope of Young's Creek valley; 6.0 miles east of Booneville, on road to Hare's old mill site; Hare's old mill site, on Big Brown Creek, 9.0 miles east of Booneville.

Alcorn—cut of M & O RR, 3.0 miles south of Corinth; cut of Southern RR, 3.0 miles southeast of Corinth; Stevenson's cut on Illinois Central RR, 2.5 miles southeast of station at Corinth; cut on Illinois Central RR, 10.25 miles southeast of Corinth.

Tishomingo—cut on Southern RR, 2.0 miles northwest of Burnsville.

RIPLEY / chiefly marine sands and sandstones, with local beds of clay containing coelenterates, mollusks, scaphopods, gastropods, a few sharks' teeth, and some of those peculiar tubes, *Halymenites major* Lesquereux. Ripley is found in the following counties:

Chickasaw—upper slopes of hills in woods, about 5.0 miles east of Houlka; cut on eastward-facing slope of Houlka Creek valley on State Highway 8, 2.0 miles east by south of Houston; cut of M & O RR, 7.0 miles northeast of Houston.

Pontotoc—quarry 450 feet southeast of crossing of north prong of Chiwapa Creek by old State Highway 15, 2.0 miles south of Pontotoc; bank of small stream at south end of wagon bridge on Aberdeen road, 6.5 miles southeast of Pontotoc; Bob Miller Creek (?) at crossing of State Highway 6, 4.0 miles on road east of Pontotoc; cut on Shannon road, on eastward-facing slope of Tallabinnela Creek valley, 0.4 to 0.5 mile east of Troy.

Tippah—road cut on L. T. Braddock's farm, southward-facing slope of Walnut Creek valley; Naber's Coal Bluff, near Dumas; old Lander's (Medlin's) mill site on Cane Creek, 5.0 miles northwest of Molino and 9.0 miles south of Ripley; W. O'Kelly's farm, 2.5 miles south of Dumas; Bullock's old overshot mill, 2.0 miles south of Dumas; bluff on Hatchie River, at Crum's old mill site, 16.5 miles northeast of Ripley.

Union—roadside ditch on local road on northeastward-facing slope of a branch of Brown's Creek, about 3.5 miles northeast of Wallerville; "The Caves" on land of J. A. Roberts, 6.0 miles east by north of New Albany; cut in side of hill at bridge No. 5710 on St. L–SF RR, over branch of Cherry Creek, about 2.5 miles northwest of station at Blue Springs; Lee's old mill site on a headwater branch of Tallahatchie River, 1.5 miles northeast of Keownville; bluff of small stream, 3.0 miles south of Molino; C. R. Hall's farm near Molino.

Oktibbeha—cut on Osborn road, 5.0 miles northeast of Starkville.

PRAIRIE BLUFF CHALK / Near Alabama line it is hard, brittle chalk with phosphatic internal molds of shells; in upper part, only a few microscopic fossils. Northern parts of the deposit are increasingly sandy and argillaceous, with molds in basal beds. The Prairie Bluff is found in the following counties:

Kemper—cut 3.0 miles east of Scooba on Giles road; old U.S. 45, near top of northward-facing slope of Wahalak Creek valley, about 6.0 miles north of Scooba.

Noxubee—bald spots in field west of road, about a mile north of Shuqualak; bank of Running Water Creek at crossing of DeKalb road, 7.5 miles south of Macon; bald spot on southward-facing slope of small branch of Running Water Creek, DeKalb road, about 7.0 miles south of Macon; U.S. 45, on northward-facing slope of Running Water Creek valley, 5.0 miles south of Noxubee River Bridge at Macon; bald spots on northward-facing slope of Dry Creek valley, 4.0 miles southwest of Macon; right bank of Noxubee River, 6.5 miles west-northwest of railroad station at Macon; roadside ditch, 0.75 mile east of Pope's Chapel; right bank of Noxubee River at Edmonds Bridge.

Oktibbeha—roadside exposure, 10.0 miles south by west of Starkville; cut of Illinois Central RR at overhead bridge at east edge of business section of Starkville; gullies on campus of Mississippi State University, near Starkville; Aiken farm, 2.5 miles north of Starkville; gullies east of Rocky Hill Church road, 3.0 miles north of Starkville; Lee Pearson's farm, near Houston road, 3.0 miles northwest of Starkville.

Clay—roadside exposure on State Highway 10, 2.5 miles east of Pheba; roadside ditch a few hundred yards north of Montpelier road, 4.0 miles northwest of Cedar Bluff; bald spot on top of Pontotoc Ridge, 5.0 miles north-northeast of Montpelier.

Chickasaw—bald spot in field at roadside and cut on Houston road, 1.25 miles north of Sparta; bald spot at foot of northward-facing slope of Cane Creek valley, 1.5 miles north of Sparta on Houston road; road cut on northward-facing slope of Chewawah Creek; road cut on State Highway 8, top of eastward-facing slope of Pontotoc Hills, about 3.5 miles west of Buena Vista; gullies and washes in field northwest of M & O RR, 1.25 miles

northeast of Houston; ditch at side of Houston–Van Vleet road,
1.25 miles northeast of M & O RR crossing; eastward-facing
slope of Soctahoma Creek, 0.25 mile east of State Highway 15;
roadside exposure 1.5 miles east of State Highway 15; bank of
branch stream northeast of abandoned cut of M & O RR, 4.75
miles northeast of Houston; upper part of northward-facing
slope of Chookatonkchie Creek valley, 3.0 miles east-northeast
of Houlka station.

Pontotoc—bald spots on both sides of local road (NE¼
sec. 35, T. 11 S., R. 3 E.); quarry 450 feet southeast of old State
Highway 15, at crossing of north prong of Chiwapa Creek, 2.0
miles south of Pontotoc; street exposure just east of underpass
of Gulf, Mobile and Northern RR, several blocks south of
Pontotoc station; right bank of small stream, one eighth to one
quarter mile south of GM & N RR station at Pontotoc; 1.0 and
2.0 miles east of Pontotoc, on abandoned Tupelo road; side
road to rock quarry 50 feet north of State Highway 6, 2.75 miles
by road east of Pontotoc; Old Tupelo road, on eastward-facing
slope of Bob Miller Creek valley, 5.0 miles east of Pontotoc; floor
of abandoned ballast pit east of GM & N RR, 2.5 miles northwest
of Pontotoc.

Union—cut of St. L–SF RR, a few hundred yards northwest of station at Wallerville.

OWL CREEK / Argillaceous, glauconitic, fine sand and
sandy clay, calcareous in places, containing fossils similar to
those of Coffee Sand and Ripley. Found in the following counties:

Union—cut of State Highway 15 on northward-facing slope
of Kings Creek valley, 3.25 miles south of New Albany; cut of
Pontotoc road on northward-facing slope of Kings Creek valley,
3.0 miles south of New Albany; northward-facing slope of Kings
Creek valley on first north-south road east of Pontotoc road, 3.0
miles south of New Albany; gullies near St. L–SF RR, a few
hundred yards northwest of station at Wallerville; cut at overhead bridge on same railroad, 4.0 miles southeast of New Albany; foot of northward-facing slope of Kings Creek valley on
Wallerville road, 2.0 miles southeast of New Albany.

Tippah—roadside exposure, 0.75 mile south of Dumas;

bluff on Owl Creek land of William Hill, 2.5 miles northeast of courthouse at Ripley; Yancey Hill, 3.5 miles east of Ripley, on Corinth road, at base and 10.0 feet below top; bluff on south side of White Oak Creek valley on Erastus Blackwell place, 5.5 miles northeast of Ripley; Walnut Creek, Braddock's farm, 7.0 miles northeast of Ripley; Chalybeate Spring, 2.0 miles southeast of Walnut.

AN ABUNDANCE OF AMBER among Cretaceous fossils in Mississippi is noted, especially at one place: 1.6 miles east of Iuka, Tishomingo County, in the northernmost outcrop of the Tuscaloosa Formation. It shows there in a cut of the Southern RR and (as in other outcrops in the northeastern part of the state) ranges in size from tiny globules to pellets as large as marbles. There are a few fossil leaves there, but poorly preserved.

Searchers for oil have been aided by information gained through the study of ostracods and foraminifers in the Eocene of Scott County and the Paleocene of Clay. In Scott, the Eocene Jackson Formation appears as two members: Moodys Branch marl and Yazoo clay. Only two species of ostracods, but 225 species and varieties of forams had been reported in Scott up to 1942, when the state issued special bulletins on the two counties. The lower Yazoo (in a number of exposures in the western part of the county) contains a zone of large oyster shells, and a few fragmentary bones of *Basilosaurus* have been found there. There are no recognizable exposures of Moodys Branch, and all specimens come from test holes. The Paleocene Midway Series in Clay County is rich in both types of microscopic fossils, with perhaps 120 species and varieties of foraminifers, and at least twenty-five species of ostracods. This series crops out in a three- to five-mile belt, north-south trending in the extreme western part of the country.

MISSOURI

MISSOURI IS SOMEWHAT UNUSUAL AS FAR AS ITS GEOLOGIC
column goes, and remarkable for some of its fossils. It has all
strata from Precambrian to Recent, except Permian, Triassic,
and Jurassic; and the surface rocks are either igneous (such as
those in the St. Francis Mountains) or sedimentary. Most of the
sediments were laid down in shallow sea water; a little of the
sandstone and clay accumulated in fresh; coal was formed
because swamp conditions were once just right. As A. G. Unklesbay, professor of geology at the University of Missouri, put it in
a popular handbook, the sedimentary layers, which occur in
broad areas, "can be likened to a pile of blankets spread out and
then pushed from below." Sometimes these layers are wrinkled,
torn, or overlapping. Erosion was so extensive and prolonged
that many formations have been removed from large sections,
and there are occasional knobs of granite or porphyry, where the
entire cover is gone.

Cambrian and Ordovician rocks cover about half the state,
in a squarish area that starts above a small piece of Quaternary
in the southeast corner and goes up to the center. At the southeast, it touches a rectangle of Mississippian, which also (with
lesser deposits of Silurian, Devonian and Quaternary) makes
a wishbone shape—pointed toward the east—across the center.
Except for a narrow border of Quaternary on the west, the area
within the wishbone is Pennsylvanian. Here and there toward
the southeast are small outcrops of Precambrian; and toward the
north, even smaller ones of Cretaceous.

INVERTEBRATE FOSSILS *include:*
Protozoa—fusulinids fairly abundant in Pennsylvanian lime-
stones; endothyroid forams in some Mississippian limestones.
Sponge spicules—some in Ordovician of Jefferson City For-
mation, but not easily recognized.
Receptaculites (sponge or coral?)—"sunflower coral" in

Kimmswick limestone (Ordovician) of eastern Missouri.

Stromatoporoids—abundant in Devonian limestones, especially where there are corals.

Corals—tetracorals and tabulates in Ordovician, Silurian, Devonian, Mississippian, Pennsylvanian.

Bryozoa—branching types common in Pennsylvanian, and Kimmswick and Plattin limestones of Ordovician; lacy in Silurian and Coal Age; "Archimedes' screws" (corkscrew-shaped fossils) in Keokuk and Chester limestones of Mississippian, and some Pennsylvanian; *Evactinopora* ("starfish") abundant in Fern Glen Formation of St. Louis County, and the St. Joe and Reed's Spring of southwestern Missouri.

Worms—borings and tubes abundant in Hannibal and Northview formations of Mississippian.

Brachiopods—probably most common fossils in Missouri: (1) inarticulate—linguloids in Cambrian, orbiculoids in Pennsylvanian and others; (2) articulate—seven kinds, all over state, most abundant in Paleozoic rocks.

Pelecypods—fairly common in Ordovician (especially upper Plattin and Kimmswick), Devonian, and Coal Age.

Gastropods—common throughout state.

Nautiloids—Ordovician—usually straight, but some coiled from Jefferson City Formation; Devonian—moderate number of straight and curved; Mississippian—fair number of straight, curved, and coiled in Chouteau limestone; Pennsylvanian—varied well-preserved coiled, and a few straight, found particularly in west central part of state.

Ammonoids—very rare in Devonian, but fairly common in Mississippian and Pennsylvanian.

Trilobites—range widely in age; found in all Paleozoic systems, though not common in Cambrian or early Ordovician, but fairly so in Plattin and Kimmswick beds of east central part of state, in Mississippian Chouteau and Burlington beds, and in those of the Pennsylvanian.

Ostracods—in several formations in shaly layers associated with limestones. There are reports also of related insects and eurypterids, but these are very rare.

Blastoids—fairly common, especially in Mississippian.

Crinoids—abundant in Ordovician, Silurian, Devonian,

Mississippian, and Pennsylvanian, with some beds of Callaway and Burlington formations composed almost completely of their remains. The Burlington is one of the best known crinoid-bearing formations in North America.

Echinoids—fairly large numbers in St. Louis limestone, with specimens of the genus *Melonechinus* sent to museums everywhere.

Graptolites—some of the best uncrushed in this country are from Ordovician shales in Jefferson County; poorly preserved carbonaceous films of the same creatures in Maquoketa formation of Pike County.

PLANT FOSSILS *include:*

Spores of algaelike masses in Cambrian Bonne Terre dolomite; spore-bearing plants, and molds, casts, and impressions in Devonian black shales of northeastern parts of state; microscopic "fruits" called chara, in Devonian, early Mississippian, and Pennsylvanian; many fossils, from microscopic to large trunks, in Pennsylvanian, with carbon-film impressions, resembling reeds, rushes, and ferns, and carbonized remains of treelike ferns and "scale trees"; plant leaves, including walnut, hickory, linden, and sycamore, in Eocene beds in southeastern Missouri, particularly Stottard and Scott counties.

VERTEBRATE FOSSILS *include those of:*

Fish—large numbers of teeth, conodonts (?), and bony armor plates abundant in some beds and localities from Ordovician into Pennsylvanian. One of most common forms of teeth is from the sharklike creature *Ptyctodus*.

Amphibians—a few prints of a supposed amphibian from Pennsylvanian shale near Kansas City, and a few Pleistocene frog bones from old sinkhole near Enon, Moniteau County.

Reptiles—scarce, with a few dinosaur fragments from the Cretaceous. Several dinosaur vertebrae were found in Cretaceous beds at Marble Hill in Bollinger County in 1942. A few Pleistocene remains have been reported from a fissure in limestone near Herculaneum in Jefferson County, and turtles have come from an old sinkhole near Enon.

Mammals—some excellent finds, though mammalian remains are not truly common in the state; discoveries have been isolated and unpredictable, with most from caves and sinkholes and some from alluvial deposits along creeks and rivers. Finds have included skulls, teeth, ribs, and leg bones of mastodons (something from almost every county); fewer bones of mammoths; remains of several species of ancient horses, with frequent teeth; camels, deer, musk oxen, bison, bears, peccaries; and probably raccoons, porcupines, and armadillos. Specific finds: from a sinkhole near Enon—fragmental remains of horses, young mastodons, tapir, and sloth; from cave beneath old Lemp Brewery in St. Louis—more than three thousand bones of peccaries, a raccoon, black bear, porcupine, armadillo, all now in the American Museum of Natural History.

WHEN IT COMES TO FINDING MASTODONS, those who know Missouri's history think immediately of Albrecht (now usually Albert) K. Koch, who called himself doctor, though he had no right to the title and actually had had no training. He was perhaps the first person in the nineteenth century to look there especially for mastodon bones, and made spectacular finds in such places as Rock Creek, about twenty miles south of St. Louis, and in various caves and sinkholes, which he was constantly exploring.

When Koch found a skeleton with parts missing, he made the parts. He used scientific terminology in a strange fashion. And he put together some odd bones, called the resulting monster "Missourium," and showed it not only in several cities of the United States but in foreign countries. Nevertheless, he seems to have been an honest man, hitherto much maligned, who was actually ahead of his time, and whose finds have been very helpful to later generations. Koch tried to prove that the mastodon was contemporary with man. Though that probably was not true in Missouri, authorities say it has been proved to be so in other places, like Wyoming (see p. 301).

In 1839 Koch wrote, "Besides the Mastodon's head I have found near the same place several highly interesting remains of antedeluvian animals, one of which especially merits attention. It is the head of a nondescript animal, which appears to have been superior in size to the largest elephant, and which resembles somewhat the Mastodon in the hind part of the head, but the front part is entirely different; and until it is recognized or proved to have been previously discovered, I shall name it Koch's Missourium, in honor of the state it is discovered in."

AMONG THE INNUMERABLE LOCALITIES in which hunters are likely to find fossils, many (as in other states) are on rocky slopes and ledges that have been exposed to weathering, in quarries and road cuts, and in spoil piles of coal strip mines. Moreover, authorities don't mind amateur collecting! (See p. 67.) Considered chronologically, sites include:

CAMBRIAN
A few small phosphatic brachiopods, especially in vicinity of Ironton; some brachiopods and an occasional trilobite in southwestern part of Van Buren area.

ORDOVICIAN
Fossils abundant in some beds; in others, not. In the Ozarks fossils are most common in chert that appears after dolomite and limestone have weathered, and diligent search will produce many gastropods and brachiopods, and a few trilobites and cephalopods. The Kimmswick limestone at Glen Park, Jefferson County, and in other exposures in eastern Missouri, is abundantly fossiliferous, and the only formation that contains "sunflower coral." Among other good localities for Ordovician are highway and railroad cuts near Eureka (St. Louis County), and Herculaneum, and the road cut just north of New London near Salt River bridge in Ralls County, where shale contains numerous conodonts.

SILURIAN
Limited in depth and extent, with a few typical fossils in the vicinity of Cape Girardeau and Bowling Green.

DEVONIAN
Some of the best finds come from exposures along Little Saline Creek in Ste. Genevieve County; in creek valley rock quarries in southern Callaway and Boone counties; and in western Montgomery County, especially along north side of gravel road about two miles east of New Bloomfield.

MISSISSIPPIAN

Many fossils in quarries in Burlington limestone from central part, southwestward toward Springfield and Carthage, and even more in weathered slabs on hillsides in same formation. For many years, King's Butte, north of Springfield, has been a favorite spot; and there have been excellent fossils in the old Sweeney Quarry near Clifton City in Cooper County.

PENNSYLVANIAN

Good collecting from spoil piles of strip mines in west central; well-preserved plants often in dark shales associated with coal beds; and tree trunks and stumps sometimes from fire clay pits and clay layer under beds. Pennsylvanian fossils have come also from limestone quarries in Kansas City area.

CRETACEOUS

No good collecting localities.

TERTIARY (Eocene, Pliocene, and Pleistocene)

A few well-preserved fossil leaves from old clay pits in Stoddard County.

A POPULAR STATE HANDBOOK of 1962 amplifies the story of mammals. The most prolific localities for them are swamps, sinkholes, and caves, and among those still identifiable (several of which Koch visited) are:

SWAMPS / *Bourbeuse River*—in 1843, Koch told of finding partly burned bones in a site that is thought to be that about 2.5 miles south of the Gasconade County line, in Phelps County, near what is known as Foley's Spring (SE¼ NE¼ NE¼ sec. 8, T. 39 N., R. 6 W.).

Pomme de Terre—in 1806, B. S. Barton wrote to the great French zoologist and geologist, Baron Cuvier, that someone was said to have collected seventeen mastodon tusks in this area, and Koch certainly searched there. The site is near the Pomme de Terre (or Big Bone) River, tributary to the Osage, probably on the Brashear farm (SW¼ NW¼ NE¼ NW¼ sec. 9, T. 33 N., R. 22 W.), about a tenth of a mile south of the Benton County line, in Hickory County.

Kimmswick—a favorite locality for more than a century

after Koch reported it in 1839. Systematic excavations were carried on by an amateur between 1940 and 1942.

Sedalia—remains of all sorts of animals found in 1879 and shortly thereafter, but those given to the University of Missouri had disintegrated by 1919.

Vienna—two hundred bones and teeth taken out in 1951, when a swampy patch on the farm of Andrew Buschmann was excavated; site is 4.0 miles west and a little south of Vienna, off State Highway 42 (sec. 26, T. 40 N., R. 10 W.) in Maries County.

SINKHOLES / *Cherokee Cave*—vertebrates collected in the late 1820s from this cave beneath St. Louis (now a historical and geological museum). In 1945 Dr. M. G. Mehl and students from the University of Missouri found peccary skeletons there.

MGSQV-1101 (See p. 67) in Howell, and MGSQV-1091 in Laclede County have revealed fossils, but specific localities are not given.

CAVES / *Enon*—the University acquired many teeth and bones of horses, tapirs, a sloth, and lesser animals, plus two nearly complete turtle carapaces, when a natural accumulation of Pleistocene bones was found there in 1941, because of tunneling into the area in the southeast corner of Moniteau County.

Jerry Long—Ralls County, about four miles north of Perry (NE¼ sec. 10, T. 54 N., R. 7 W.). From a fissure in the floor, in 1956–57 many unarticulated bones were excavated, representing animals from deer mouse to bear, with the most common an Eastern wood rat not found there today.

Bat—Shannon County; another mechanical trap; has yielded bears and other bones.

Carroll—Camden County (MGSQV-1079); upper arm bone of giant cave bear makes only record of this Pleistocene bear from middle of North America. Also found in this site were remains of an extinct giant wolf, and beaver.

Bat—Pulaski County; giant wolf and many smaller.

Cox—Pulaski County (MGSQV-1103); bones of large canid and giant cave bear.

Nameless—Crawford County (MGSQV-1104), not far from Sullivan; giant cave bear.

Stark (commercial) Caverns—Miller County (NE¼ NW¼ sec. 28, T. 41 N., R. 15 W.); broken pieces, probably elk and deer.

OTHER SITES, not completely identified are Jasper County MGSQV-1009; Benton County MGSQV-1006 and 1013; Atchison County MGSQV-1936; Hickory County MGSQV-1001; New Madrid County MGSQV-1003; Jackson County MGSQV-1035.

The state puts on many temporary exhibits, and has an outstanding permanent one in the State Museum of Natural Resources, Capitol Building, Jefferson City, and a small collection in the headquarters of the geological survey in Rolla.

MONTANA

SOME OF THE MOST ASTONISHING FOSSIL FINDS (SUCH AS *Tyrannosaurus rex* of the Cretaceous Hell Creek beds) have been made in Montana. Yet there seems to be comparatively little popular literature about the finds, and not a great deal to which the amateur can refer, as there is no handbook yet.

Extraordinary discoveries have not ceased, and the paleontological world is still flocking to Montana, especially because of what was found in the summers of 1962, 1963, and 1964 at or near Bug Creek.

The fact that the area contains important fossils was discovered by Newell F. Joyner, regional museum curator of the National Park Service, Omaha, Nebraska, and the families of Donald C. Beckman and Eugene Kuszmaul of Fort Peck, Montana. Collections have already been made by and for many institutions, including the St. Paul Institute Science Museum, the American Museum of Natural History, the universities of Minnesota, Kansas (K.U.), and Nebraska, and Yale, Montana

State, Harvard, and Princeton universities. Various grants are helping to support expeditions.

The Bug Creek fauna is late Cretaceous, found in three localities: Bug Creek Anthills (W½ sec. 9, T. 22 N., R. 43 E.); Bug Creek West (NE¼ sec. 17, T. 22 N., R. 43 E.); and Harbicht Hill (sec. 32, T. 25 N., R. 43 E.). The richest and most exciting of these is Bug Creek Anthills, which contains the lowest of the three newly discovered Cretaceous mammal faunas, which are transitional between late Cretaceous faunas and those of the early Paleocene. These transitional discoveries have revealed that they include the earliest species of four families previously thought to be restricted to the early Tertiary.

In the first ten weeks of field work scientists unearthed about 26,000 mammal teeth, some 1,000 mammal jaw fragments, hundreds of mammalial postcranial elements, and numerous remains of fish, amphibians, and reptiles (including teeth of seven species of dinosaurs).

It is reported that collections thus far show mixtures of three coeval communities: the usual aquatic and semiaquatic Cretaceous and early Tertiary community of gar pike, bowfin, sturgeon, ray, crocodile, alligator, champsosaur (a smallish reptile with slender jaws), turtle, salamander, frog, and aquatic bird species; and two terrestrial vertebrate communities in very unequal proportions, with the less abundant represented by the well-known late Cretaceous assemblages of dinosaurs, lizards, didelphid opossums, and ptilodontid multituberculate mammals (herbivores having many and differentiated teeth—best known from the Lance Formation of Wyoming), and the second (more abundant) community dominated by previously undescribed species whose descendants are characteristic of the early Paleocene Puercan age.

As the result of these excavations, specialists are making new evaluations of community changes from Cretaceous into Paleocene. There is a continuous reduction in the diversity of types of flora between the lower Hell Creek Formation, through the Tullock Formation (which is lower Paleocene), up into the Lebo Formation of mid-Paleocene age. Among the deductions is one that the rate of evolution of mammals was high during this transition. Paleontologists have also been able to restore the skeleton of a multituberculate, and to revise the multituberculate classification, as well as to make certain changes in their estimate of the evolution of mammals, and to add to their knowledge of climate.

Of course the Bug Creek is not yet a place for amateurs to poke around.

Montana's site in the Tertiary Ruby Valley basin was first worked in 1947 by Dr. Herman F. Becker, research associate of the New York Botanical Garden. This area, in southwestern Montana on the fringe of the West Yellowstone–Madison-River region, has turned out to be one of the most rewarding sites on the continent for plant and insect remains. Dr. Becker has carried out exceedingly successful excavations during the summer since 1947. Many of the fossils are now in the Botanical Garden.

The locality is private property; and, in addition, scientific investigation is not yet completed. Therefore, the person who collects only for the joy of doing it should not even try to dig there for the time being. When the moment *does* come that scientists will not mind his being there, naturally he should get permission before venturing in. He will then enter the basin between the (Precambrian) Ruby and Gravelly ranges, to a place about sixty miles west-northwest of Hebgen Lake. Volcanic activity still continues, and there are several thermal springs.

During the 1959 season alone, Dr. Becker collected approximately five thousand specimens, representing about two hundred species of plants, insects, and fishes. The Ruby Valley deposit seems to be inexhaustible, and (from fifteen sites, all within about six square miles) has revealed such specimens as lantern, crane, damsel, May, and caddis flies, grasshoppers, mosquitoes, beetles, earwigs, leafhoppers, ants, bees, wasps, snails, feathers, and even an occasional bird. New things keep coming to light, as in 1961, when a notable florule (unit within a larger flora), now known affectionately as the "Badger Flora," was dug up from a badger burrow on the side of a V-shaped gulch. From that site have come such unique specimens as the remains of a lotus or water lily leaf with petiole. Flora and fauna range from the Eocene through the Miocene, with Oligocene most abundant.

The Oligocene shales are finely laminated and sometimes

paper-thin, made up of clay, silt, and volcanic ash, where plant remains were quickly covered over. Greatest care must be taken in excavating and preserving the finds. Among plants that have been recovered are mosses and ferns, cattails, sedges, horsetails, pondweed, false mermaid, liverwort, maple, beech, dogwood, ironwood, *ailanthus* (tree of heaven), elm, oak, ash, roses, dawn redwood, cedars, grasses, pennycress, barren (or false) strawberry, cinquefoil, smoke trees, spiraea, snowberry, gooseberry, vetches, cilmbing grapes, *smilax* (greenbriers), milfoil fernbush, Katsura tree, and mountain mahogany. This whole assemblage is very similar to the Florissant flora of Colorado, and also helps to connect the Colorado area with certain floras of Oregon, to make a common botanical province. Paleontologists have worked out some intricate relationships and drawn a number of significant conclusions from this.

What is called the Mormon Creek flora has been collected from only one small site—near Mormon Creek, in siltstone composed of quartz and mica in minute particles of clay. As of 1960, the flora was known to include nineteen orders, thirty-four families, forty-five genera, and fifty-four species, with three additional unidentified forms. These finds are more than ordinarily important for the clues they offer to the age of the rock in which they lie. Because of what Dr. Becker (who has written about them for several publications) calls "a deplorable lack of geological data and contributary faunal remains for this area," determination of the age of the basin deposits must depend "entirely on their plant contents." About three miles from the Mormon Creek site, scattered teeth and small bone fragments seem to have been left by Miocene horses and camels. But, on the basis of various evidences, the Mormon Creek assemblage is now established as upper Eocene.

Finds in the long-famous Fort Union beds of Sweet Grass County have been the subject of papers by well-known paleontologists. In 1901 Dr. Earl Douglass came on fossil plants, mollusks, and vertebrae at Bear Butte, "in a mesa-shaped hill east of Widdicombe Creek on the John and William Widdicombe ranch"; this site is sixteen to eighteen miles northeast of Melville. In a quarry later named for him, A. C. Silberling had unearthed a number of small mammals not known anywhere else —in most cases represented only by teeth. Fossils had also been taken from a mine not far away, called the Gidley, and from a third site, opened up in 1933, and called the Scarritt. Many of the bones found in the Fort Union are now in the American Museum of Natural History. When, in 1937, George Gaylord Simpson wrote of the Fort Union beds, fossil mammals had been found in fifty-seven localities, with at least twenty-five of them of real value to scientists. The Silberling is in the NE¼ SW¼ sec. 4, T. 5 N., R. 16 E., in an embayment near the east side of Bear Butte; the Gidley, in the NW¼ NE¼ sec. 25, T. 5 N., R. 15 E.

From the Gidley and Scarritt, important discoveries included ten multituberculates; eleven insectivores (primitive insect-eating mammalian forms); six primates (of the same order as man, and probably something like lemurs); fourteen carnivores of the *Artocyonidae* (carnivorous quadrupeds with forty-four teeth); two taeniodonts (with threadlike teeth); and two pantodonts (large, hoofed, herbivorous five-toed quadrupeds). In most instances the specialists figured out what they had from jaws, teeth, and occasional fragments.

From eighty-two places in the Crazy Mountain field in the south-central part of the state, numerous invertebrates were taken, and among them one champsosaur.

In 1963 certain specific types of fossils, and localities where they may be found, were listed for us by the Department of Earth Sciences of Montana State College in Bozeman. They are:

Trilobites (Cambrian)—Nixon Gulch; Horseshoe Hills north of Manhattan; Sawtooth-Lewis and Clark ranges west of Augusta; and Bridger Range north of Bozeman.

Corals, brachiopods, and bryozoans (Mississippian)—in Bridger Range and at Shell Mountain south of Big Timber.

Dinosaurs—Hell Creek area in Garfield and McCone counties; on Fish Creek, Sweet Grass County; and at confluence of Judith and Missouri rivers south of Bearpaw Mountains.

Cenozoic flora—above Ruby Reservoir on Ruby River (see foregoing).

Tempskya (petrified plant)—near Harlowtown.

Mammalian remains—Madison Bluffs south of Three Forks, and near Fort Logan (White Sulphur Springs).

Mammalia and plants—Pipestone Springs area near Whitehall.

IMPORTANT FINDS, as recorded in the general literature, include Precambrian burrow fillings, worm trails, arthropods, blue-green algae, fungi, and consularians in Glacier National Park; the horned *Montanoceratops* in very late Cretaceous sediments at St. Mary's.

In the Belt Series (Montana's oldest sediments) in Glacier National Park, fossils of algae are exceedingly well shown, especially at a number of places along Going-to-the-Sun Highway, which crosses the park. The algae are of the group known as Spongiostroma, which grew as thin mats of threadlike filaments, but seldom show microscopic structure. Masses, known as heads, occur in all sorts of shapes—columnar, fan shaped, dome shaped, and conical; they are composed of limestone layers separated by layers containing less silt, and showing clearly on the rock surface.

Montana contains 147,138 square miles of land and water, but its boundaries were created with little regard for its physical history, and its geology is difficult to differentiate from that of the whole Rocky Mountain region. The serious fossil hunter will find it helpful to know a good deal about the state's formations. He will find:

ARCHEOZOIC and PROTEROZOIC
Rocks—western part, such as Belt Series in Glacier National Park.

CAMBRIAN
Flathead sandstone, Gros Ventre limestones and shales, and the thick Gallatin Group of limestones, above Proterozoic.

ORDOVICIAN
Middle—Big Horn dolomite in south-central part of the state. Upper Ordovician in central and western.

SILURIAN
Only in north-central part of state and eastward into Dakota.

DEVONIAN
Late—Jefferson limestone and Three Forks shale, western part of state, in great unconformity, on upturned edges of earlier rocks.

MISSISSIPPIAN
Early—in southwestern part of state as Sappington car-

bonaceous shale; elsewhere as Madison limestone (best known formation in state); well found in Gallatin, Madison, and Beaverhead valleys. Late Mississippian in Big Snowy Group in southwestern, central, and eastern parts of state.

PENNSYLVANIAN

Sketchy. Early Pennsylvanian—Amsden over late Mississippian; middle Pennsylvanian—Quadrant quartzite in west, Tensleep sandstone in central.

PERMIAN

Only in phosphate beds in southwestern and south-central parts of state.

TRIASSIC

Early—only in southwestern, as Dinwoody, Woodside, and Thaynes formations of conglomerates, sandstones, shales, and impure limestones, and in south-central as Dinwoody and Chugwater, especially around end of Big Horn Mountains. There is no Middle or Upper Triassic.

JURASSIC

Middle—Sawtooth formation of basal sandstone overlain by dark shales, limestones, and gray siltstones spread by sea over most of Montana. Late—Rierdon Formation (claystones and limestones); Swift Formation of marine sandstone, shales, and thin limestones, everywhere except over Sweetgrass arch; and varicolored conglomerates, sands, clays, and impure limestones of Morrison Formation conformably over the Swift formation.

CRETACEOUS

Especially complete, with more than twenty formations recognized. These include Kootenai in the western part of the state; Dakota sandstone and Fuson shale, eastward; Colorado Group; Montana Group (alternately marine and nonmarine); thick Hell Creek Formation of fresh-water sandstones and clays over swamps and huge floodplains—last Cretaceous sediments to accumulate in Montana. The famous *Tyrannosaurus rex* of the American Museum of Natural History was found in the Hell Creek, on the John Willis ranch, now under the Fort Peck Dam. The bones were so heavy and required so much protection that blocks weighing 4,150 pounds were sent back, carted 130 miles from the site to the railroad. In this period came the Laramide Revolution, in which there were profound crustal disturbances along the Rocky Mountain geosyncline, resulting in the intrusion into westernmost Montana of the Idaho batholith, and into the area between Helena and Butte of the Boulder batholith.

TERTIARY

Primarily nonmarine in interior, with coal-forming swamp conditions followed by deposition of mud and sands in cycles, until sediments were two thousand feet thick in some places, to make the Fort Union Formation, which is overlain more or less conformably by the Wasatch Formation in southeastern and north-central. Unconformably over Wasatch is the White River, widely scattered over state. Westward, on plains and within intermontane basins, thin sheets of Flaxville gravels.

QUATERNARY

Only along courses of present streams, and difficult to distinguish from Recent.

NEBRASKA

ALL OVER THE WORLD, MUSEUMS, UNIVERSITIES, AND INDIVIDuals glory in fossils representing the magnificent deposits for which Nebraska is famous. And in the state itself, the University of Nebraska is especially active in taking practical steps to conserve the fossils and to let the public know what has been found there, and what still may be found. One of the most helpful activities was the opening in 1961, near Crawford, of the natural history Trailside Museum, in what was once the Post Theater at Fort Robinson (now a state park). This museum is a branch of the university's State Museum in Lincoln. The large institution has already installed in the Trailside a representative collection from its more than 2 million specimens. There is no popular handbook for would-be diggers, but those who want to hunt in Nebraska may ask the director of the Trailside Museum to suggest localities. Probably the most famous in the state are

Weeping Water Valley, near Weeping Water, in Cass County, for invertebrates; and the northwestern corner (in the region of the Badlands and Agate Springs) for vertebrates.

Nebraska's fossil deposits first began to attract public attention immediately after 1877, when Capt. James H. Cook, a scout and rancher, discovered the Agate Spring Quarries, known sometimes as the Agate Bone Beds. These Miocene deposits center around the flat-topped Carnegie Hill and University Hill, in Sioux County, about twenty-three miles southeast of Harrison, and it was there that an estimated 4,300 skulls and other bones (representing 1,700 skeletons) were found in one forty-four-foot-square slab of sandstone. Millions must still lie undiscovered.

Almost a quarter of the bones in the famous slab were those of a tiny rhinoceros, *Diceratherium cooki,* which must have roamed the plains in tremendous herds. There were also remains of a truly "giant pig," *Dinohyus,* at least seven feet tall, and of the claw-hoofed *Moropus,* one of the large perissodactyls, who looked as if he were made up of odd parts of several animals— horse, rhino, tapir, and bear.

Some 25 million years ago, there was a stream running approximately parallel to the present Niobrara River, and sediments form part of the Niobrara Formation—one of the best known in the world—which is loaded with fossils almost everywhere it appears. A few miles below Agate Springs, another especially good area in Nebraska's Niobrara has supplied dozens of small camels, almost all of them complete.

In 1907 Dr. F. B. Loomis of Amherst College found a Miocene camel near Agate Springs, and by the next year five institutions already had field workers digging in the hills. In 1908 twenty-one camel skeletons were excavated from the area; and in 1909, nine more were dug up for the American Museum of Natural History. Altogether, more different kinds of camels have been found than in any other collecting ground in the world. The bones found by the early expeditions were usually articulated, and no one knows why so many chanced to be in one spot. Some paleontologists subscribe to the theory that all the animals died as the result of some sort of cataclysm.

Since 1891 the University of Nebraska has been sending

field expeditions into the area; fossil quarries have been opened in all western Nebraska counties; and other rich finds have been made in many places.

Displays in the Trailside Museum are arranged in chronological order, beginning with the Cretaceous and going up into the Recent, including certain invertebrates as well as vertebrates from the early beds, and records of man from the late ones.

The finding of the remains of a man-creature of any great antiquity is very unusual in this hemisphere, but for a time it was thought that an epochal discovery had been made in western Nebraska.

As anyone who has dug for animal fossils knows, identification is often made by a tooth, or even a fragment of one. Leg bones of mammoths and mastodons, or horses and camels, may be confusingly alike, but their teeth give them away. So when teeth that looked as if they had come from an early hominid came to light in Nebraska, scientists leaped too quickly to the conclusion that they had something remarkable, and named the hypothetical creature *Hesperopithecus,* or the "western ape." Alas! The teeth were those of a peccary.

In the "Age of Dinosaurs," inland seas covered the greater part of the state, and it may therefore seem natural that only one dinosaur has ever been found in the deposits. On the other hand, land once covered by the seas has given up fine fossil mosasaurs, plesiosaurs, and other marine fauna.

Romantic stories surround the earliest discovery of Cretaceous sea monsters. The first mosasaur was unearthed in 1780 in a sandstone quarry near Maastricht, Holland. The find created such a commotion that work was suspended until a French surgeon arrived and took charge of the bones, to prepare them for mounting. Canon Godding, the man who owned the land where the reptile had been found, insisted that the fossil belonged to him, and confiscated it. When the French invaded the town in 1794, he hid it in a cave. The story goes that he was persuaded to part with it in exchange for six hundred bottles of wine. The bones were taken to Paris, and may still be seen there.

In twentieth-century Nebraska, there is now a road on

which it is possible to reach the Badlands northwest of Fort
Robinson, where a region long known as Toadstool Park contains Oligocene fossils. One of the characteristic animals of the
Oligocene is the rhinoceros, which may have appeared first on
this continent, and in any event ranged the Great Plains for
something like 35 million years, beginning in the Eocene.
Nebraska's Tertiary deposits have given up more rhinoceros
bones than have come from any other part of North America.
Among exhibits in the Trailside are *Diceratherium,* who had two
horns, side by side, on the tip of his nose; a mid-Pliocene type,
Aphelops, from the Andrew Hottell ranch, west of Harrisburg,
Banner County—the largest mounted rhinoceros skeleton from
this continent; *Hyracodon,* called the "running rhinoceros"—a
small creature that looked like an early horse; and the late
Miocene and Pliocene *Teleoceras,* which was small and short-
limbed. Many of the fossils have been taken from the university's
extensive excavations near Bridgeport and Hemingford.

Camels lived in Nebraska for many millions of years, and
have left fossil evidence all the way. The earliest is from the
Chadron Formation in the Badlands, where little *Poëbrotherium*
of Oligocene times laid down his bones. The Trailside Museum
shows, too, the small *Stenomylus,* in its sandy matrix; the early
Pleistocene *Giganticamelus fricki,* more than eleven feet tall;
and *Camelops,* somewhat smaller, from later Pleistocene.

The late Pliocene was a period of extinction for 70 per cent
of the large mammals living at that time, and a great many more
species disappeared in the Pleistocene. Fossils show the big
game animals with which the plains and forests of Nebraska
teemed during the so-called Ice Age. Records have remained of
mastodons, "shovel-tusked" mastodonts, mammoths, wild horses,
camels, tapirs, saber-toothed cats, jaguars, and the enormous
bear *Arctodus,* along with numerous small mammals such as
rodents. *Arctodus* was twice as large as the present-day Alaska
brown bear. The largest so-far-recorded giant bears have come
from mid-Pleistocene deposits in Sheridan and Cass counties.

Remains of mastodons and mammoths have been found in
all ninety-three counties in Nebraska; and deposits in Sheridan
County, south of Rushville and Hay Springs, have been known

since 1867, when they were discovered by the government survey led by Ferdinand Vandiveer Hayden. The largest mastodon skeleton came from near North Platte, and woolly mammoth remains have come from Dawes, Sioux, and other counties in the western part of the state.

Visitors travel from all parts of the world to see the mounted Tertiary and Pleistocene fossils in the University of Nebraska's museums, and for almost forty years vertebrate paleontologists on the staff of the museums and the state's geological survey have been specializing in fossils of Pleistocene mammals. As a result, the largest stratigraphic collection of such specimens on the continent is on view there.

One aspect of the study has been of the mass migration from Asia; and this has led to detailed information about the Kansan (second glacial period of the Great Ice Age). In post-Kansan deposits of Nebraska, the following forms, which are believed to be of Asiatic origin, have been found and are on exhibit: giant bison, musk-ox-like creatures, true musk-ox, wild cow, giant stag-moose, moose, deer, caribou or reindeer, mountain sheep, giant bear, ordinary bear, wild cat, cougar, and jaguar. Man, who had come across the Bering Bridge, is believed to have lived on the Great Plains during at least the last four warm periods of the Wisconsin or Fourth Ice Age. Besides the Asian types of animals, there are certain odd forms such as *Platycerabos dodsoni*, from Cass County, which seems to furnish the first evidence of wild cattle. *Archidiskodon imperator maibeni*, known at the museum as "Archie"—a remarkable example of the world's largest elephant, at the shoulders more than twice as high as a man—came from the Sangamon or third interglacial period. He was dug up in Lincoln County.

Nebraska is very proud of its fossils, and tries in every way to preserve the beds in which they have been found. When the Medicine Creek Dam (completed in 1949) was being constructed at the Medicine Creek Reservoir in Frontier County, the university and other institutions undertook an intensive archeological and paleontological program in seven major localities, to get as much information as possible while they could, and preserve as many as they could of the invaluable fossils. Several fossiliferous localities were destroyed in the construction, and many are now covered by the reservoir.

Late Pleistocene animals were found, associated with human remains, in the Lime Creek, Red Smoke, and Allen sites —all in the lower part of the terrace of the Republican River, which flows across the lower part of the state. Coyote bones like those of the modern animal, bison bones of an extinct species, and other late Pleistocene remains were the first of this extensive fauna to be reported from the Great Plains region. Principally in the Kimball Formation of the Ogallala Group, paleontologists found fossils of the shovel-tusked mastodont *Amebelodon fricki,* various other new mammals, and (most important) the skull and a bone from the jaw of a hitherto unknown form of saber-tooth, which is *not* an ancestor of *Smilodon*—the horrifying variety of the Pleistocene. These excavations throw new light, scientists say, on the boundary line between Pliocene and Pleistocene.

The Queen Hill Quarry, thirty miles south of Omaha, has revealed many marine invertebrates, including fine pieces of horn coral, and the impression of a large shark. A complete fossil fish was found there not long ago. Examples of the fossilized burrows ("devil's corkscrews") of primitive beavers or other large rodents may sometimes be seen from Highway 20, west of Fort Robinson, sticking out of the banks on either side.

On May 24, 1965, a bill became law making the Agate Fossil Beds a national monument. These beds are owned by Harold J. Cook, son of James H. Cook, who discovered them, and the son has donated land for headquarters, where there will probably be a visitors' center, an Indian museum, a post office, and other facilities. The monument is to cover 3,150 acres, and a free camping ground will be established on the site the Cooks had already set up. A foundation has also been created, with the Cook scientific literature as nucleus for a research center, and it is hoped that there will be a foundation building, with offices, auditorium, and lecture rooms.

Paleontology exhibits were set up at the University of Nebraska State Museum soon after it was established almost a century ago, and the institution has had a lively history. In

1963 the Mastodont Quarry in Ogallala beds of Red Cloud in south Nebraska were reopened, and again important finds were made. Among them was the fairly complete skeleton of a four-tusked mastodont, now mounted for the museum's Elephant Hall. The museum has also acquired a forty-two-foot plesiosaur (from Graneros shales, near Valparaiso in Saunders County)— the most complete ever found in the state. Work on this was a cooperative effort with the state geological survey and other institutions.

Because of the fame of the state's vertebrate fossils, it is easy to forget that there are also invertebrates and plants. The university and the geological survey publish scores of bulletins. Naturally, many of them are about bones, but it is possible to get some printed information on fungi, echinoderms, insects, and diatoms, and a good deal on specific Carboniferous flora and invertebrates—fusulinid forams, cephalopods, crinoids, and corals.

Anyone who wants to dig in Nebraska—and who doesn't? —should have little difficulty in finding out how to go about it.

NEVADA

IN GOLD RUSH DAYS, WHEN MORE ROOM WAS NEEDED IN NEVADA'S Carson City Gaol, sandstone inside the walls was blasted to make building material for a workshop, and a whole area of fossil tracks was found. These were not identified, however, until 1882, when the National Academy of Sciences decided that they were those of Pleistocene animals, including mastodons, horses, lions, wolves, and giant sloths, along with birds. These prints, with some skeletons, were found at a depth of twenty to twenty-five feet on what had apparently been the shore of an ancient lake.

Despite this early discovery, there has been little orderly investigation in Nevada, and what had been done has often been by paleontologists from other states, with the result that, though museums throughout the country have been enriched, almost none of the fossils are to be seen within the state itself, except for a few in the museum of the University of Nevada.

One of the most famous sites is Ichthyosaur Park, where Charles L. Camp of the University of California at Berkeley found, in Triassic shales and limestones, remains of ichthyosaurs, those largest of sea reptiles, some of which had skulls as long as eight feet. Their skeletons are shown in the original places in the rock. The park is in northern Nye County, in the center of the state, twenty-five miles east of Gabbs, and is reached by taking U.S. 50 west of Austin, and going south on State Highway 21. In the early 1960s, Dr. Camp found another, and a nearly complete, ichthyosaur skeleton at the Luning Farm, near Berlin.

Nevada's first organized field work was at Eureka (between the Lake Lahontan and the Lake Bonneville basins, at 6,000 feet), in a still richly fossiliferous area that has produced more than five hundred identified species from the Cambrian, Devonian, and Carboniferous; many of these species—chiefly mollusks and fresh-water shells—were previously unknown.

Fossils of invertebrates, vertebrates, and plants are common in the hundred or more mountain ranges of Nevada, and a number of the localities that have been, and sometimes still are, good hunting grounds are listed in a guide to the state:

Virgin Valley—a semiarid area in the northwest, discovered early in 1900; many mammals, including two types of horses, two cameloids, a mastodon, a large cat, and probably a rhinoceros. These came from three formations; the top and bottom layers yielded animal remains, and the middle one, logs, stems, and leaves. In 1908, in Virgin Valley opal beds, stones were found in shape of casts of limbs, twigs, or crack fillings in petrified trees.

McKnight Ranch—forty miles northeast of Elko, at head of north fork of Humboldt River; fragments of foot bones, and teeth and cheekbones of camels, and remains of horses and several reptilian creatures.

Esmeralda Field—in midwest counties, largest fossil area in the state; mammalian fossils in shore deposits of former fresh-water lakes. From Sedar Mountain beds southeast of Walker Lake, in 1912, a slab was taken with parts of an early horse, plants, mollusks, and fish. From the Ione and Stewart valleys, in the same formation, have come plants, fish, and fresh-water mollusks; from Black Springs, near the line between Esmeralda and Nye counties—many important finds; from a site fifty miles south of Mina—remains similar to those of Cedar Mountain, including two hedgehogs (two of three found in entire U.S.) and more cameloids than other places all put together.

Truckie Beds. In 1914, fragments of Miocene rhino, mastodon, and numerous fresh-water mollusks were found in the Kawich Mountains and in the Virginia Range, northeast of Reno.

Astor Pass. In excavations for railroad near Pyramid Lake, in gravel deposit evidently formed along Lake Lahontan—horse skull, several other large skulls, large leg bones, and fragments of an elephant creature, bison, and camel.

Prison Hill—in Eagle Valley near Carson City, about twenty to twenty-five feet down; best fossil footprints yet found in West, including mammoth tracks twenty-two inches in diameter and two to six inches deep; several other sets resembling human prints, eighteen to twenty inches long; largest group, twenty-four tracks of giant sloth; also remains of early horse, mammoth, mastodon, huge ground sloth, lions, very large saber-tooths, and birds, including large four-toed birds. These curious human-like prints have been the cause of endless debate. The general consensus is that they were made by some form of sloth, but they seem to be bipedal.

Carlin Beds—small fossil area in low foothills near Carlin, in a thin layer between others of diatomaceous earth; bones of camels and primitive horses.

Thousand Creek Beds—north of Thousand Creek Ranch, which is reached by State Highway 8A; saber-tooths, mammoths, camels, and other mammals, in gravel.

Caves, especially Lehman (now a national monument) and Gypsum—numerous fossils. M. R. Harrington of the Southwest Museum found a ground sloth skull while he was collecting Pueblo Indian pottery in 1930; later, he found other bones of the same creature.

PRE-TERTIARY ROCKS, exposed along the west flank of the

Shoshone Mountains, south of the town of Ione in the northwest part of Nye County, show a nearly complete sequence of units from late Paleozoic to mid-Triassic, with a base of volcanic rock. Many of the invertebrate Triassic species are of stratigraphic importance, or were previously little known. In the Hawthorne and Toponah quadrangles (7,700 square miles) in west-central Nevada near the western border of the Basin and Range Province, along an imaginary line between Reno and Las Vegas, there are fossiliferous Paleozoic and Mesozoic rocks. This area is crossed by an excellent improved highway, from which secondary roads lead in all directions.

NEW HAMPSHIRE

NEW HAMPSHIRE IS ONE OF THE STATES IN WHICH VERY, VERY few fossils are found, and then only in isolated areas. This is due to the character of the rock, which is often thoroughly metamorphosed.

As one authority says of the geologic conditions in this state: "The sedimentary and volcanic rocks that constitute the framework into which the plutonic rocks have been emplaced range in age from Ordovician (?) to Mississippian (?)." Dating them, surely, is a difficult task. In some instances, New Hampshire rocks of a supposedly given age are dated by their relationship to fossils found within New Hampshire itself; at other times, they are referred to fossiliferous rocks in Vermont, Quebec, Maine, or Massachusetts. Devonian and other older sedimentary and volcanic rocks have been regionally metamorphosed, to greater or less degree, but the Mississippian are too young to be thus affected. As for the vast quantities of plutonic rocks—radioactive dating has given them ages from pre-Cambrian at Newburyport, to Mississippian in the White Mountains. Among fossils found are:

SILURIAN
Corals, crinoids, brachiopods, trilobites, and bryozoans—

Fitch Formation, 1.7 miles west-northwest of Littleton (in 1873 by C. H. Hitchcock); corals and crinoids—four other localities in the same belt; crinoid columnals, along Ammonoosuc River, 2.3 miles west-southwest of Littleton, and 1.0 mile north-northeast of Lisbon; crinoid columnals and chain coral (in marble), along east bank of Ammonoosuc River, 2.0 miles northeast of Lisbon; crinoid columnals, 1.0 mile west of Franconia.

DEVONIAN

Branchiopods, crinoid columnals, and gastropods—in Littleton area (first found in 1912–13 by F. H. Lahee)—best localities:

Tip Top Farm, 3.5 miles west-southwest of Littleton, and Mormon Hill, 6.0 miles southwest of the same town; and from the northeast end of Dalton-Mountain, 2.0 miles west-northwest of Whitefield.

In 1958 geologists became very excited about a New Hampshire discovery they think is unique—that of "generally identifiable fossils in metamorphosed rock." In the upper part of the Clough Formation (preserved as a coarsely crystalline calcite in a matrix of quartz, hornblende, and other minerals) they found a shell bed. This is in the extreme western part of the state, in Croyden Township, near Claremont—part of a region of lower Silurian rock about 140 miles wide, which goes into New York, New Jersey, and Pennsylvania. It is noted that a similar sequence seems to go through central Massachusetts and into Connecticut. In the newly discovered bed, there had obviously been a certain amount of current action because, for one thing, the brachiopods had been disarticulated.

NEW JERSEY

SUCH UNFORTUNATE THINGS HAVE BEEN DONE IN NEW JERSEY BY greedy and irresponsible fossil hunters that its geologists and professional paleontologists are far from anxious to encourage amateurs. So the state puts out no guide, although the area is rich in fossils of many kinds, and very exciting specimens have been found there. In the interests of all nonprofessionals who want to hunt the past through fossils, anyone who goes collecting in New Jersey should be even more than ordinarily careful to abide by all the rules, and to be on his best behavior.

In geologic age, rocks run from the oldest, in the upper part of the state, to Quaternary, in almost all of the southern half, with Recent making the beach sands of Sandy Hook and off-shore bars; a broad band of Triassic (Newark Group) through the middle, in which there are narrow strips of igneous rock; then come Cambrian, Ordovician, Silurian, and farther north-west, a little Devonian.

In general, the state's geologic survey reports, going from south to north, there are virtually no fossils in the Cohansey (topmost Tertiary formation); usually fossils are moderately abundant in stream banks and in new excavations in the Ter-tiary and Cretaceous marls; there are sharks' teeth and a few other forms in the Greensand marls, from which most of the spectacular vertebrate discoveries have come; there is little except foraminifers and Bryozoa in the Vincentown Formation, in the vicinity of the type locality; there are plant remains in the argillite and occasional dinosaur footprints in the Brunswick shale of the Triassic, with rather remarkable vertebrate finds sometimes in the shale or sandstone, but poor pickings generally in rocks of that age; moderately abundant Devonian remains in the massive limestones of the upper Delaware, though it is diffi-cult to collect them; and only a few fossils in Ordovician and Cambrian limestones and shales.

Important finds began very early, and occur every now and then. In 1838, John Hopkins of Haddonfield found a Cretaceous herbivorous dinosaur, *Hadrosaurus*, but it occasioned no especial concern (except that curio seekers broke some of the bones and went off with the pieces) until 1858, when William Foulke heard of it, and sent what was left to Leidy in Philadelphia. At the other end of the state, about a half mile from where the George Washington Bridge now crosses the Hudson, in sandstone under the Palisades cliffs, a Triassic phytosaur (a carnivorous armor-covered reptile) was found in 1910. Hundreds of Triassic coela-canths came to light in 1946 below the library building of Princeton University. A lot of specimens of a small, bony fish of the same epoch, *Diplurus,* and vast numbers of the crustacean *Cyzicus* were also found in Princeton, in fresh-water shales. Great masses of Silurian marine fossils have come to light in iron ore beds dug out near Clinton. And of course everyone who read the news in 1960 knows about the gliding reptile, the coelacanth, and other early forms found in the Granton Quarry near West New York, New Jersey, by young Alfred Siefker and two friends. Those specimens have become potential exhibits at the American Museum of Natural History, and late reports say that the museum has been working on a publication about the quarry, and the gliding reptile, which helped to fill a gap in the understanding of evolutionary change.

Pleistocene remains have been discovered since the early days. In 1869 the almost complete skeleton of a mastodon was excavated from a bed of gray marl in Mannington Township, Salem County; this is now in the museum at Rutgers. The creature is twenty-two feet long, and nine feet eight inches high. Six other mastodon finds have been made between Vienna and Hackettstown, and teeth have been dredged up off the coast. In Cape May and the Atlantic counties, when sand was pumped up from the bottom of the marshes, shells and a few larger specimens came to light, including bones of deer, whales, and fishes.

Quarries near Blairstown and Columbia have yielded fragments of Cambrian trilobites and brachiopods. Ordovician sponges, corals, shells, and trilobites have occasionally been found, especially near Jacksonburg, Newton, and Branchville. A fossil cycad of the Triassic was discovered at Woodbridge. Marine invertebrates of the Cretaceous have come from deposits in such places as New Egypt, Marlton, and Crosswicks.

As early as 1894 the U.S. Geological Survey noted that one kind of brachiopod, one crustacean, more than sixty pelecypods, and more than forty gastropods had been found in New Jersey's Miocene. Localities from which they came—all on or near the south reaches of the state's seashore—include Cape May, Atlantic City, Bridgeton, Mullica Hill, Heislerville, and (oftener than any others) Shiloh and Jericho. Collections in which these shells were placed are at Rutgers University in New Brunswick.

the Pennsylvania Academy of Sciences in Philadelphia, and the National Museum in Washington.

The most comprehensive and detailed analysis made in a long time has been of the Cretaceous—an analysis begun as early as 1907, but brought up to date in 1958 and 1962 by Horace G. Richards and other noted authorities.

For invertebrates, the commonest fossils, this work covers localities in eleven formations: Raritan, Magothy, Merchantville, Woodbury, Englishtown, Marshalltown, Wenonah, Mount Laurel, Navesink, Red Bank, and Tinton. Many of the earlier collecting localities are no longer accessible, but those that still were in 1958 include:

Raritan: Sayreville, Middlesex County—Sayre and Fisher pit and New Jersey Clay Products Company pit.

Magothy: Cliffwood, Monmouth County—bluff along Raritan Bay; beach near bluff (fossils in material loose on beach); Oschwald's pits, near Whale Creek.

Merchantville: Oschwald's pits, above the Magothy Formation.

Woodbury: Lorillard, east of Keyport, Monmouth County (only poorly preserved specimens); Crosswicks, Burlington County—in J. Braislin and Company (later Franklin Company) pits on Crosswicks Creek, 0.5 mile west of Crosswicks (a few fossils recently); Bordentown, Burlington County—in Church Brick Company pit, 1.0 mile south of town; Haddonfield, Camden County—small stream tributary to Cooper Creek (near corner of Maple Avenue and Grove Street, near where the hadrosaur was found in 1838)—from clay in stream bed.

Marshalltown: 1.0 mile southwest of Swedesboro, Gloucester County (a few specimens of the oysters *Exogyra ponderosa* and *Gryphaea*); Penns Grove, Gloucester County—abandoned marl pits along U.S. 40, between Penns Grove and Woodstown; Fellowship, Burlington County—excavations for New Jersey Turnpike at crossing of Pennsauken Creek.

Wenonah: Matawan, Monmouth County—road cut, 1.5 miles south of Matawan on east side of Route 34 (numerous tubes of *Halyminites major* and a few obscure mollusks); same locality, but newer exposure, in burrow pit 200 yards east of highway; Runnemede, Camden County—along Turnpike north of Interchange 3 and along King's Highway south of the Turnpike (numerous tubes of *Halyminites major*).

Mount Laurel and Navesink: Atlantic Highlands, Monmouth County—bluffs along Raritan Bay, east of railroad station; Middletown, Monmouth County—along a brook on both sides of bridge 2.5 miles south of Middletown on road to Lincroft; Cream Ridge, Monmouth County—marl pits on "Schank farm" and along tributary on east side of Crosswicks Creek, about 0.5 mile southwest of Cream Ridge; Crosswicks Creek, Ocean City—various exposures along west bank of creek, especially on Nutt farm, 2.0 miles south of Walnford; Runnemede, Camden County—about a half mile north of Interchange 3 (a number of fossils); Mullica Hill, Gloucester County—on south side of Route 322 at its junction with State Route 45, immediately south of Raccoon Creek (a classic locality, where Cretaceous fossils have been found for many years, but where there are not too many fossils now); Hurfville, Gloucester County— Chestnut Branch Creek and road cut 0.8 mile southeast of Five Corners in Barnsboro; and ravine of Edwards Run, 1.7 miles west of Five Corners.

Red Bank: near Middletown, Monmouth County—overlying Navesink along the brook, 2.5 miles south of Middletown; Beer's Hill, Monmouth County—cuts on road between Hazlet and Holmdel, just south of Garden State Parkway, and 0.75 mile north of Crawford's Corner.

Tinton: Beer's Hill, at same locality; Tinton Falls, Monmouth County—"just below the mill."

RECENTLY SIX WELLS have yielded forty-eight species of invertebrates (twelve of them new). The wells are 2.0, 2.5, 4.0, and 6.0 miles north of Chatsworth, Burlington County; in Harrisville, Ocean County; and 8.0 miles north of Manahawkin, Burlington County.

Emphasis in the report on the Cretaceous is placed on the similarity between invertebrates found in New Jersey and those of the Chesapeake and Delaware Canal. It also gives the range of species outside New Jersey, especially along the Atlantic and Gulf Coast Plains.

Something more than fifty species of vertebrates are recorded as coming from the Cretaceous. These are found in formations from the Raritan up through the Navesink and include plesiosaurs, chelonia (shield reptiles such as turtles), crocodiles, Squamata (true lizards and snakes) and a few dinosaur tracks.

Plants have been few, and little scientific work has been done on them. Foraminifera are much like those of Maryland. A number of Cretaceous shark teeth have been found in and near such localities as Maple Shade, Mullica Hill, and Holmdel. Fish have been infrequent, and their sources vaguely recorded. Long ago, Marsh identified eight species of birds found in New Jersey as being Cretaceous, but paleontologists now say that they probably were Eocene, and no specimens have been found in recent years.

Finds continue to be made in the famous Granton Quarry, and the American Museum of Natural History is now preparing a phytosaur found there by Robert Salkin.

Late reports tell us that the New Jersey State Museum at Trenton has expanded its exhibits, and the Newark Museum is increasing its exhibits of vertebrate paleontology.

NEW MEXICO

"FEW STATES CAN BOAST A MORE COMPLETE REPRESENTATION of the geologic column than New Mexico. Every period of the geologic time table is represented somewhere in the state by rocks containing fossils."

So said Dr. Stuart A. Northrop, research professor and curator of the state university's geology museum, in a 1961 lecture from which much of the material presented here is gratefully derived.

New Mexico (121,666 square miles) is a fossil hunter's paradise. Precambrian rocks form about 3 per cent; Paleozoic, 17 per cent; Mesozoic, 19 per cent; and Cenozoic, 61 per cent.

Many of them are abundantly fossiliferous. More than 3,300 species of plants, invertebrates, and vertebrates have been found in the state during the past century, and more than one hundred new genera and about seven hundred new species have been founded on New Mexico type specimens. The periods represented are:

CAMBRIAN

Probably all late—marine Bliss Formation—found in southern third of the state, south of line from Reserve through San Marcial to Carrizozo; in narrow strips along escarpments of Sacramento, Oscura, Caballo, Organ, and San Andres Mountains (with some fine localities in San Andres no longer accessible because of the White Sands Missile Range); and scattered localities near Winston and Silver City. Finds have included a few species of marine brachiopods and trilobites, worm borings, and one species of dendroid graptolite.

ORDOVICIAN

All marine, and all three epochs of period—found in southern third of the state, usually in narrow strips or belts along steep escarpments of north-trending mountains, mostly as limestones or dolomites, with northernmost outcrops near north end of San Andres Mountains, and south end of Oscura; also in Organ, Sacramento, Caballo, Franklin, Cuchillo Negro, Cooks, Florida, Victorio, Hatchet, and other ranges in southwestern part. Fossils include more than two hundred species of marine invertebrates —brachiopods, gastropods, nautiloid cephalopods, corals, trilobites, bryozoans, pelecypods, sponges, algae, an amphineuran, a cystoid, and stromatoporoids—with great variety of finds in different age levels. In the Bat Cave Formation are algal or stromatolitic bioherms (reefs) up to four hundred feet in diameter and three hundred feet in height.

SILURIAN

All marine, restricted to southern part of state, in limestone or dolomite containing locally much chert and jasper. Sixty-six species found of: corals, brachiopods, gastropods, bryozoans, stromatoporoids, one pelecypod, and a nautiloid.

DEVONIAN

Virtually all marine, in southern third, south of line through

Reserve, Carrizozo, and Roswell, with most fossils from Sly Gap or Percha Formations. Well over two hundred species of fossils include: corals, bryozoans, gastropods, pelecypods, cephalopods, and other marine invertebrates; two suborders of placoderms, two subclasses of chondrichthyans, and seven species of other fishes (teeth). At Sly Gap (no longer accessible) two men collected more than five thousand specimens in five hours. Percha shale has large outcrops in the southwest part of the state, and there is good collecting in the San Andres, Hillsboro, and Silver City areas. Not one species is common to Sly Gap and Percha, though they are of the same geologic age.

MISSISSIPPIAN

Chiefly south of line from Reserve through San Marcial and Carrizozo to Sacramento Mountains, east of Alamogordo; small scattered exposures near Socorro, Ladron Peak, and in Sandia, Nacimiento, and Sangre de Cristo Mountains, in central and south-central part of the state. The most widespread and fossiliferous formation is Lake Valley—of limestones, soft marls, and siltstones—with bioherms (some huge) composed chiefly of crinoid and other fossil debris. Among finds are at least eighty-five species of crinoids, two hundred and two brachiopods, fifty-seven corals, thirty-three bryozoans, twenty-two gastropods, nine trilobites, eight pelecypods, seven nautiloids, six blastoids, and several other classes, including earliest forams, starfish, and definite land plants. Plant finds have included a horsetail rush (in the Magdalena mining district, near Socorro), and probably of the same age, a scale tree and a horsetail (from the Big Hatchet Mountains).

PENNSYLVANIAN

Ranging across middle from Colorado to Texas line, changing from marine to nonmarine and back again, chiefly limestone imbedded with other rocks, and all known as Magdalena Group, offering good collecting localities in mountain ranges from Sacramento, San Andres, Organ, and Franklin Mountains, through Caballo, Oscura and Los Pinos, to Manzano-Sandia, Nacimiento-Jemez and Sangre de Cristo. Finds have included 157 species of brachiopods, 118 forams, eighty-seven gastropods, eighty-five pelecypods, sixty land plants, forty-one bryozoans, thirty-four corals, thirty-four cephalopods, twenty-five ostracods,

and several other classes, as well as tremendous numbers of
forams, especially fusulinids. Traces of color have been found in
certain brachiopods from northwestern New Mexico, and there
are numerous instances of parasitism.

PERMIAN

Dominantly marine, in almost every part of the state, reaching a thickness of 12,000 feet in the southwest, (with that of
most Texas) offering "the most complete and significant Permian sequence known in the United States. From the Permian
have come about three hundred species of marine forms, chiefly
invertebrates; a few fresh-water fishes; ten amphibians; fifteen
reptiles; twenty land plants. Marine fossils from Bluewater Lake
in Zuñi Mountains are unusually large. Several species of brachiopods from black limestone near Tularosa, northwest of Alamogordo, have nacreous luster and make fine museum specimens.
Land plants include horsetails, seed ferns, and ancestral conifers. Among land vertebrates are notable collections of tetrapod
amphibians and reptiles, with several new genera or species
from red beds of Jemez-Chama area, including *Ophiacodon nava-
jovicus,* a fish-eating lizardlike reptile which must have weighed
about sixty pounds; the larger *O. mirus; Edaphosaurus novo-
mexicanus* (a huge vegetarian "ship lizard"); and *Aerosaurus
greenleeorum,* a new genus. A new *family* had to be established
for *Limnoscelis paludis,* a reptile from Cobre Canyon near
Abiquiu, and a new *suborder* for *Sphenacodon ferox,* whose even
more ferocious relative, *Sphenacodon ferocior,* found at the old
Spanish Queen copper mine near Jemez Springs, was the most
powerful carnivore of its day in that part of the world. Many of
these fossils were gathered in the 1870s by David Baldwin (a
professional collector).

A report of the New Mexico vertebrate fauna of the Permo-
Carboniferous was published in 1913 by the Carnegie Institution. And way back in 1878 and 1879, Carboniferous invertebrates were listed by the USGS as having been found near the
head of Mora Creek; Ferdinand Creek; on Taos Peak; at Cebolla,
Manuelitos Creek, and at Coyote Creek, especially near Black
Lake; and near Taos.

Up to 1958, Permian invertebrates (mostly as molds or
silica replacements) had been taken from such places as a cut-

off member of the Brockoff Mountains, from Panther, Last
Chance, and Cherry Canyons, from Victorio Peak, Goat Seep Reef,
Grayburg (southern Brockoff Mountains), and Queen Mesa.

TRIASSIC

Chiefly late, in northwestern and northeastern parts of
state, yielding only a few dozen species. Plants include horsetails, cycads, cordaitales, and conifers such as the ancestor of
the monkey-puzzle tree. From fresh-water streams and lake deposits: an alga, a river clam, a few snails, an ostracod, and a
fish. There are also the giant labyrinthodont *Eupelor* (once
Buettneria), and some semiaquatic and dry-land reptiles. A
large slab full of amphibian skulls, now in the National Museum,
came from near Lamy (see hereafter). Teeth, bony armor
plates, vertebrae, and a few skulls of the carnivorous, crocodilelike phytosaurs have been found at several localities in the
Chama and Santa Rosa–Tucumcari areas, and in Union County
north of Clayton; and *Typothorax*, a heavily armored herbivorous pseudosuchian, from the Chama–Ghost ranch area north of
Abiquiu. In 1947 an American Museum of Natural History party
found at Ghost Ranch what G. G. Simpson called "probably the
most important discovery ever made in the American Triassic"
when it came on a bed crammed with complete skeletons of a
tiny dinosaur, *Coelophysis*, many of them still articulated.

JURASSIC

Very few exposures, in three formations (Entrada sandstone, Todilto limestone and gypsum, and Morrison) in northern
half of state, with best displays in cliffs called Red Wall, north
of U.S. 66 and Santa Fe RR, from vicinity of Grants and
Bluewater, through Thoreau and Fort Wingate, nearly to Gallup.
Almost no Jurassic fossils had been found in the New Mexico's
Morrison until not so long ago, although in nearby states the
formation had yielded plants and many animals, including large
dinosaurs and primitive mammals. Then, in 1953, William
Chenoweth, a graduate student at the University of New Mexico,
made epochal discoveries in three places west of Albuquerque
(near Correo and Mesa Gigante, near Acoma, and near Grants):
scraps of bones of *Stegosaurus*, of a brontosaur, and of *Allosaurus*—three characteristic dinosaurs of the Morrison, long ago
found in adjoining states.

CRETACEOUS

Lower—thickest in southwestern parts of state; Upper—extensively exposed over northern half. Seven formations, with maximum thickness at any one place of some 21,000 feet, have yielded about nine hundred species of flora and fauna: Lower —mostly marine invertebrates, with gastropods up to eighteen inches across; Upper—marine invertebrates of about 450 species, usually large, and scores of plants, including fourteen species of ferns, sixteen figs, eight honeysuckles, five willows, plus seventy-one species of pollen and spores from near the city of Cuba, and logs more than thirty feet long from north of Chaco Canyon. Vertebrate finds in the Upper Cretaceous have included a few crocodiles, at least sixteen species of turtles, and numerous dinosaurs—ornithopods, ceratopsians, sauropods, the carnivorous *Gorgosaurus* up to twenty-nine feet long, and possibly the huge *Deinodon.* Not long ago, a seven-year-old boy, David Thomas, discovered the largest ammonite found in this formation—*Mantelliceras canitaurium*—sixteen inches in diameter and six and a half inches thick.

PALEOCENE

Extensive swamps in Raton region have produced a profusion of plants; floodplain deposits in San Juan Basin, many animals and some plants, including single palm leaves as much as nine feet across, taken from coal mines. The Puerco Formation has produced remains of a snail, a fish, a rhyncocephalian, two crocodiles, sixteen turtles, and at least forty-two mammals, including multituberculates, marsupials, taeniodonts, carnivores, condylarths, and those early Eocene mammals the amblypods. These remains include a bone showing the oldest known fracture in a mammal—the humerus of *Ectonus,* an amblypod. The famous Puerco Formation has been known since 1875, and large numbers of fossils began to be found there in 1881, when David Baldwin spent much time in the region collecting for Cope. After 1892 several paleontologists from the American Museum of National History went in, and the sequence of strata in the San Juan Basin where the formation lies has become standard by which to judge any Paleocene formation in the world.

EOCENE

Richly fossiliferous deposits in the San Juan Basin. Fossil logs from Cerrillos-Galisteo area were probably first New Mexico fossils to attract wide attention. From this area have come only a few plants, but a hundred and twenty species of animals, including clams, snails, fishes, a seven-foot bird, *Diatryma,* and approximately eighty mammals of twenty-three families and ten orders.

OLIGOCENE

Almost no fossil record, and no diagnostic fossils.

MIOCENE and PLIOCENE

From Rio Grande Valley and Jornada del Muerto, especially near north end of Fra Cristobal Range, north of Caballo Mountains, south of San Marcial—gemlike opalized wood. Especially from Española Basin north of Santa Fe—masses of material, mostly mammalian (freight-car-loads sent to the AMNH), including four-tusked elephantines, rodents (especially beavers), rhinoceroses, and three-toed horses.

PLEISTOCENE AND RECENT

Notable collections from several caves. An unusual find of vertical tree molds one to three feet in diameter, along with impressions of bark, probably of pine trees, from lava flow into the San José Valley southwest of Grants, is perhaps only a thousand years old. Sixty-five species of birds have come from Shelter and Conkling caves; many mammals from the latter; two reptiles, seventeen birds, and forty-three mammals have come from Burnet Cave, west of Carlsbad; many mammals have been found at Sandia, near Placitas; more than forty mammals have come from Isleta, ten miles west of Isleta Pueblo. From the east slope of the Sandia Mountains at 8,470 feet came what is probably the altitude record for *Mastodon americanus.* In 1956, nine-year-old J. Nicholl Durrie, Jr., who was looking for arrowheads, found there remarkably preserved mastodon teeth, now in the University of New Mexico museum. Horse and mastodon bones have been found in gravel pits within Albuquerque city limits. In 1928 the partly mummified and completely articulated skeleton of a ground sloth, *Nothrotherium shastense,* was found by three boys at a hundred feet below the surface of Aden Crater, southwest of Las Cruces. Total count for Pleistocene and Recent mammalian species for New Mexico in 1961 was forty-one.

The original "Folsom Man" remains were found in 1926 near Folsom, twenty-two miles east of Raton; and in 1937 a road construction crew dug up quantities of bison and mammoth bones, along with artifacts, in Black Water Draw, between Clovis and Portales, which in 1933 had revealed many animals, artifacts, and 140 species of diatoms.

THE GENERAL HISTORY OF FOSSIL HUNTING in New Mexico, as in most western areas, began with early explorers, though the objects they picked up were probably not so dramatic as those that startled scouts and trackers in some other regions. Apparently there is no record of fossils until 1845, though the Spaniards were there from 1539 until a few years before 1850, when New Mexico became a United States territory.

In *Commerce of the Prairies*, 1844, Josiah Gregg, a famous Santa Fe trader, described beautiful specimens of silicified wood. In 1846 F. A. Wislizenus, scientific observer with an exploratory expedition, saw and mentioned fossils. And Lieut. J. W. Abert, who was in the territory between 1846 and 1847, wrote about petrified trees, shark teeth, shells, and bones he collected, in a report incorporated into a longer report by J. W. Bailey (professor of chemistry, mineralogy, and geology at the U.S. Military Academy), published in 1848 as a Congressional Document. Many other reports followed.

Then, between 1853 and 1856, when several parties were sent out to prepare for a transcontinental railroad, the geologists wrote careful papers about fossils and sent specimens to James Hall in Albany for identification. Other equally famous paleontologists soon came into the picture. Joseph Leidy named a new mastodon, *Mastodon obscurus*, from bones sent to him. And between 1871 and 1893 Edward Drinker Cope (see Wyoming) wrote sixty-six papers on New Mexico fossils.

Many of the papers came after 1874, when Cope went into New Mexico with the G. M. Wheeler Survey and found bones of what is now called *Coryphodon*, which gave first evidence of Eocene mammals in the Southwest. He also dug up mastodon, camel, deer, horse, dog, and crocodile remains. His discovery of

ninety Paleocene species helped to increase his reputation, as it
led to firm establishment of that epoch in the United States. The
long official Wheeler report on New Mexico (invertebrates by
Charles A. White, M.D., and 136 vertebrates by Cope) was published in 1877. Prof. O. C. Marsh of Yale (Cope's mighty antago-
nist) received fossils of mastodon, rhinoceros, and camel from
G. K. Gilbert, who found them near San Ildefonso.

One of the most colorful paleontological figures of the time
was David Baldwin, who wove back and forth with no companion
except a burro, on whose back he carried out his precious loads.
Among Baldwin's great finds were reptiles in the Permian beds
of the Chama-Jemez region, and it was he who discovered the
Paleocene Puerco fauna.

Museums, schools, and geological surveys have enormously
enriched their collections with New Mexico fossils. Paleozoic
and Cretaceous marine invertebrates have gone to many schools
and museums and to the U.S. Geological Survey; land plants,
chiefly to the Geological Survey and the National Museum;
Permian and Triassic amphibians and reptiles, to the National
Museum, Yale's Peabody, the American Museum of Natural History, the Academy of Natural Sciences in Philadelphia, to Harvard
and to the universities of Michigan, Chicago, Oklahoma, and
California at Berkeley; upper Cretaceous turtles and dinosaurs,
to the National Museum and the AMNH, with a complete dinosaur skeleton to the Paleontological Institute in Upsala, Sweden;
Paleocene and early Eocene mammals, chiefly to Philadelphia,
New York, Berkeley, Washington, St. Louis, and Lawrence,
Kansas; vast numbers of Miocene-Pliocene mammals of the
Española Valley, to the AMNH as its Frick Collection; Pleistocene
and Recent, to museums and universities from coast to coast.
Great masses of material, collected since approximately 1925,
are still being prepared.

A fantastic cache of amphibians was discovered in 1936.
It seems that Mr. and Mrs. R. V. Witter, collecting for Harvard's
Agassiz Museum, at a spot about sixteen miles south of Lamy in
Santa Fe County, saw fragments of amphibians washing down
a small stream that came from some distance up the hill. They
had just time to discover that there was an almost solid mass of
amphibian bones up there, nearly all of them of one (Triassic)

species—*Buettneria perfecta* (now called *Eupelor*). Two years later, with Dr. T. E. White, the Witters returned and undertook a complete excavation, learning that the deposit extended laterally for about fifty feet, and back into the hill for some distance. It was covered by a six-foot overburden of sandstone, which had to be broken up and carried off.

Triassic amphibians are very rare in North America, but from this mass were taken about fifty good skulls, large numbers of the dermal plates of shoulder girdles, and many isolated members of backbones and limbs. These are thought to represent as many as a hundred individuals, and the deposit to have been only the fringe of a much larger one that perhaps contained thousands. In the process of excavating, the scientists took out a 6 x 8-foot slab, and many smaller ones, poured at least six hundred pounds of plaster onto the big slab, and reinforced it with iron, wood, and burlap until it weighed a ton and had to be raised and turned over with jacks. Dr. A. S. Romer, writing of the discovery, finds in this example of extraordinary mass death (reminding one of the Agate Springs Quarry) perhaps the end of a drought in which the pools dried up.

NEW YORK

NEW YORK HAS A GOOD REPRESENTATION OF PRECAMBRIAN AND Paleozoic rocks, then almost a complete gap through the whole of the Mesozoic and the early part of the Cenozoic. However, taken as a whole, the state is richly fossiliferous.

The largest area of surface rocks is Devonian, with isolated patches of other periods appearing here and there. A wide strip across virtually the entire southern portion of the state, from Chautauqua County to Greene, is Devonian, and is bordered on the east and northeast by Ordovician, which curves northwestward below a great mass of Precambrian, which in turn is bordered on the north by Cambrian and Ordovician. Precambrian also appears in much of Manhattan. North of the westernmost stretch of Devonian is a large area of Silurian. Long Island is almost entirely Tertiary-Quaternary.

The late Ordovician is especially significant because it is part of a piedmont and coastal plain that was growing westward into an inland sea while the eastern border of our continent was rising into mountains.

In New York State up to 1933 (when a famous handbook was printed—see Bibliography) finds included few fossils, except those of jellyfish from the Cambrian, and no vertebrates from the Ordovician—though there were eurypterids from that period. From Niagara Gorge at Lewiston and other places in the western part of the state come what are probably the earliest land plants, and primitive ostrachoderms, sharks, and many specimens of lagoon-and-bay-living eurypterids.

The state is world famous for its Devonian rock, and has been since 1843, when W. James Hall described its flora and fauna for the state's geological survey. Even today, this is one of the best documented periods in the United States. Devonian fossils include ostrachoderms (oldest vertebrates), small arthrodires (fish with massive head shields, and plates over the shoulders), chimaeroids (rat-tailed fishes), dipnoans (lungfishes), and crossopterygians. In fact, fish fossils are so abundant and varied that New York has provided more information about Devonian fish life than comes from any other state (though, since 1965, Ohio may have surpassed it—see p. 233). In general, New York fossils (except those of the Pleistocene) have been thoroughly petrified.

Devonian deposits are divided into six strata, each consisting of two or more elements—limestones, sandstones, and shales —altogether more than 4,000 feet thick. Many of them contain records of land plants—enormous seed ferns, club mosses, and horsetails. Marine animals include sponges (some huge), corals, mollusks, starfishes, brachiopods, trilobites, and eurypterids, as well as fishes.

Specific sites where Devonian finds have been made through the years include:

Eighteen-Mile Creek, south of Buffalo—in a concretionary layer of Moscow shale—conodonts.

Cortland County—in Ithaca beds—fin spines of fishes.

Buffalo area—in Portage rocks—scales, cranial plates, and incomplete ganoid fishes.

East Bethany area, along Lackawanna RR—in gray shale famous for well-preserved specimens—many brachiopods, snails, molds of clams, corals, and hydras (very simple animals).

Glory Hill, near Waverly—varieties of brachiopods.

Schoharie Creek Forest, near Gilboa—late Devonian plants.

Discovering Gilboa Forest, which was unearthed piecemeal between 1869 and 1921, was much more than even coming on an extraordinary number of late Devonian plants. That forest was undoubtedly one of the very first ones to establish itself anywhere on earth. Among the plants that grew there were seed ferns (*Eospermatopteris*), two species of lycopods (like ground pines and club mosses), and an undergrowth that has yielded fossils of creeping vines, plants that looked like horsetails, and several true ferns.

Though New York provides no fossil reptiles of the Mesozoic, the small area of Triassic rock that lies in the southeast corner of the state, and runs over into New Jersey, has produced a phytosaur from the Palisades.

Above older rocks, as well as in Quaternary surface outcroppings, late Pleistocene animals left their bones in swamps, potholes, lake beds, and river channels. Some of those that have been restored are tremendously famous.

The first-reported find of mastodon remains in the state was near Albany in 1705, and altogether up to 1933 about a hundred such finds had been made. In the 1840s a complete skeleton was discovered near Newburgh, in shell-marl. This creature, known as the Warren Mastodon, was in such remarkable condition that Dr. Asa Gray (an American botanist with whom Darwin corresponded) was able to analyze the contents of its stomach, and draw conclusions about the forest in which it had been feeding. The Warren Mastodon is now in the American Museum of Natural History. Two others of its kind are noted for their misfortunes. The Otisville Mastodon, mounted in the Peabody Museum at Yale, had fractured his skull at the back, had necrosis of the bone in another part of his skull, had broken two ribs at some time, and existed with a deformed and apparently diseased breastbone. The Cohoes Mastodon, found in 1866 and 1867, and now in the New York State Museum, Albany, is especially famous because the poor animal had abscessed teeth and pyorrhea. Above him, when he was found, almost sixty feet deep, was a deposit of soil containing bits of trees and beaver-gnawed wood.

Among other Pleistocene animal remains found in the state are mammoths (only fifteen up to 1933), giant beavers, peccaries, tapirs, foxes, bears, seals, deer, elk, caribou, bison, and horses.

The New York State Museum, arranged to show the state's fossil record in chronological order, contains a collection of plants, and some twenty thousand invertebrates, as well as bones of vertebrates of many kinds, including the giant peccary, giant beaver, black bear, and the mastodons and mammoths, plus the extraordinary record of Devonian fish.

And then, in the Farmer's Museum in Cooperstown, one of the greatest and most successful *hoaxes* of all time may be seen. There, reclining in an open grave like the one from which it was supposedly disinterred after thousands of years, is the Cardiff Giant, which fooled even some of the paleontological experts for a very long time.

In 1868 George Hull, a resident of Binghamton, very discreetly had an artist design, and a stonecutter chisel from a block of gypsum, the agonized form of a man ten feet four and a half inches tall. After the result had been treated with sulphuric acid, it was shipped back to Hull's home in a box marked "machinery," and he buried it secretly on a farm owned by his cousin in Cardiff. By what was made to look like the purest chance, the figure was unearthed the next spring.

Even the scientists were taken in. The story goes that the great Othniel Marsh of Yale and James H. Drator of the New York State Museum accepted it as a fossil, and that Oliver Wendell Holmes—physician, physiologist, and anatomist—still thought the giant was of "great antiquity," though he found no brain when he bored a hole in its head.

Hull showed the fake in a tent and later in a hall, and eventually took it all around New England, New York, and Pennsylvania. Even after a reporter dug up and published the true facts, the public still wanted to see the famous object.

The project, in fact, was so successful that P. T. Barnum hired a sculptor to make an exact copy, which *he* of course showed as the one and only original Cardiff Giant. No one knows what happened to Barnum's gypsum gentleman. The probability is that it was destroyed in a great fire in which many of his animals perished.

The epic of the Cardiff Giant is, indeed, a far cry from what is being done with *true* fossils nowadays.

In 1963 John W. Wells, a professor of geology at Cornell, set the paleontological world agog by reports of his experiments on Devonian corals, through which he has been attempting to find out just how accurate a determination of age is being made by "atomic clocks," which base their conclusions on radio-activity. Those tests have been accepted, Dr. Wells says, "as the best approximations now known, even though they rest on a series of assumptions, any one of which may be upset at any time." There has been "no fossil evidence concerning variations in the length of the day, the rotation of the Earth, or diurnal variations, in the geological past." The two chief approaches have been radioactive isotopes and astronomical data. But accepting figures thus set up is really "an act of faith."

From astronomical data, he notes, it appears that the length of the day has been increasing throughout geological time and that the number of days in the year has been decreasing. He therefore set about finding "some means of determining the number of days per year for the different geological periods." And he found a method of initiating such study, in the growth rings common on many Paleozoic corals.

The study has been a complex and difficult one, using Middle Devonian coral of New York and Ontario; and Dr. Wells (as a true scientist) draws no positive conclusions. In a 1963 article in *Nature* magazine he says, however, "These results imply that the number of days a year has decreased with the passage of time since the Devonian, as postulated by astronomers, and hence the values of the isotopic dates of the geophysicists agree well with the astronomical estimates of the age of Earth. It is not claimed that coral growth proves that either is right; but it is suggested that paleontology may well be able to supply a third stabilizing, and much cheaper, clue to the problem of geochronometry, and that further search for diurnal or circadian records in groups other than corals may result in strengthening this weak anthozoan prop."

As so often happens, completely unknown to each other, several paleobotanists in this country and in England have been working on the same problem. S. K. Buncorn, director of the School of Physics at Newcastle upon Tyne, discusses the matter in an article of 1966, in the *Scientific American*. It has been known, he says, that the length of the day increased slowly in geologic time, while the number of days decreased, with 428 at the beginning of the Cambrian, and 400 in mid-Devonian; but everybody had been looking for a more accurate record, and certain corals may provide it.

It looks as if narrow bands were made monthly, and finer ones, perhaps daily (as first suggested by Dr. Wells), and what has been learned seems to support conclusions arrived at by other means. Now, when the geophysicists get into the act, they bring in the laws of planetary motion, suggesting that study of enough corals may give "information on the early history of the earth-moon system," and a clue as to the origin of the moon! Moreover, corals may not be the only fossil assistants. Fossil algae and other marine organisms also have tempting bands!

A new investigation of Devonian *plants* in New York State (see p. 48) undertaken by Prof. Harlan P. Banks, also of Cornell, is reported and illustrated in one of the recent Geograms published by the state's geological survey. This publication gives the kinds of Devonian plants found in the state, and explains that a group of Cornell students has worked with the author, carrying on studies initiated in 1922 by G. R. Wieland, and continued by others. Dr. Banks listed twenty-four localities in which such fossils may be found. These are:

1. Riverside Quarry (now abandoned) on west side of Schoharie Creek, 0.2 mile south of bridge on State Route 341, near Gilboa.

2. Road cut on State Route 10, 1.4 miles south of Richmondville; and another road cut 2.1 miles north of crossroads at Summit.

3. Hawk's Nest, 4.0 miles northwest of Port Jervis along east side of State Route 97 on steep cliffs overlooking Delaware River.

4. Abandoned roadside quarry, north side of State Route 97, just west of Fish Cabin Creek, approximately one mile east of bridge in Pond Eddy.

5. Large quarry 2.0 miles northwest of Cairo on State Route 145.

6. A quarry on west side of State Route 296, 1.0 mile southwest of Hensonville.

7. East side of Mount Peter, 1.25 miles below the summit, along State Route 17A.

8. Quarry on north flank of South Mountain, 1.1 miles west of Schoharie-Greene county line on West Durham–Conesville road.

9. Quarry on west side of Cave Mountain, on road running south from East Ashland on State Route 23 toward Jewett.

10. Davidson Quarry, on hill on south side of State Route 23, 0.25 mile west of bridge in Davenport Center.

11. Fayette Quarry, 0.25 mile west of Fayette.

12. Hungerford and adjacent Finger Lakes Stone Corporation Quarries, Ithaca.

13. Taughannock Gorge, west side of Cayuga Lake, upstream from bridge on State Route 89 at Taughannock Park.

14. North bluestone Quarry 3.5 miles south of Sidney, east of State Route 8.

15. Cazenovia Creek, near Springbrook.

16. Spring Creek near Alden, on State Route 20.

17. Cattaraugus Creek at its junction with South Cattaraugus Creek, southeast of Gowanda.

18. Menteth Creek, alongside State Route 21 just south of Cheshire.

19. Kimble Gully, 1.0 mile southeast of Penn Yan.

20. Gooding's Landing Ravine, near Cottage City, at stream's edge 1.0 mile east of Gooding's Landing.

21. Outcrops along State Route 10 east from Stilesville in the vicinity of the new Cannonsville Reservoir on the west branch of Delaware River.

22. Grimes Gully, 1.0 mile south of Naples.

23. Sandstone quarry 1.0 mile northeast of Rock City, near Olean.

24. Abandoned quarry on State Route 28, 0.5 mile west of West Hurley.

NORTH CAROLINA

MANY FOSSILIFEROUS LOCALITIES HAVE BEEN DISCOVERED ON the Coastal Plain of North Carolina—a region approximately east of an imaginary line drawn through Roanoke Rapids, Southern Pines, and Rockingham. Early Mesozoic flora are very similar to those of Virginia (see p. 277). On rare occasions specimens come from coal beds, but most are from higher strata, with at least nine species of plants peculiar to North Carolina, and a great number of cycads and conifers are found. Floral and faunal localities from the Cretaceous and later ages (as of 1950, and *possibly* accessible now) include:

CRETACEOUS
Upper Black Creek Formation—thinly laminated sand and clay, with some glauconite, much lignite, and iron sulphide locally: (1) tributary of Cape Fear River about five miles south of Fayetteville—petrified wood; (2) other plants—Rockfish Creek (7.0 miles south of Fayetteville, near Highway 87), Prospect Hill Bluff near milepost 93, mouth of Harrison's Creek near milepost 83, Court House Landing near milepost 77, Mines Creek twenty miles below Fayetteville, road cut near bridge in Elizabethtown. Plants also have been found along Black River above Wilmington, N.C. at: Bradshaw's Landing, Sykes' Landing, Big Bend, ACL RR bridge fifty-eight miles above Wilmington, Corbitt's Bridge near Ivanhoe, and Horrell Landing; (3) mollusks— Mossy Log Landing, milepost 69, Bryan Newkirk's marl pit sixty-six miles above Wilmington, Corbitt's Landing, Kerr's Cove, Hatcher Reaches, and Iron Mine Landing.

A stage of the Black Creek Formation appears in bluffs of the Neuse River from Blackmans Bluff (117½ miles above New

Bern) to Whiteley Creek Landing (ten miles above Kinston,
Lenoir County). Better known localities are: Blackmans Bluff,
right bank—plants; near Arringtons Bridge milepost 92—plants
and casts of shells; 87.05 miles above New Bern—plants and
casts of shells; 79.05 miles above New Bern, right bank—shells;
Seven Springs—shells; Auger Hole Landing, left bank, milepost
73—many mollusks; Whiteley Creek Landing, right bank—many
mollusks.

EOCENE

Lower—a few poorly preserved fossils; Upper—Castle
Hayne Formation of marl, often finely broken and calcareous.
Typical fossils include two species of gastropods, eleven of
pelecypods, two brachiopods, four echinoderms, many Bryozoa,
and are found in the following counties:

Pitt—(1) 3.0 miles east of Quinnerly, on Green farm, in
marl pits along Highway 118—marine invertebrates; (2) Clay-
root Swamp, just south of Quinnerly Bridge—similar.

Craven—Turkey Trap Farm, 4.0 miles northeast of Dover,
on Halfmoon Creek—numerous shells.

Lenoir—4.0 miles south of Kinston—bryozoa.

Wayne—at bridge of Route 111, between mileposts 82 and
83—oysters and pectens.

Jones—(1) Simmons farm 0.75 mile southwest of Comfort
Depot—bryozoans and others; (2) 1.0 mile east of Pollocksville
—large shells; (3) Pollocksville, in marl pit at ACL RR station—
shells.

Onslow—Richlands marl pits on New River at crossing of
Route 258—bryozoans.

Duplin—(1) 2.0 miles south of Magnolia on B. D. Johnson
farm—numerous; (2) Rose Hill, on farm of A. L. Bland, 1.5
miles northeast of Rose Hill station—similar; (3) Cedar Fork
Swamp about five miles east of Beulaville—marl pits apparently fossiliferous; (4) on left bank about a hundred yards
below Chinquipin Bridge over Northeast Cape Fear—abundant
casts.

New Hanover—rock quarry 0.5 mile south of railroad station—excellent fossils (including some that are Cretaceous and
Pleistocene, with sharks' teeth abundant.

Miocene
In three formations:

TRENT / In narrow north-south belt between New and
Neuse rivers, as consolidated shell rock used as building stone,
with numerous fossils, usually casts. Typical—twenty species of
gastropods, twenty-one of pelecypods. Found in the following
sites in Craven County: (1) Camp Battle, 3.0 miles above New
Bern on Neuse, one quarter mile above pumping station—
pelecypod casts; (2) Spring Garden—landing on right bank of
Neuse, 3.5 miles northeast of Jasper—casts; (3) B. S. Dawson
farm, about 1.5 miles east of Jasper; (4) White Rock Landing,
left bank of Trent River, twelve or thirteen miles above New
Bern—casts.

YORKTOWN / Especially twenty-nine species of gastropods, forty-three of pelecypods, three of scaphopods, and one of
crustaceans, in the following counties:
Halifax—(1) road cut on Highway 561 between Heathville
and Nevill's store—pectens; (2) ravine on branch of Quankey
Creek on Ponton farm—mollusks and whale bones; (3) canyon
off Roanoke River, 0.5 mile north of center of Halifax on Highway 301—poorly preserved fossils; (4) about four miles east of
Scotland Neck—whale vertebrae; (5) Palmyra Bluff on south
bank of Roanoke about a mile east of Palmyra—shells and many
bones.
Hertford—(1) along Meherrin River just above and below
Murfreesboro—shells; (2) Thompson farm, near Murfreesboro
—whale bones; (3) along road to Tar Landing Ferry across
Wiccacon Creek—excellently fossiliferous, with about sixty
species.
Martin—(1) Hamilton Bluff on south bank of Roanoke—
many small shells; (2) about 0.5 mile below Poplar Point Landing on south bank of Roanoke—pectens; (3) Abbitt's Mill, at
bridge of Highway 125 over Beaver Dam Creek—numerous
specimens.
Beaufort—Pamlico River at Washington—sharks' teeth.
Bertie—(1) Colerain Landing, in bluffs on south bank of
Chowan River—good large shells; (2) eight-foot section of bluff

on west bank of Chowan about 1.5 miles above Eden House Point —rich in fossils.

Edgecombe—(1) left bank of Tar River, 2.0 miles northwest of Tarboro along Highway 44—oysters, fragments of large bones, and large sharks' teeth; (2) site of Old Bell's Bridge on Tar River about three miles northwest of Tarboro in low bluffs —shells at water line; (3) about 150 yards below Bryant's Bridge over Fishing Creek, 3.5 miles northeast of Leggett— shells.

Pitt—(1) banks of Little Contentnea Creek on Highway 258 between Farmville and Fountain—shells; (2) along creek on east side of East Carolina College campus—shells; (3) road ditch 2.0 miles northwest of Greenville on Highway 43—shells; (4) Conetoe Swamp, about five miles west southwest of Bethel —good fossils.

Craven—(1) probably Miocene in pits 0.5 mile south of Maple Cypress—whale bones; (2) Cannon's marl pit on bank of Neuse River, 2.0 miles east of Fort Barnwell—some twenty-five species of mollusks; (3) marl pits on property of Z. B. Broadway, 1.0 mile north of Fort Barnwell—shells (overlain by Pleistocene with bones of mastodons, tapirs, etc.); (4) marl pits on John Daugherty property at Rock Landing, 2.0 miles west of Jasper— once contained large collections, but in 1950 only a few specimens; (5) along bank of Neuse 3.0 miles above New Bern— barnacles.

DUPLIN / Typical are thirty-five species of gastropods and forty-seven of pelecypods, in marl exposed locally in southern part of state. Best developed near Magnolia (Duplin County), but found also in Sampson County, near Clinton (whale bones); Bladen County, near Elizabethtown; Robeson County, near Lumberton and Fairmont (sharks' teeth); Columbus County, at Lake Waccamaw; and New Hanover County, near Wilmington. This formation extends into South Carolina, where the best collections have been made at Mayesville, Sumter County of that state.

PLIOCENE

Occurs only south of Neuse River, best exposed in several places along Cape Fear River, and found in Columbus and

Onslow counties. From Waccamaw and Croatan Formations (sometimes undifferentiated) at least twenty-five species of gastropods and forty-six of pelecypods have been identified. In Columbus County, good collections still obtainable from pits of Acme Fertilizer Company, in Acme, which is type locality for the gigantic shell *Fasciolaria papillosa acmensis* Smith, and has produced bones of *Equus complicatus*.

PLEISTOCENE

Early—abundant marine fossils in certain areas. Late—one species of crustacea, thirty-three of pelecypods, and twenty-four of gastropods may be found in the Pamlico Formation in the following counties:

Perquimans—along canals from Nicanor toward Pasquotank County line near western border of Dismal Swamp—shells, including rare varieties.

Camden—best material from spoil banks of Dismal Swamp Canal, about five miles north of South Mills—shells.

Hyde—spoil banks of Intracoastal Waterway between Pungo and Alligator rivers—abundant shells.

Pamlico—(1) north and east of Bayboro—shells abundant; (2) spoil banks of Intracoastal Canal, in land cut about a mile west of Hobucken—shells; (3) along several small canals near Cash Corner and Alliance—shells; (4) marl pits on Lucas Benner's plantation on left bank of Neuse, sixteen miles below New Bern—marine and vertebrate specimens.

Craven—(1) southwest bank of Neuse, ten miles below New Bern—large truncated cypress stumps; (2) shallow marl pits on left prong of Bryce's Creek, 1.0 mile west of Croatan RR station—shells.

Carteret—(1) canals for Open Land Project about ten miles northwest of Beaufort—Pamlico Formation fossils; (2) along Waterway Canal near Core Creek Bridge—mixture of Pleistocene and Pliocene.

Onslow—spoil banks of Intracoastal Waterway Canal at Tar Landing—mostly Pleistocene.

New Hanover—(1) gravel pit at Gander Point—coquina abundant; (2) crossing on Intracoastal Waterway Canal of Highway 421, near Carolina Beach—bones of mastodon; (3) beach at old Fort Fisher—coquina.

Brunswick—bluff along Cape Fear River, 0.25 mile north of ruins of Old Brunswick—shells.

LOCALITIES (noted by counties) where important Pleistocene vertebrates (many of which are in the North Carolina State Museum in Chapel Hill) have been found include:

Halifax—*Equus*, and a whale.

Pitt—*Equus complicatus* found near Greenville.

Carteret—mammoth bones and mastodon teeth found in dredgings from Intracoastal Waterway Canal; cetaceans and a mastodon found in Harlowe.

Edgecombe—the mastodon *Mammut americanum* (now in the Smithsonian), from Tarboro.

Nash—*M. americanum* found at Rocky Mount.

Washington—*Equus leidyi*.

Craven—tapir, mastodon, and a cetacean found in a muck deposit on property of Z. B. Broadway.

Jones—horse and mastodon found in Maysville; horse and manatee found on Bender farm.

Pamlico—*Carcharodon megalodon* found at Minnesott Beach; *M. americanum, Elephas, Equus,* and several cetaceans, at Benner's plantation.

Onslow—*M. americanum* found at Jacksonville.

Duplin—mastodon bones, on William Hatcher farm.

Wayne—*M. americanum*.

Pender—*M. americanum*.

New Hanover—mastodon bones found near Carolina Beach; mammoth, at Ross and Lord's Quarry; *Elephas columbi,* nine miles south of Wilmington; *Equus,* at Wrightsville Beach.

Brunswick—mastodon found at Winnabow.

Dare—walrus (*Odobenus rosmarus*), at Kitty Hawk.

NORTH DAKOTA

A GUIDE, *Fossil Collecting in North Dakota,* IS BEING PREPARED by the University of North Dakota, and is promised soon, as one of the Miscellaneous Series of the state's geological survey. Meanwhile, in response to requests from eager hunters, a letter is often sent out, which says in part:

"Fossils can be found, in some places abundantly, in North Dakota, but one has to look carefully for them. Since all the state north and east of the Missouri River was covered by the glaciers in the Pleistocene or Ice Age, the best fossil hunting is in the southwestern part of the state. The glaciers brought large amounts of till, sand and gravel from Canada with them and covered all but little patches of bedrock outcrops (mostly Niobrara, Pierre and Tongue River shales). In these small outcrops some fossils can be found in the glacial deposits. Limestone and dolomite pebbles in the gravel should be inspected and cracked with a hammer to look for fossils brought by the glaciers. . . .

"Southwest of the Missouri River one should work up and down the bluffs, creeks and gullies to search for fossils in the shale and harder rock layers. Shale should be split with a chisel along the bedding planes to look for leaves. 'Scoria' or 'clinker' (clay baked by burning of the underlying lignite) pits are a good place to look for leaf impressions. Concretions should be cracked open with a hammer to find fossils. A good deposit of fossils is a rare find, however. . . .

"Further information should be sought in the publications of the North Dakota Geological Survey. . . . You will probably be especially interested in the state geologic map and the guide books. . . . Those books were written especially as guides for Boy Scouts and tell of places to collect interesting rocks and fossils near the principal centers of population in North Dakota."

A chart obtainable from the same source tells where various kinds of rocks appear at the surface, and what they may contain:

CRETACEOUS
Niobrara Formation: Pembina Escarpment and Valley City area, bluish-gray, calcareous marine shale—fish scales, rarely bones, and microscopic fossils; Pierre shale formation—Pembina Escarpment, Valley City area, and along Missouri and Little Missouri rivers, dark gray to black marine shale with concretions —fish scales, snails, clams, and ammonites in concretions,

rarely in shale. Fox Hills Formation: along same rivers, brown-ish marine sandstone and sandy shale—snails, clams, and am-monites. Hell Creek Formation: along same rivers, light-colored shaly sandstone and sandy shale—leaves and bones, very rare.

PALEOCENE

Ludlow Formation: southwest of Bismarck, buff-colored sandstone and shale with lignite—rare leaves, poorly preserved. Cannonball Formation: southwest of Bismarck, buff marine sandstone and shale—very rare snails and corals. Tongue River Formation: western half of state, light and dark shale, fine sand-stone containing lignite and "clinker"—fresh-water clams and snails, leaves in some shale and clinker, and petrified wood.

EOCENE

Golden Valley Formation: along Knife River, banded clay, shale, silt, and sands—plant fossils in dark layers.

OLIGOCENE

White River Formation: Little Badlands southwest of Dick-inson, white clay, shale, and sandstone—rare bones.

PLEISTOCENE

North and east of Missouri River, till, gravel, and lake clay —rare fresh-water clams and snails.

AS THE LETTER SAYS, the state puts out a number of geologic guidebooks (see Bibliography) which may be of help to the fossil hunter. Though they are not concerned with fossils as such, and there is only a very occasional notation, like "Poorly preserved fossils such as clams and snails are found in some of these outcrops," the guides, nevertheless, tell the reader a good deal about general geology, for each guide is prefaced with a short introduction about the science, and even more about the geology of North Dakota. There are maps, drawings to explain certain geologic phenomena, lists of sediments of the various ages, and such comments as the one about the Cannonball in the Minot area: "The rocks of this formation are the last rocks of a marine origin laid down in the interior of the North Ameri-can Continent."

A publication of the North Dakota Academy of Sciences contains a paper by Dr. F. D. Holland, Jr., head of the depart-

ment of geology at the University of North Dakota, giving the
status of paleontology in the state; this paper is of much interest
historically, and should be of special help to any amateur who
lives or hunts in that area and is thinking of making a career
from a hobby.

Dr. Holland writes that recent excavations have revealed a
collection of fossil shells from the Fox Hills and Tongue River
Formations, in an early Mandan Indian site. But, although all
kinds of explorers, trappers, traders and other entrepreneurs
moved back and forth during the eighteenth century, it remained for the Lewis and Clark Expedition to carry back the
first fossils collected by white men. When Meriwether Lewis and
William Clark mapped the course of the Missouri River and
made other observations between 1804 and 1806, they found
sandstone concretions at the Cannonball River about which
Lewis wrote, "wood first carbonated and then petrefyed [sic] by
the water of the river, which I have discovered has that effect
on many vegitable [sic] substances when exposed to it's [sic]
influence for a length of time." This is thought to be the first
written record of fossils from North Dakota.

It was not until 1833 that another such keen observer came
along—the German Alexander Philip Maximilian, Prince of
Wied-Neuwied. The Prince noted that "the strata of sand-stone
occurring in the above-mentioned hills [upper Missouri country]
are filled, at least in part, with impressions of the leaves of
phanerogammic plants, resembling the species still growing in
the country." He apparently made an extensive collection, but it
was destroyed by "fire on board the steam-boat"—a catastrophe
in 1835 near what is now Bismarck.

No less a person than John James Audubon visited the area
in 1843, and evidenced some interest in fossils. But he found
only poor specimens of petrified wood and had bad luck with
marine shells, which crumbled when exposed to the air.

When the federal government began to make extensive
surveys of land in the upper Missouri country, in the mid-nine-
teenth century, John Evans (a geologist with the Northern
Pacific Railroad Survey) wrote, "From the Sioux River to the
falls of the Missouri, both sides of the Missouri, you pass through

the cretaceous and tertiary formations, perhaps as rich in fossil remains as any other region in the country, or it may be in the world."

Evans, who had collected extensively in the Badlands of South Dakota and in Wyoming (see p. 255), sent vertebrate remains to Leidy, who reported on them in a series of papers that have been spoken of as "marking the beginning in America of studies in vertebrate paleontology."

The men who had most to do then with paleontology in North Dakota, however, were Dr. Ferdinand V. Hayden and Dr. Fielding Bradford Meek—"giants in the early days of the Federal surveys," who went on to even greater things, including organizing the U.S. Geological Survey in 1879. Reports by Evans and Leidy attracted W. James Hall, geologist of New York, whose name is famous especially as having done a definitive job on the Devonian of New York State. Hall dispatched Hayden and Meek in 1853 to the Badlands, where they collected enormous quantities of fossils. Of these, the mammalian remains were described by Leidy; the others, by Hall and Meek themselves.

During ensuing years, Hayden and Meek worked together or apart, described invertebrate fossile in joint papers, and collaborated between 1856 and 1876 on a series of papers on Cretaceous and Tertiary fossils from the western U.S., the last of which, by Meek, has been called "one of the most important contributions ever made to the science of paleontology in any portion of the world," and is still the standard work on invertebrate paleontology in North Dakota.

Like other early explorers, these men had to cope with hostile Indians and had plenty of opportunities to show their courage. It is told of Hayden that, once when he was collecting alone in the Upper Missouri country, marauding Indians caught up with him, emptied a bag he was carrying, and discovered that it contained nothing but fossils. After looking them over, the Indians decided that he was crazy and left him alone.

Significant additions were made in the invertebrate field by Arthur Gray Leonard, state geologist from 1902 to 1932, who found many new localities.

Of course Edward Drinker Cope looked for vertebrate fossils in North Dakota—for the first time in 1883—and listed the fossils and described two new species of fish from the White River Formation. Dr. Holland says that this locality became so famous that it has been completely mined out. Then, in 1905, Earl Douglass was sent out by the Carnegie, and wrote extensively about the fossils of the region.

Among the important finds made early in this century are a mosasaur from the Pembina Escarpment, a dinosaur from Marmarth, a titanothere from near Buford, and a mammoth from near Watford City. Many plant fossils were collected, but early paleobotanists created great numbers of form genera and form species on the basis of nothing but fragments, and revisions have had to be made. It is certain that the now nearly treeless plains were once covered by great forests of hardwoods, containing oak, elm, hickory, and walnut, interspersed with conifers, ginkgoes, fig trees, sequoias, and other trees. Even the concretions hold beautiful impressions; petrified wood of various kinds is often found; and occasionally, fossil amber.

Dr. Holland is especially anxious that further exploration be made of the Cannonball Formation, of the Pleistocene terrestrial and aquatic faunas, of the significance of abundant ostracods in the sediments of Glacial Lake Agassiz, of the exact age and correlation of the various Pierre shale outcrops, of the subsurface of the vast Williston Basin, and of the paleogeography and stratigraphy of the lignite deposits. There aren't enough paleontologists at work in North Dakota, and it is certainly a field for young enthusiasts who want to make names for themselves.

Meanwhile, finds go on.

Fossilized conifer cones are very rare, but some fine ones of the Cretaceous have come from a gravel pit near Mandan, on Highway 10, with those of *Sequoia dakotensis* among them. Complete tree sections, weighing as much as fifty pounds apiece (some with worm borings), come from the same locality. Petrified wood in large hunks, log fragments, and smaller pieces has been found in sandy ground above Thirty Mile Creek, reached by following Highway 10 to about twenty-five miles south of Richardton.

Strikes—occasionally very significant ones—are being made from time to time by professional paleontologists. Between

1963 and 1966 several Pleistocene mammal skulls were found in the state and described in the scientific literature. A new Cretaceous echinoid was unearthed from the Fox Hills Formation, and new lobsters from the Cannonball. But the most important discovery was a specimen of *Triceratops* (a three-horned late Cretaceous dinosaur), found in the summer of 1963 by Charles I. Frye. This is the best specimen of its kind ever found, though early geologists dug up numerous fragments of horn cores, ribs, and leg bones. This fossil, excavated through funds made available by several state and national organizations, was in the light gray bentonitic clay of the Hell Creek Formation, forty feet below the Tullock of the Paleocene, on the southwest side of a butte in the NW¼ NE¼ sec. 32, T. 135 N., R. 106 W. (referring to the Dickinson sheet, on the 1:250,000 scale—see p. 72) about eighteen miles north of Marmarth, in Slope County. Excavating was done by Dr. Holland, Jack W. Crawford, and Michael F. Archbold of the department of geology of the University of North Dakota at Grand Forks, with Marshall Lambert of Ekalaka, Montana. As parts of the skeleton were recovered and jacketed, they were shipped to the university, where they will form an exhibit sure to attract visitors from far and near. (See chapter on Montana for finds in the same stratum, in Bug Creek.)

An original educational, visual demonstration of the appearance and quality of geological deposits, with special reference to paleontology, may now be seen on the campus of the university, in the new geology building, Leonard Hall. Though the brick exterior conforms in general to the traditional architecture of the campus, outside trim is made of limestone; and rock ranging through many classifications and geologic ages, from all parts of the United States and Canada, is used in the interior. For decorations of the exterior, a volcano, a brontosaur, a triceratopsian, and a woolly mammoth were cut from the limestone and applied to the brick; and prints that look like those of The Jurassic dinosaur *Allosaurus* are imbedded in the side walk in front.

Interior stone, which was chosen and obtained by members of the geology department, ranges from Precambrian to Recent. The rocks are in walls, on laboratory bench tops, counter tops, lecterns. Many of them contain fossils and have been sawed in such a way as to show those fossils to the best possible advantage.

In the lobby is a small museum, where visitors may rest on benches made from southwestern Minnesota dolostone from the Lower Ordovician (up to 500 million years old) and look at the minerals, rocks, and fossils on display.

OHIO

OHIO IS ANOTHER OF THOSE SATISFYING STATES WHERE FOSSILS may be found almost anywhere, sometimes just waiting to be picked up, and often in astonishing abundance.

The best places are quarries (to be investigated, of course, only with permission), railroad and highway cuts, old strip mine workings, and areas where the soil has weathered for a long time. Fossils include plants, invertebrates, and vertebrates. The hunter may find whole specimens, casts, molds, tracks, trails, burrows, and coprolites (fossil dung); and the original material may have been replaced by minerals, or the remains—especially those of fishes—may be encased in rocks from which all liquids have been squeezed out. Like numerous other states, Ohio has a gap between Permian and Pleistocene, so that Mesozoic and early Cenozoic fossils are missing.

In the following summary, based on an extraordinarily complete and many-faceted guide put out by the state's geological survey, extremely rare occurrences are omitted. *Abundant* refers to fossils so numerous and so widely distributed that they are likely to turn up in the majority of collections; *common* to fossils numerous in some localities but not in others; *rare* to those found only occasionally. The guide contains much additional useful information not included here.

ORDOVICIAN
At surface in southwest part of state, in triangle bounded

by Miami County on north and by state line on west from Preble
County southward, and on the south from the Indiana line to
Adams County. Good specimens are still found in Cincinnati,
though there has been collecting for more than a century.

Good sites: Greene County, in streams and railroad cuts—
corals, and abundant bryozoans and brachiopods; Preble and
Butler counties—near campus of Miami University, in river
banks and road cuts—abundant; Fort Ancient, Warren County
—abundant brachiopods and others in Stony Run; Blanchester,
Clinton County—abundance of brachiopods and pelecypods, and
some trilobites in certain zones.

Commoner fossils: corals (both horn and colonial), bryozoans (dozens of types), brachiopods (many genera and species),
pelecypods (more than eighty species, of some twenty-five
genera), gastropods, cephalopods (straight, and fewer coiled
and curved), ostracods (sometimes abundant), annelids (sparingly), trilobites (though these are comparatively rare in complete form), edrioasters ("seated stars"—unique echinoderms—
rare), crinoids (abundant, but perfect specimens not common),
starfish (very rare), graptolites (rare).

SILURIAN

Broken sequence from outer edge of Ordovician outcrop to
Indiana line at west, Michigan line and Lake Erie at north, and
Devonian contact at east. Fossils not so abundant as in Ordovician, but varied and worthy of study. Possibility of finding unknown species.

Good sites: Highland County—numerous fossils in road
cuts and quarries, especially near Hillsboro; Clay Center, Ottawa
County—many kinds; northwest of Crawford, Wyandot County
—numerous fabulites and one sea scorpion found; Carey, Wyandot County—fabulites; Gibsonburg, Sandusky County—characteristic fossils, especially pelecypod *Megalomus;* Genoa, south
east Ottawa County—abundant; Maple Grove, Seneca County—
in quarries; Yellow Springs, Greene County—especially in abandoned quarry at southeast edge of Antioch College campus and
Yellow Springs Creek; Piqua, Miami County—in quarry—corals
and brachiopods, a few cephalopods and gastropods.

Commoner fossils: plants (a few poorly preserved specimens, assumed to be impressions of seaweeds), foraminifers,

stromatoporoids (hydrozoans—especially hemispherical or globular—two species), corals (great variety—at least eighteen
genera), bryozoans (ten genera common, and a few others rare),
brachiopods (very abundant, in variety of forms and some very
large), pelecypods (three species), gastropods (common),
cephalopods (straight, curved, and coiled), ostracods (many
species), eurypterids (scarce, but should be looked for, for record), trilobites (greatly varied), cystoids and crinoids (usually
only portions).

DEVONIAN

Curving band from south-central Ohio to northeast has
numerous fossiliferous localities, many of them in quarries or
along creeks and runs into the Scioto and Olentangy rivers. Most
finds made in limestone and shales, which are packed with tiny
scales, spines, and teeth of fish, foraminifers, scolecodonts
(worm jaws), ostracods, and plant spores.

Good sites: quarries north of Silica, Lucas County, which
for many years have yielded beautifully preserved and abundant
fossils (note that permission *must* be obtained before entering);
at top of Columbus limestone in central Ohio; about twenty-five
feet above base of Delaware limestone—abundant "button corals"; quarries at East Liberty, Logan County. Devonian is also
exposed—and contains abundant fossils—in several northwest
counties.

Commoner fossils: plants (most are rare and poorly preserved, but tree trunks, branches, spores, etc., in black shale,
abundant in places); foraminifers; sponge spicules (common but
inconspicuous); stromatoporoids (three genera—especially in
coral-bearing beds); corals (famous in many localities), including colonial and horn (some very rare); bryozoans (small but
worth looking for—nine genera common); brachiopods (varied
and abundant); gastropods (large and small—fairly common);
cephalopods (very large, fairly common); ostracods (many, but
not easy to identify); trilobites (in many places, but few complete specimens); blastoids (two genera, common only in Columbus and Delaware formations, and usually silicified); crinoids
(six genera fairly common, but usually fragmentary); fishes
(great number from upper Devonian black shales in north Ohio
—long famous).

MISSISSIPPIAN

Exposed in wide belt from Ohio River in south to vicinity of Lake Erie in north, and east to Pennsylvania line. In the extreme northwest, in Defiance, Williams, and Fulton counties, is a smaller, separate area.

Good sites: northeast Ohio—in lower part of Mississippian section, a few brachiopods throughout, but abundant and varied in some beds; east-central—around Licking County, where there are many fossils in silt and particularly in shale, and also around Granville and Newark, an area that has been worked since 1887 for pelecypods, for rarer cephalopods and conularians (early jellyfish), and for brachiopods (some of the best of which have come from iron concretions); south-central—some parts abundantly fossiliferous, with thirty-six species named (a famous early site, Sciotoville bar, a ledge of Byer sandstone in the Ohio River, has yielded thousands of marine invertebrates).

Commoner fossils are similar to those found in Pennsylvanian deposits (see below) and include conularians (some of finest specimens), brachiopods (most abundant fossils in this rock, remarkably varied in size, but only nineteen genera common), gastropods (six genera), and plant remains (poorly preserved).

PENNSYLVANIAN

Exposed in an irregular crescent from the Ohio River in Lawrence County to Geauga County in north and Trumbull County in northeast; fossiliferous beds throughout, but varying in abundance. One of the oldest known reptiles was found at Linton.

Commoner fossils: plants from all periods of the upper Paleozoic, and representing all phyla except possibly angiosperms and cycadophytes, are found in coal seams, particularly in shales and sandstones with coal; specimens include roots, logs, twigs, leaves, cones, sporebearing organs, and isolated spore coats of variety of true fern or fernlike plants; invertebrate fossils include those of bryozoans (common in limestones and shales), brachiopods (amazing wealth and variety, equal to Devonian and more than Mississippian), pelecypods (abundant, with twenty-two genera common), gastropods (abundance of many genera), ostracods (abundant in some beds), cockroaches (nearly fifty species, from two sites, near Steubenville and near Richmond), crinoids (complete specimens rare, but stems abundant in many beds), conodonts (in many formations); vertebrate fossils include fish scales and spines (common in some beds), a few amphibian skeletons, and some prints of amphibians and reptiles.

PERMIAN

Outcrop in narrow crescent bounded by Pennsylvanian on west and north, and Ohio River on southeast. Few beds have fossils, but plants are in some abundance above and below coal.

Good sites: plants—Cameron and Clarington, Monroe County, and Beckett Station, Crabapple, and Vallonia, Belmont County; animals—Beckett Station, Crabapple, Vallonia, Little Short Creek, Shadyside, Pleasant Grove, and Raven Rocks in Belmont County, Clarington in Monroe County, and 1.0 mile east of Elba and Marietta in Washington County.

Commoner fossils: ferns and sections of tree trunks (in Washington Formation of Monroe and Belmont counties), brachiopods (one species, in black shale of same formation), pelecypods (three genera), gastropods (three species), ostracods (common, probably several genera), fishes (variety of material, but no complete skeletons), amphibians (only coprolites), reptiles (finds have included only one fragment, from spine of *Edaphosaurus*).

PLEISTOCENE

In almost every county, with plants, vertebrates, and invertebrates from beaches of Lake Erie; gastropods, pelecypods, and ostracods from extinct lakes.

Plants—usually like contemporary; much pollen from lake beds.

Invertebrates—nearly all are species now living in state.

Vertebrates—amphibians and reptiles like those now alive; occasional birds, but no complete skeletons; mammals—mammoths, mastodons, moose, deer, bison, bears, giant beavers, ground sloths, peccaries, horses—isolated bones, teeth, and antlers, occasional skulls, but few complete skeletons.

ON OF THE MOST IMPORTANT of all Devonian finds was made in the spring of 1965. The Ohio Bureau of Public Roads and the state Highway Department worked with the Cleveland Museum of Natural History to save Devonian fish fossils from a six-mile stretch in the southwest quadrant of Cuyahoga County, being disturbed by construction on Interstate Highway 71, circling Cleveland. Dr. David Dunkle of the Smithsonian took charge, and scientists said they hoped to recover as many as fifty thousand fish fossils, including those of both sharks and bony fishes. In November 1965, it was reported that sixty *new* vertebrate forms had been added to the sixty already known, and those were in addition to truckloads of other material!

OKLAHOMA

A WONDERFUL ARRAY OF FOSSILS, RANGING THROUGH PALEOZOIC, Mesozoic, and Cenozoic rocks, is to be found in Oklahoma—so large an array, in fact, that generalized directions (courtesy of the department of geology of Oklahoma State University) should be sufficient guide for the enthusiast:

CAMBRIAN

Fort Sill limestone and rocks of the Timbered Hills Group of the Arbuckle limestone near Turner Falls in the Arbuckle Mountains—some trilobites and graptolites, though collecting is not too good.

ORDOVICIAN

Several formations of the Simpson Group (Champlainian) over a widespread area in the Arbuckle Mountains provide excellent localities: at Rock Crossing in the Criner Hills—several species of brachiopods, trilobites, bryozoans, ostracods, and a few primitive echinoderms, in Bromide limestone, and a classic graptolite locality showing prolific *Climacograptus,* in Viola limestone; southwest of Ardmore—fine specimens of *Isotelus* trilobites.

SILURIAN

Best localities are from the Henryhouse Formation on northern flanks of Arbuckle Mountains. There are wide exposures of this light-cream-colored, marly shale south of Lawrence, in T. 2 N., R. 6 E.—*Calymene* trilobites along with an impressive fauna of brachiopods, bryozoans, echinoderms, and sponges.

DEVONIAN

In Lawrence and also at White Mound, south of Platt National Park, in Haragan marl—almost unparalleled variety of marine invertebrates, with excellently preserved specimens of many phyla available from several outcrops.

MISSISSIPPIAN

Best localities are in northeastern part of state, where the system is most clearly exposed. A few conodonts are found in Chattanooga shale (Kinderhookian), and Osagian, Meramecian, and Chesterian rocks yield splendid faunas. In Boone chert (Osagian) silicified brachiopods and echinoderms are common; in Meramecian, trilobites and brachiopods prolifically distributed; the Chesterian series just south of Fort Gibson Dam yields some exquisite specimens of *Pentremites* blastoids; from shale banks of the Fayetteville Formation, at many points, *Archimedes* spirals; east of Adair, near Grand Lake, massive deposits of productid and rhynchonellid brachiopods.

PENNSYLVANIAN

A complete succession of rocks in this series affords better collecting and greater variety than in any other state. Lowermost (Morrowan) at Greenleaf Lake in eastern Muskogee County— blastoids. Desmoinesian rocks in Pontotoc, Coal, Hughes, Okfuskee, Okmulgee, and Tulsa counties provide very fine collecting sites; Upper Pennsylvanian (Missourian and Virgilian) of Osage, Pawnee, and Payne counties—some of the best fusulinids, brachiopods, bryozoans, and pelecypods. Footprints that may be of an unknown type of amphibian have been found in Pennsylvanian shales; and paleoniscid skulls (i.e. those of extinct ganoid fishes—having enamel-like plates), within very small nodules.

PERMIAN

Conditions similar to those of the Pennsylvanian continued, so that a rich lower Permian fauna is obtained from outcrops in Payne, Pawnee, and Kay counties in the north-central area. Insects, branchiopods, and a few amphibians (including stegocephalians) are found in redbeds of Logan, Noble, Grant, and

Garfield counties. *Pseudoschwagerina* (a giant Permian foram) is obtainable from Wolfcampion rocks near Pawnee.

TRIASSIC

From Dockum Group in western area have come a very few reptiles and amphibians.

JURASSIC

A few localities of Morrison (Upper Jurassic Formation) in the western part of the state provide rather good dinosaur bones. Not long ago a new carnivore, *Saurophagus*, was found near Kenton, in the northwest part.

CRETACEOUS

Lower (mostly Washita Group): in Marshall and Love counties just north of Red River—locally prolific faunas of pelecypods, echinoids, and immense ammonites; good collecting from several outcrops of argillaceous limestone near Marietta. In road cuts and other exposures in Bryan, Choctaw, and Mc-Curtain counties—Upper Cretaceous assemblages of oysters *Ostraea* and *Exogyra* are common.

TERTIARY

Several exposures of Ogallala (Pliocene) in high plains of the western part of the state provide vertebrate remains of various sorts. Horses, camels, and creodonts have been found and are now in museums.

PLEISTOCENE

Occasional gravel-pit excavations reveal mammoth and mastodon teeth and tusks. Several complete skeletons are on record from sites in different parts of the state.

IN THE DOBY SPRINGS AREA, in Kansan (glacial) time, a stream cut through the underlying Ogallala Formation into the Permian strata. In Yarmouth time, a caliche (crust of calcium carbonate) was formed in the top of the formation, and still later, in Illinoian, a collapse basin was developed. In that lake have been found ostracods, mollusks, seven kinds of fishes, amphibians, reptiles, birds, and twenty-four different mammals. Specific collecting localities are from three layers, within ten feet of stratigraphic section, in five localities, all in the N¼ SW¼ sec. 10, T. 27 N., R. 24 W.

OREGON

GEOLOGICALLY SPEAKING, OREGON IS ONE OF THE MOST DRAMATIC areas in North America, with a complex history of inundating seas, searing and smothering volcanoes, both gentle and violent upheavals, and voracious rivers eating downward through thousands of feet of igneous, metamorphic, and sedimentary rock.

Exciting finds have been made for more than a century, and continue. One of the most important of recent years was made in 1962, in Eugene, Lane County, when two University of Oregon students found some thirty-five bone fragments and fifteen teeth of a crocodile, probably about eight feet long, 45 to 60 million years old. This is the only crocodile ever reported west of the Rockies.

The most famous region, the John Day country, is usually considered to be the mountainous region between the Cascade Range and the Blue Mountains, drained by the John Day River. The oldest identifiable fossils there are from the Cretaceous, when a great sea covered much of the state. Then, in late Oligocene and Miocene times, ashes fell from nearby volcanoes, preserving the abounding life of those epochs. More than a hundred species of mammals—including cats, dogs, camels, rodents, rhinoceroses, oreodonts, and *Miohippus*—have been recognized from between Picture Gorge and Spray alone. Innumerable plant fossils from various periods have been found. Tertiary formations in the amazingly colorful earth include Clarno, which is late Eocene; John Day, late Oligocene to mid-Miocene; Columbia River, mid-Miocene; Mascall, upper Miocene; and Rattlesnake, Pliocene.

The John Day region became famous in the early 1860s after a company of soldiers returning to Fort Dalles in 1861 from the Crooked River country took back fossilized bones and teeth, including a fine rhinoceros jaw. Thomas Condon, then pastor of the Congregational church at the fort, and intensely interested in geology and paleontology, was much excited by the finds. So the next year he went out with a party of soldiers carrying supplies to Harney Valley and collected fossils on the way out as they passed through the Crooked River locality and on the way back as they went through the John Day. The next summer Condon returned to Bridge Creek, and continued to collect summer after summer, when he could leave his church. In 1864 he saw and realized the importance of the large exposures in the John Day River valley north of Picture Gorge.

Condon had no scientific books to help him identify specimens; so he sent to Prof. Othniel Marsh at Yale (see p. 112) some fossil teeth that turned out to be from the theretofore unknown Oligocene horse. Marsh asked Condon to guide an expedition into the field, and later other expeditions went into the John Day beds, with or without Condon's guidance, sending vast amounts of material to the Smithsonian Institution, the American Museum of Natural History, and various universities.

In 1876 the University of Oregon made Condon its first professor of geology and he taught there for many years, during which he wrote geologic reports on the state. These later became a book, *The Two Islands* (1902), on which all later Oregon geologic study was based. In 1954, in recognition of the man who had made the region famous, the John Day Fossil Bed State Park was renamed Thomas Condon State Park.

The fact that Oligocene fossils are found in the John Day country and other parts of the state is particularly remarkable because almost all other important finds from that epoch have been made in the Great Plains. Oregon's Sunset Highway area, a region about thirty-five miles northwest of Portland, extending from Mist at the north to Gaston at the south, was covered by Eocene and Oligocene seas, and some time later was uplifted permanently, warped into folds, and then eroded. The result is certain areas of great stratigraphic thickness, containing shells, other invertebrates, and plant remains. Formations include the Cowlitz, which is upper Eocene; Keasey, lower Oligocene; and Pittsburg Bluff, middle Oligocene. One looks for such fossils as gastropods, scaphopods, crinoids, echinoderms, crustaceans, and plant remains. Many new varieties have been found. Localities are:

Mist crinoid locality—most remarkable deposit of rare speci-

mens—on high bluff, west side of Nehalem River, 0.3 mile south
of junction of State Highways 47 and 202, plainly visible from
47; reached by crossing river on Burn Road bridge just south of
Mist and walking upstream several hundred feet along the west
bank of the river to the bluff, then walking a short distance along
the base of the bluff at water's edge. The site can be reached
only in late summer and, as one Oregon geologist puts it, "should
be treated with respect"—because it contains very rare, complete crinoids, as well as spiny echinoderms, and various
mollusks.

Pittsburg—sandstone bluffs along Nehalem River near
Pittsburg, well exposed in road cuts along State Highway 47,
especially 0.2 mile north of Scappoose Road junction—narrow
bands thick with gastropods.

East fork of Nehalem River—both sides of fork near highway bridge crossing east fork 5.0 miles southeast of State Highway 47, outcrop about thirty feet above highway at west end
of bridge, and along railroad on opposite side of valley (one may
reach outcrop from east end of railroad bridge by walking
northwest across wooded pasture to the west end of the first
railroad trestle, then climbing to the railroad bed, going west to
a second trestle, and crossing it)—most fossils in hard concretionary masses.

Rock Creek—in high banks between Vernonia and Keasey
railroad station—type locality for Keasey Formation—formation
now exposed in more readily accessible places.

Rocky Point Quarry—small basalt quarry west of Nehalem
River, on west side of Timber-Vernonia road, 5.8 miles north of
Sunset Highway, about an eighth of a mile west on private road
that starts opposite Longview Farm sign—basal conglomerates
containing Eocene marine fossils, including pelecypods and occasional sharks' teeth.

Nehalem River—in prominent cut along river, east side of
road from Timber to Vernonia, 3.0 miles north of junction with
Sunset Highway and about 3.0 miles south of Rocky Point
Quarry—large pelecypods.

Sunset Tunnel—exposed in certain places in road cuts for
about two miles from either end of tunnel, and especially in
Empire Lite-Rock Quarry. (Permission must be obtained.)

Railroad trestle—abundantly fossiliferous in cliffs at both ends of curving railroad trestle crossing Highway 47 about 6.2 miles north of Sunset Highway and 8.5 miles south of Vernonia (reached by climbing steep foot trail to railroad bed and going along tracks)—many well-preserved Oligocene shells and some crinoids. Freshly exposed fossils in Smithwick-Haydite Quarry about one-quarter mile beyond north end of trestle. (Permission required.)

Timber—prominent cut at sharp bend in Timber-Glenwood road, 1.3 miles south of railroad crossing in Timber—well-preserved shells.

Gales Creek—two road cuts (one 3.5 miles west of the center of Forest Grove, and the other 1.2 miles beyond) on State Highway 6, on north side of valley, west of Forest Grove—a few Oligocene shells in harder layers, and crabs in concretions.

Scoggin Quarry—on north side of Scoggin Creek Road, reached by going 5.0 miles south of Forest Grove on Highway 47, then west 1.0 mile—numerous well-preserved Oligocene fossils, especially a triangular mollusk, in basaltic sandstone, but difficult to remove.

Cherry Grove Road—hard ledge in open hillside on north side of road, reached by going 6.0 miles south from Forest Grove on Highway 47, then west 1.0 mile, where ledge is about one hundred feet above road—shells abundant and well-preserved, but difficult to extract.

IN THE EUGENE AREA FOSSIL collecting began about eighty years ago. Important collections have been taken out, and typical fossils are shells and leaf imprints. The strata are late Eocene to late Oligocene, and fossiliferous beds crop out in hills, which dip gently eastward because of folding. Eleven localities are identified. The first seven contain marine remains; the last four, plant fossils. During Eocene and Oligocene times the sea level fluctuated considerably, at some times receiving marine sediments, and at others, terrestrial deposits. Therefore shells and plants are often found close together. Formations are Spencer, which is of tuffaceous marine sandstones; Fisher, of ash, tuff, breccia, and other volcanic materials; and Eugene, of gray tuffaceous and highly fossiliferous sandstones. Collecting localities include:

Fern Ridge Dam—in buff-colored sandstone on Richardson Butte at west end of dam, on barren hillside at extreme southeast end, and above dirt road leading north from west end—abundant marine fossils, including at least twenty-five species of Eocene mollusks.

Lenon Hill—west from Coburg on Harrisburg road to junction of Brownsville road, then north on Brownsville road for 1.9 miles, and east for 1.5 miles on dirt road to farmhouse, and (with permission) along lane to hill—Oligocene mollusks about halfway up steep south slope and on west slope.

Smith quarry—north side of U.S. 99 between highway and millrace, at junction of westbound lane of U.S. 126—abundant large white pelecypods, in tuffaceous sandstone.

Railroad cut reached from Glenwood by following Henderson Road 0.5 mile south from U.S. 126, crossing Southern Pacific RR tracks, going 0.5 mile west on Judkins Road to Sears warehouse, then backing along railroad grade about 0.25 mile to steep bluff—has yielded large marine fauna and still contains many fossils.

U.S. Highway 99—prominent road cut east of Eugene, 0.7 mile southeast of junction of U.S. 99 and U.S. 126—abundant Oligocene marine fossils, including beautifully preserved crab claws in concretions, even along roadside at base of cliff.

Reservoir Hill—road cuts and basement excavations along Jefferson and Washington Streets, city of Eugene, near 26th and 28th Avenues, high on west slope—molds and casts of marine life in weathered sandstone.

Lorane Road—shallow road cut at top of high hill near south edge of Eugene, about 2.3 miles southwest of Willamette Street, and 29th Avenue—marine fossils.

North Goshen—road cut in small hill on north side of junction of U.S. 99 and State Highway 58—fossil leaves of late Oligocene, as black carbonaceous films and impressions beautifully preserved in thin layers of shale; occasional fossil salamanders.

South Goshen—road cut through small hill on old Highway 99, beneath overpass, 1.75 miles south of Goshen (partly destroyed by recent excavation), contains true "Goshen flora"— a large group of plant remains of Oligocene age, in whitish tuff.

Hayden Bridge—road cut near bridge, reached by going almost 3.0 miles northeast on Marcola Road, crossing McKenzie River on Hayden Bridge, and continuing 0.2 mile—thin layers of late Oligocene fossil leaves at several levels, in black carbonaceous shale that breaks very easily.

Jasper—three outcrops in vertical cuts of sandstone, 5.0 and 7.0 miles southeast of Springfield, via Jasper Road. From bridge across middle fork of Willamette River, outcrops are (1) 0.75 mile north, (2) 0.25 mile north, (3) about one mile south—late Eocene to early Oligocene carbonized wood, including some logs, scattered through sandstone; leaf impressions in streaks of cream-colored ashy shale.

The Eugene area is characterized by great variety. Among plant remains are leaves, wood, occasional flowers, fruits, and seeds. *Meliosma,* magnolia, fig, and other subtropical plants are among the older flora; pine, oak, maple, sassafras, among the younger. There are also numerous marine fossils, including pelecypods, gastropods, scaphopods, barnacles, sea worms, echinoids, and crabs. Late Oligocene salamanders are found in the north Goshen leaf locality; sharks' teeth from Oligocene marine sediments; and rarely, finds are made of teeth and fragments of Pleistocene elephantine creatures along Spencer Creek and in Willamette Valley.

The Salem-Dallas area, in the center of the Williamette Valley, in Polk and Marion counties, contains numerous fossiliferous localities, twelve of which are especially good. All are easily reached by paved highways or good secondary roads. Thousands of feet of fossiliferous sediments were laid down here during Eocene, Oligocene, and Miocene times, and because of tilting, the old rocks crop out near Dallas, whereas the younger are seen near Salem. Occasionally, later sediments produce fossils from river banks and excavations, but this is unpredictable. The best places to look for fossils are in sedimentary beds recently exposed or well enough cemented to have resisted weathering. Exposures may be man-made (such as quarries and road cuts), or natural outcrops on hillsides and banks of streams. Good localities are:

Eola Hill—outcrop near top of divide on road that crosses Eola Hill from McCoy to Lincoln (reached from Rickreall by going north on U.S. 99 West toward Amity for 8.0 miles to Lincoln Road, then turning right and going east 3.0 miles to road junction at top of hill).

Holmes Gap—between hills where U.S. 99 crosses the Southern Pacific RR, 5.0 miles north of Rickreall—outcrops in bank of shallow gully about two hundred feet west of a farmhouse and on side of small ravine in steep bluff near highway contain well-preserved mid-Oligocene pelecypods and gastropods.

Illahe Hill—south end, about five miles southwest of Salem (reached by following South River Road to Roberts and going 1.4 miles to driveway at farmhouse)—outcrop behind farm buildings at base of hill, about five hundred feet north of road, contains fossils similar to next locality.

Finzer Station—on Oregon Electric RR, 5.0 miles southwest of Salem, directly across South River Road from Illahe Hill locality (reached by climbing to tracks at railroad overpass and walking along railroad about one hundred feet to deep cut through hill)—fossil casts of gastropods and more especially of pelecypods, which are very abundant.

Frontage Road—about 10 miles south of Salem (reached from Center City by driving south on U.S. 99 for 11.0 miles to Jefferson overpass, turning right onto Frontage Road, and backing parallel to main highway for 1.0 mile to road cut about 3.5 miles south of junction of U.S. 99 through Salem and By-pass)—abundant chalky white mollusks which disintegrate on exposure and leave internal casts.

Turner Quarry (reached from center of Turner, by driving east on county road for 0.5 mile to Oaks Cemetery road, turning left, and proceeding toward Witzel for 2.3 miles, to old shallow quarry and dump on west side of road)—casts and molds of pelecypods.

Helmick Hill—highway cuts 1) on new U.S. 99W through south bank of Luckiamute River, 4.5 miles south of Monmouth; 2) through old U.S. 99W, one third mile due west—pelecypods, gastropods, and occasional sharks' teeth.

Cooper Hollow Road—outcrop on north side of highway rising out of Luckiamute Valley, 6.5 miles west of U.S. 99W in Monmouth, and 1.2 miles east of State Highway 223—a few mollusks in soft shale.

Polk County lime quarry—about a mile east of Oregon Portland Cement Company quarry (reached from Dallas Court House by driving south on State Highway 223 for 2.2 miles to Liberty Road, then driving west on Liberty Road for 1.5 miles)—numerous Eocene fossils, especially oysters.

Oregon Portland Cement Company quarry (reached from Dallas Court House by taking State Highway 223 for 1.0 mile south to intersection of Oakdale Road, turning west on Oakdale, and proceeding 3.7 miles to quarry road)—crabs, pelecypods, large species of nautilus, sharks' teeth, sea urchins, and foraminifers. (Permission should be obtained.)

Ellendale Quarry—on Ellendale Road, 3.0 miles west of junction in north Dallas with State Highway 223 (easily accessible from south side of hill)—gastropods (including rare *Pleurotomaria*), pelecypods, brachiopods, and bryozoans.

Buell limestone quarry—2.0 miles west of Buell on State Highway 22, with entrance marked by sign on south side of highway, quarry plainly visible about one eighth mile to southwest, in bottom of valley—coquina composed of oysters and other mollusks; above, in black grit, large round foraminifers (easily seen without hand lens) and brachiopods.

THE STATE IS NOTED for its petrified wood, scattered through Tertiary volcanic and alluvial rock; but identifying it is difficult for various reasons, including the fact that it sometimes has no living counterpart. The most famous location is the Thomas Creek area—unique in that most of the wood is where it grew. This area includes the Thomas Creek and Jordan Creek drainage, above the confluence of the two streams in Linn County. Many stumps and logs from one to four feet in diameter are imbedded in exposed tuff. Some are carbonized; some silicified or partly opalized. In the former creek there is one unusual group of seventeen stumps. Thirteen genera have been identified —conifers and hardwoods. Those identified are *Alniphyllum*, hornbeam, hickory, cinnamon, persimmon, beach, ash, pine, sycamore, oak, *Gargura*, redwood, and hemlock. The most abundant specimens are of redwood and sycamore, which are found in almost all Oregon localities.

The Clarno Formation was originally described in 1901, when it was found in outcrops at Mitchell and at Clarno's Ferry. It is now known to be widely distributed throughout the state, and its sediments contain not only an abundance of plant remains but a newly discovered vertebrate fauna. Until recently, the formation was thought to belong to the Upper Eocene, but discoveries of animal fossils near the type locality have suggested that it may be lower Oligocene. It covers a larger area than was previously thought. Localities are:

West Branch Creek, Wheeler County—best collecting in tuffaceous and shaly sediments in secs. 20, 29, and 30, T. 11 S., R. 21 E.—most notable finds have been leaves of *Platanophyllum angustilobus*, thought to be ancestor of the sycamore; seventeen genera of plants have been identified, with nine of ferns.

Clarno type locality—1.5 miles east of Clarno's Ferry (SE½ sec. 27, T. 7 S., R. 19 E.), Wheeler County—remarkable fruits and seeds; eight genera identified, with small walnut most common; some leaf impressions; a cycad; silicified woods (palm, walnut, *Cinnamomum*, sycamore, and several unidentified). This is one of the few localities in the world where fruits, wood, and leaves of a plant are found together.

Cherry and Currant creeks—first studied in 1883 by Lesquereux and others; sixteen genera of plants from Cherry Creek; three from Currant.

Post locality: north and east of Post, Crook County—silicified remains in NW corner of sec. 27, T. 16 S., R. 20 E.; (1) 8.0 miles due east of Post on small tributary of Crooked River (Lost Creek); (2) 3.0 miles farther north—seventeen species differentiated, with sycamore *platanus* predominant.

Pilot Rock localities—on East Birch Creek, about ten miles southeast of Pilot Rock, Umatilla County—extensive collections of leaf impressions, including twenty-seven species (three of them new), but only twelve species recognized as to genera.

Arbuckle Mountain localities: (1) about twenty miles southeast of Heppner—abundant remains of palms; (2) 1.5

miles northwest of Arbuckle Mountain, at junction of Heppner-Ukiah road with Arbuckle corral road, 24.0 miles southeast of Heppner—fossil leaves; (3) and (4) mine No. 1, in SW¼ NE¼ sec. 20, and mine No. 3, in SW¼ NE¼ sec. 19 (both in T. 4 S., R. 29 E.)—leaf imprints; (5) mine No. 7 in NW¼ SW¼ sec. 34, T. 4 S., R. 28 E.—six species of plants and numerous other dicotyledonous leaves.

Riverside Ranch locality—34.0 miles up Crooked River from Prineville, 0.5 mile north of highway on west bank of Wickieup Creek in Crook County—five species of leaves.

Bear Creek and Hampton Butte localities: (1) and (2) near junction of road in upper Bear Creek Valley (secs. 9 and 17, T. 18 S., R. 17 E.)—fossil leaves; (3) a few miles to southeast—extensive deposits of fossil wood, with best collecting at Hampton Butte in sec. 36, T. 19 S., R. 19 E., 12.0 miles north of Bend-Burns highway. Wood often colored green or reddish. Fossil wood also at Lowry's (SW corner sec. 8, T. 19 S., R. 18 E.)—only conifers and sycamore.

Mitchell locality—1.5 miles south of Mitchell in sec. 15, T. 12 S., R. 21 E., on east side of Nelson Creek—silicified wood, more than half of which is pine.

PENNSYLVANIA

OUTCROPS OF EVERY KIND OF ROCK, FROM PRECAMBRIAN TO Quaternary, appear somewhere in Pennsylvania, with almost the entire western half of the state consisting (suitably) of Pennsylvanian.

The Pennsylvania Geological Survey publishes specific trip guides for Lebanon County (which is largely Ordovician, with smaller sections of Silurian and Devonian) and has supplied a list of selected fossil localities throughout the state.

Swatara Gap, a water gap in Blue Mountain, twelve miles north of Lebanon, where Silurian and Devonian rocks meet, is in the heart of the coal fields. Bedding planes are almost vertical, "on the south flank of a great syncline whose axis strikes north-east." Hunters search chiefly in an old quarry. To get there from Harrisburg, after about twenty miles on Route 22, one turns right, then left onto Route 72, and on for 4.4 miles to the gap. This quarry, and the hillsides to the south, where some 235 feet of fossiliferous beds are exposed, has yielded a great variety of late Ordovician fossils, including trilobites, mollusks, brachiopods, graptolites, crinoid stems, bryozoans, pelecypods, ostracods, and starfish.

To reach a fine fossil plant locality, one goes to Swatara Gap, then along Route 443 and, after 1.6 miles, turns left toward Tower City. About five miles farther along, beyond the crest of Sharp Mountain, on the south flank of Stony Mountain, is a small strip pit, on left side of the road. At the end of the strip pit are mine dumps containing the Post-Pottsville Formation of the Pennsylvanian. Beds are almost vertical with the axis of a major syncline about one-quarter mile south of the pit. Many kinds of plant fossils may be collected here, including *Mariopteris, Odontopteris, Sphenophyllum, Pecopteris plumosa, Pecopteris pennaeformis, Cordaites, Sphenopteris* (?), *Pecopteris orenulata* (?), *Neuropteris, Diplothemema,* and *Annularia.*

Selected collecting localities in Lebanon and nine other counties are:

Crawford: (1) along Grassy Run in Wayne Township, in Meadsville upper limestone—abundant fishes and brachiopods; (2) along bluffs on French Creek at Franklin—fishes and brachiopods.

Dauphin—Rockville, in Susquehanna Gap, 5.0 miles north of Harrisburg, in quarries of Little Mountain, just north of Kittatinny Mountain—fauna of the Hamilton Formation.

Fayette—J. V. Thompson quarry, on U.S. 40, east foot of Chestnut Ridge—shells abundant in limestone.

Jefferson—Humphrey quarry at Brookville—plant fossils numerous on floor.

Juniata: (1) north side of Tuscarora Creek, at bridge 0.3 mile north of East Waterford—abundant brachiopods in Helderberg limestone; (2) site reached by going 1.5 miles north of East Waterford, turning left, and proceeding for approximately 0.35 mile along dirt road, to outcrop on east side of small stream where it crosses the dirt road—abundant brachiopods, trilobites, bryozoans, corals, etc., in shale.

Lancaster—small borrow pit in shale at Fruitville, about four miles north of Lancaster, along Fruitville Pike—fragments of trilobites.

Lebanon—2.0 miles south of Lickdale on Route 72, shale quarry at south end of Swatara Gap through Blue Mountain, in shale at top of Martinsburg Formation—many fossils.

Mifflin—east side of Lewistown, quarries in limestone.

Perry: (1) Dyson's quarry, about 0.4 mile north of Landisburg, along Route 850—exceedingly fossiliferous, with excellent specimens of stromatoporoids, ball sponges, honeycomb coral, crinoid stems, bryozoans, brachiopods, gastropods, orthoceroids, and pelecypods; (2) road cut one-quarter mile south of Pine Grove on Route 17—limestone fauna; (3) 2.8 miles north of Amity Hall, along Juniata River—outcrops in Hamilton sandstone and shale; (4) Fossil Bank (reached by turning left on first dirt road [less than 0.5 mile] south of New Bloomfield, to old borrow pit on left side of road).

Schuylkill—old coal strippings along road from Lickdale to Tower City—abundant plant fossils.

THROUGH THE YEARS, unusual finds in Pennsylvania, chiefly in Devonian sediments, have added to biological knowledge. The track of a land creature, possibly an amphibian, providing the earliest evidences of a land vertebrate, was found near Warren. Amphibian remains were discovered, along with fossils of primitive fishes, in a late Devonian stratum. Elsewhere, they have been found chiefly in the far north, especially in East Greenland. The tracks of a creature identified as certainly amphibian had been left near Pottsville during the Mississippian epoch, in the red shale of the Mauch Chunk Formation, and are now in Harvard's Museum of Comparative Zoology. Princeton University and the New York State Museum have Silurian chordate fish remains (*Palaeapsis bitruncata*) found in Bloomsburg shale in Perry County.

RHODE ISLAND

THOUGH RHODE ISLAND, LIKE MOST OF THE REST OF NEW ENG-
land, is far from fossiliferous, it does contain coal deposits that
frequently are rich in plants; and many years ago the state
became famous for insect remains, of types then new to science.
There are few animal fossils, though occasional amphibian tracks
have come to light.

The eastern end of the state is part of a down-folded trough
of bedded sediments a great deal younger than the ancient
igneous and metamorphic rocks that form much of New England.
Those Pennsylvanian sediments of Rhode Island are black shales
and slates, which have retained imprints of trunks, stems, and
leaves of plants. The region was later folded and faulted in the
movements that made the Appalachians, and the coarse sandstones of that period contain little except a few casts of horsetails and club mosses. One of the most dramatic of such relics
is a trunk sixteen inches in diameter, of a plant that must have
been fifty feet tall, taken out when a sandstone quarry was
opened in East Providence.

Brown University has a large collection of plants, many
of which were found when a car tunnel was made in 1914
through College Hill. Others have come out of coaly shales lying
from Valley Falls eastward to Sockanosset, and thence southward.

The first specimen of remains of a fossil insect—the wing of
a cockroach—was found in Pawtucket just before 1893, by a
Providence clergyman. Later, a fair number and variety of
insect forms were discovered, as was a creature now named
Anthracomartus (the first arachnid discovered in the Carboniferous deposits of the eastern United States). A new genus of
Neuropteroid (the word means resembling the Neuroptera, the
order of net-winged insects) and a Protophasmid (an early plant-
eating insect), both very different from any form that until then
had been found in this country, but like some from France, plus

a number of cockroaches (represented by their wings alone) in several genera and many species, and all new to science, also came to light in this area.

SOUTH CAROLINA

PHOSPHATE OFTEN PRODUCES INTERESTING FOSSILS, AND PHOS-phate rock from South Carolina has been known for more than a hundred years, having been most actively mined in the latter part of the nineteenth century. However, there has been a continuing difference of opinion about its age. In 1959 a survey of the beds in the Charleston area led to the conclusion that the lower portion (Cooper marl) is Oligocene, and that fossils from the spoil banks of abandoned phosphate mines are deposited Oligocene, plus some Pleistocene.

Extensive collections have been made, beginning in 1956, from the spoil banks of the Old Bolton mine, which is 0.3 mile south of the site of the Atlantic Coastline's old Johns Island station and 9.0 miles southwest of Charleston on Route 17. The site first came to real attention when Washer Creek was dredged in 1957. On the spoil bank were two kinds of material, thoroughly mixed up: phosphate nodules (Pleistocene) and arenaceous limestone (Oligocene). In the irregular nodules were fossils—usually as casts and molds. The limestone contained many shells, and scattered throughout were sharks' teeth, fish vertebrae, rays' dental plates, and miscellaneous fish bone fragments. Numerous species were identified, and a set of specimen fossils is in the Academy of Natural Sciences in Philadelphia.

The following collecting localities in South Carolina were known in 1936, and some are still accessible:

UPPER CRETACEOUS
In three formations:
Tuscaloosa (sands and clays)—characteristically exposed in a cut of the Seaboard Air Line RR at the crossing of the Harts-

ville-Ruby road, 2.0 miles northeast of Middendorf, Chesterfield County. No animal remains have been found, but sixty-three species of plants, from (1) cut 2.0 miles northeast of Middendorf; (2) Rocky Point near Sumter Junction; (3) Congaree River, twenty-five miles below Columbia; (4) near Langley, and at Miles' Mill, Aiken County. Among the plants are five species of fig, two of eucalyptus, one walnut, three willows, one oak, one laurel, three magnolias, one pine, and one sequoia. Many of them also occur in New Jersey, Maryland, and Alabama.

Black Creek (black shaly clays and sand)—typical outcrop near crossing of Cashua Ferry road, east of Darlington (fifteen species of plants, with *Araucaria bladenensis* characteristic). This formation is also found in Florence County, with a section at Mars Bluff, about ten miles east of Florence, where it contains many kinds of coelenterates, pelecypods, scaphopods, gastropods, one bryozoan, and one fish; and in Marion County, especially at site of Hodge's mill, 200 feet west of the Nichols–Galivants Ferry road, 0.5 mile north of its junction with Sandy Bluff Road—sixteen kinds of shells.

Peedee (gray sandy marl and hard marlstone)—highest portion of upper Cretaceous, with best exposures on Pee Dee River, between Burches Ferry (type locality in Florence County) and Yauhannah Ferry. At Burches Ferry are several kinds of mollusks; Sewitt's Bluff, five or six miles below Burches Ferry, is sparingly fossiliferous; Davis Landing has nine species of mollusks; in Williamsburg County, Murray's Ferry road, 0.7 mile south of Santee River road, has small sharks' teeth.

EOCENE

In three formations:

Black Mingo (laminated sandy shale)—characteristic at "Dr. Boyd's place," 3.0 miles north of Salters and on scarp of Santee River 1.5 miles south of Gourdin Station—small group of fossils, including two corals (*Coelohelia wagneriana* and *Haimesiastraea conforta*) formerly known only from Alabama, and a species of oyster (*Ostrea arrosis*). This formation is found in Georgetown County on Murray's Ferry road between Kingstree and Heinemann, east of Mill Swamp, 5.8 miles southwest of Kingstree—corals and shells; and north of Bennett Swamp, 6.6 miles southwest of Kingstree and 5.5 miles north of Heinemann—shells; in Clarendon County, at Tindall's Mill, on road from Manning to Paxville, 6.0 miles west of Manning—nine species of shells; in Sumter County, where River Road crosses Fuller's Earth Creek, 4.0 miles north-northwest of Pinewood—shells and a coral; and on descent to valley of Wateree River, 2.0 miles west of Catchall and 4.0 miles northeast of Claremont—five kinds of shells, and an echinoid fragment.

McBean (sand, marl, clay, fullers' earth, and limestone) contains (in widely separated places) many varieties of fossils; found also in Alabama, Mississippi, Louisiana, and Texas. Found in South Carolina in Aiken County—several places on Tinker Creek, a tributary of Upper Three Runs, especially south side, about three quarters of a mile below Cox's Bridge—ten varieties of shells; Lexington County—fossiliferous fuller's earth 3.0 miles southeast of Gaston, on west side of Sandy Run; Orangeburg County—(1) Caw Caw Swamp, 2.5 miles west of Orangeburg—forty-four species of shells, (2) on the Columbia road south of Early Branch, 5.5 miles north of Orangeburg—sixteen species of shells, (3) Pooser's Hill, 5.1 miles north of Orangeburg—more than fifty varieties of shells, (4) old brickyard, Orangeburg—eighteen varieties of shells; Calhoun County—(1) Senn Farm, north of the Kennerly road and near Calhoun-Lexington county line, 7.0 miles east of Swansea—large shells of *Venericardia claiboplata*, abundant, (2) Keitt's Ravine, 4.5 miles northwest of Creston—eighteen varieties of shells.

Jackson (in three parts, of widely different textures)—in 1842 Charles Lyell found invertebrates in the Grove on Cooper River, in Santee Canal, Cave Hall, and Eutaw Springs. Fossil localities noted in 1937 include those in Williamsburg County at (1) Doctor Lake, about one mile north of Leneud's Ferry—many bryozoans and some oysters; and (2) Rock Spring, on edge of Santee Swamp, about four miles above Leneud's Ferry—bryozoans; in Clarendon County at crossing of Wyboo Swamp, eleven miles south of Manning—bryozoans; in Berkeley County on Santee River, probably near St. Stephen—sharks' teeth; in Orangeburg County at (1) Eutaw Springs, 3.0 miles north of Eutawville—fifty-eight species of bryozoans; and (2) Leneud's Ferry—twenty-eight species of bryozoans, with nine otherwise unknown; in Calhoun County at Belle Broughton Plantation,

0.5 mile southeast of Creston, on a branch of Halfway Swamp, 400 yards northeast of the Moncks Corner road—oysters, sharks' teeth, bryozoans, a crab claw, and others; in Berkeley County at (1) pit about a mile south of Moncks Corner on U.S. 52— small foraminifers and sharks' teeth, (2) old Charleston water-works on Goose Creek near Saxon—pectens; (3) pit at Wood-stock, 0.75 mile northwest of Ingleside—type specimen of *Xenorophus sloanii* Kellogg, an archaic toothed whale; in Charles-ton County at Bees Ferry—noted for sharks' teeth; and in Allen-dale County in bed of Miller Creek about three hundred feet southeast of railroad station at Baldock—thirty-eight species of bryozoans, and many oysters.

MIOCENE

In three formations, nowhere deeply buried:

Hawthorn (marl)—few identifiable fossils, with best along Savannah River. Especially good sites: (1) 0.5 mile above Por-ter's Landing—twenty-three species of shells; (2) in dump of Old Cherokee phosphate mine north of Stono River and about a mile west of Dupont—eight species of shells; (3) Old Bolton phosphate mine at Johns Island—five varieties of shells; (4) east side of Ashley River, ten miles from Charleston—in stone ballast from wreck of a ship on Block Island, Rhode Island— eight varieties of shells; (5) Ninemile Run near Tenmile Hill, 9.0 miles from Charleston—same as on ship; (6) upper edge of phosphate deposit, Ashley River near Charleston—four species; Hampton County, old well at Duke's siding on Seaboard RR, 2.75 miles north of Gifford—twenty-seven varieties, not well preserved.

Raysor (marl)—near Raysor Bridge on Edisto River, 8.0 miles southwest of St. George—more than forty species of shells.

Duplin (marl)—a large fauna, chiefly mollusks, with most prolific locality in Sumter County on Muldrow place, near Brick Church, 5.0 miles southeast of Mayesville, where about 250 species of mollusks have been identified.

PLIOCENE

East of Pee Dee River in northern part of Marlboro County, and probably also near Wateree, Congaree, and Savannah rivers —in one formation, the Waccamaw. Especially fossiliferous lo-calities: Horry County at (1) Little River at Timber Landing—

twenty-eight varieties of mollusks; (2) three to five and a half
miles southwest of village of Little River, on southeast bank of
a canal—mollusks and sea urchins; and (3) sites near mouth of
Tilley Lake, near Nixonville—great variety of shells; Georgetown
County on (1) Pee Dee River at Yauhannah Ferry, between
Georgetown and Conway—fifty varieties of shells; and (2) on
west bank of Black River on Evans Farm, 1.5 miles by water
below Pea House Ferry—eighteen varieties of shells; Berkeley
County at (1) The Grove, written about by Lyell; and (2) bluff
on southeast side of Goose Creek, one third of a mile southeast
of Seaboard RR, and three quarters of a mile southeast of Mel-
grove—eleven varieties of shells.

PLEISTOCENE

In five formations, with fossils very rare except in the
Pamlico (sand and clay), from which many shells (mostly
marine mollusks) have been collected, chiefly at Simmons
Bluff on Yonges Island, and on the Stono River.

THE STATE ITSELF HAS PREPARED no publications dealing specifically with fossil hunting, but geologists at the University of
South Carolina nowadays recommend the following localities:
(1) Santee River, along shores of Lake Marion within sight of
bridge crossed by U.S. 301; (2) along diversion canal leading
from Lake Marion to Lake Moultrie; (3) along banks of Intracoastal Waterway at Myrtle Beach, where Cretaceous fossils
dredged from the bottom of the canal may be mixed with
Tertiary fossils from near the surface. All these sites are said to
be good.

SOUTH DAKOTA

AGAIN, NO PUBLICATION SPECIFICALLY FOR THE AMATEUR FOSSIL-
hound, because although South Dakota has been a wonderful
collecting ground for a very long time, organized amateur paleontological endeavor here is in its infancy. Fossils can be found in

many places throughout the state, though it is hard to pin down specific localities. Initial help may be found occasionally in early geological surveys, but looking those over one is back in the time before many state boundaries were drawn as they are now. The Indians were then fighting to recover their lands, and many areas were territories—later to become states. People spoke of the "Black Hills of Dakota," meaning hills in the southwest part of what is now South Dakota and Wyoming—an area of about six thousand square miles, between the Belle Fourche and Cheyenne rivers.

What we now call South Dakota contains one of the greatest treasure troves of Tertiary mammalian fossils in the world —a trove that has been studied for more than a hundred years by all the great museums and other institutions. This is the so-called White River Badlands, or the Big Badlands, which lie mostly in southwestern South Dakota but extend through northwestern Nebraska into eastern Wyoming in the form of an "arm" known as Pine Ridge.

First knowledge of the importance to paleontology of this area came in 1847 when Dr. Hiram A. Prout described a fragment of a jaw of a titanothere from there in the *American Journal of Science*. Shortly afterward, Leidy described the first *Poëbrotherium* (Oligocene camel) from the same general locality. These papers prompted the government to direct an expedition to the area; the results of it were described by Leidy, and the next year, 1850, the Smithsonian collected there. From then on, expedition followed expedition, and tons of marvelously preserved specimens, many of them complete and still articulated, were brought back to all the leading museums of the country. Exploration was still continuing when, in 1920, the South Dakota School of Mines issued its famous Bulletin No. 13, which surveyed the whole field of results up to that time. This bulletin contains a list of the animals found from the lower Oligocene to the upper Miocene—a list of no fewer than twelve pages in small print! And the work also gives detailed descriptions of the Badlands and the places where the various kinds of fossils had been found.

In a USGS report of 1877 all the fossils discussed, except for a few plants, are invertebrates. Those from the "Primordial

Rock" were taken from the head of Red Valley and from sites on Red Canyon Creek and its headwaters and on Castle Creek. Jurassic fossils came from the east side of Spear-Fish Creek, near its junction with Red Water Creek, northeast of Crow Peak at a spring called simply "T——," west of the hills; from the Red Water Valley; and from sites on Belle Fourche and Red Canyon Creek, and near Sun-Dance Hills, northwestern Black Hills, in what is now *Wyoming*. Cretaceous fossils were unearthed at Old Woman's Fork; on the Belle Fourche, about ten miles west of Crow Peak; on the Cheyenne River near French Creek and near Rapid Creek; at two places on the east fork of Beaver Creek; and at Dead Man's Rapids in upper Missouri.

These Cretaceous fossils are much the same as those of Wisconsin and, in certain instances, other neighboring states. The period gave up many interesting remains, including aberrant forms of the ammonite group.

As was predicted in the 1877 report, the field offered great opportunities for collectors. Take the expedition sent out into the Badlands in 1940 by the South Dakota School of Mines and Technology and the National Geographic. The expedition acquired a fine and valuable Oligocene collection (including 175 or more species) which weighed several tons and is now at the school in Rapid City. Among the bones are a rhinoceros skull twenty-eight inches long; remains of a pig creature that must have been eight feet long; fossils of tapirs, three-toed horses, small rodents, and several little-known mammals; and (very rare) bones of birds. The best find was a fossil egg imbedded in matrix. Among the few plant finds were hackberry seeds and wood. Some of the heaviest specimens had to be lowered with block and tackle from near the top of slender, tall pinnacles. The strata are Channel sandstones, on which very little work had been done before.

In June 1947 an expedition from the School of Mines to the White River Formation of the Badlands found rhinoceroses, saber-tooths, "giant pigs," the antelopelike *Protoceras*, tapir, horse, and other mammals. The famous White River Formation had its origin in the Oligocene, when the sea withdrew, leaving several hundred feet of black shale on which hundreds of streams deposited more land, drained from the newly formed

Rockies and Black Hills. This resulted in plains crossed by broad, meandering streams, shallow lakes, and marshes, with some uplands; and sand, ash, and dust from volcanoes helped to create beds as much as six hundred feet thick. This White River series of sediments contains titanothere beds in the lowest third, oreodont beds in the middle, and beds of *Leptauchenia* (a hoofed, water-loving mammal) in the top third. Close to the base of the *Leptauchenia* beds, in two places, are small areas of grayish-green sandstone known as the Protoceras Channels, because *Protoceras* is one of the characteristic fossils.

The White River Badlands is made up of two great formations—the Chadron (lower) and the Brulé, which once made a continuous sheet, but which now appear in isolated outcrops all the way from northeastern Colorado to southeastern Saskatchewan, and which contain some of the world's best sources of Tertiary mammals, providing the most complete record of the first two thirds of the Oligocene. One of the best places to see this formation is along Wyoming State Highway 220, between Casper and Muddy Gap. From the Chadron come, especially, descendants of the Asiatic titanotheres. These descendants developed during the Eocene through such types as *Brontotherium* and *Brontops*, which were huge beasts, to those of the Oligocene, which were even more enormous. The Brulé gives up a great variety of creatures, including rhinoceroses, three-toed horses, tapirs, crocodiles, the herbivorous oreodonts, and the carnivorous creodonts.

Titanotheres have been fascinating to all fossil hunters since even before they were named in 1852 by Joseph Leidy, who at that time was with David Dale Owen's survey of a part of Nebraska. The first recorded brontothere bone (a fragment of a jaw) was found by a trader, and Leidy described a collection made between 1853 and 1857 by Ferdinand Vandiveer Hayden and others, and also wrote *The extinct mammalian fauna of Dakota and Nebraska, including an account of some allied forms from other localities, together with a synopsis of the mammalian remains of North America.* Marsh came along in 1874 with *The Structure and Affinities of the Brontotheridae* and *Principle Characters of the Brontotheridae;* and Cope, in 1886, with *The Vertebrata of the Tertiary Formation of the West.* The classic work on the titanotheres was a monograph by Henry Fairfield Osborn in 1919 when he was president of the American Museum of Natural History.

General literature of our time tells of the finding in South Dakota of middle or late Ordovician ostracoderms similar to those from near Canon City, Colorado; a plesiosaur near Edgemont; forams and mollusks (especially oysters) in the Cannonball at the base of Fort Union (known only from there); several examples of the *Poëbrotherium* (about a foot tall) from the Big Badlands; and *Archelon,* the largest turtle of all time, and over eleven feet long, from the south fork of the Cheyenne River, thirty-five miles southeast of the Black Hills.

Cycad National Forest is very much a misnomer, for although some one thousand beautifully agatized specimens of cycads were unearthed there a generation ago (and others doubtless lie in the ground) the fossil hunter cannot go to the spot, because the land is now leased for grazing. Fossils of those early plants may, however, be found in various other places in the state, such as along the Little White River, especially twelve miles west of Mission. One of the best localities is on the slopes of Parker Peak, reached by following U.S. 18 for twelve miles west of Hot Springs, taking a forest service trail to the top of the mountain, and then going along a left fork of the trail, past a dam and three gates, into an area where it is possible to park. There are cycads on the slopes and at the foot of the peak, though they are not easily found. Several other kinds of petrified wood are seen in the Black Hills, and remarkable agatized coral comes from the White River Badlands. Fossil sharks' teeth are found near Belle Fourche at Orman Dam, and the print of a dinosaur came to light in Perkins County, south of the town of Bison. In a pit in Mission, bones were found of a three-toed horse, toe bones of a camel, the opalized tusk of a giant elephantine creature, the jaw of a rhinoceros, and a tooth of a saber-tooth.

TENNESSEE

Tennessee is such a long, narrow state, and spreads over such varied topography, that, from east to west, it is technically divided into seven distinct physiographic provinces. These provinces—most of which continue unchanged into states lying north and south—conform to the geologic structure of the underlying strata. They are (1) Unaka Range (mostly Cambrian and Precambrian granite, schist, etc.), (2) Valley of East Tennessee (early Paleozoic—mostly Cambrian—limestone, sandstone, shale, and conglomerate), (3) Cumberland Plateau (Mississippian and Pennsylvanian sandstone, conglomerate, shale, and coal, with outcrops of earlier limestone), (4) Highland Rim (peneplained at end of Eocene, often very steep cliffs, all Mississippian, beginning with Chattanooga shale), (5) Central Basin (mainly Ordovician limestone, uplifted several times), (6) Plateau Slope of West Tennessee (all the uplands west of Tennessee River; Cretaceous, Tertiary, and Quaternary sand, clay, and loam), (7) Mississippi River Alluvial Plain. In the center of Tennessee is the Nashville Dome.

The first three provinces belong to what is known as the Appalachian Highlands; the Highland Rim, with the enclosed Central Basin, makes the Interior Plains; the Plateau Slope is like the Gulf Coastal Plain; and the Alluvial Plain is part of the Atlantic Plains Division. The Valley of East Tennessee (between the Cumberland Plateau and the Blue Ridge and Great Smoky Mountains and not considered a province) is part of the Appalachian Valley that stretches north as far as New York, and south into Alabama and Georgia.

Little is available to the novice of the careful and detailed geologic work that has been done by the state. Much of that work is of a broad and fundamental nature, often establishing strata, and none of it is of recent date. But, in no state is there greater evidence of the value of fossils as handmaidens of geology. As Walter F. Pond (state geologist in 1932) wrote in a Division of

Geology bulletin, any such study requires "an expert who has a thorough knowledge of fossils, their appearance and relationships, and their relative ages."

There is perhaps no area in the world where the Ordovician strata and their fossils can be studied better than in the Central Basin—an irregular ellipse that runs northeast and is about fifty to sixty miles wide and 120 long. Here is a much simplified survey of typical localities and formations where Ordovician fossils have occurred, all in limestone:

Murfreesboro—at type locality—sponges, brachiopods, gastropods, cephalopods, ostracods, and trilobites.

Pierce—Stone's River, 7.5 miles north of Murfreesboro—corals, brachiopods, crinoids, bryozoans, gastropods, ostracods, trilobites.

Ridley—Marshall Knob, Rutherford County—sponges, corals, brachiopods, bryozoans, gastropods, cephalopods, trilobites, ostracods.

Lebanon—Rutherford County—many, though small, fossils in some places; algae, sponges, corals, crinoids, starfish, bryozoans, brachiopods, gastropods, trilobites, ostracods.

Lowville—near Nashville—tubes of coral, other corals, brachiopods, bryozoans, gastropods, pelecypods, cephalopods, crustacea, hydrozoans, trilobites.

Kimmswick—1.0 mile south of Aspen Hill—calcareous algae, hydrozoans, corals, bryozoans, brachiopods, cystoids, trilobites.

Hermitage (Upper Ordovician): (1) Smith County, particularly 4.0 and 6.0 miles northwest of Carthage—algae, sponges, corals, brachiopods, bryozoans, pelecypods, trilobites, ostracods; (2) old road to Petersburg, 1.0 to 3.5 miles south of Belfast, Marshall County—sponges, corals, bryozoans, brachiopods, gastropods, cephalopods, annelids, trilobites, ostracods; (3) 1.0 mile south of Woodbury, Cannon County—very fossiliferous.

Cannon: (1) hill at Cannon-Rutherford County boundary, 1.5 miles east of Milton; (2) cut on Louisville and Nashville RR, 0.5 mile northeast of Thompson's Station; (3) Rhodes quarry, 1.5 miles southwest of Franklin; (4) Battlefield Hill, just south of Franklin; (5) Nashville, along Tennessee Central

RR; (6) St. Cloud Hill, Nashville; (7) near Hermitage Station; (8) Harvey Knob, 5.0 miles east of Franklin, Williamson County; (9) along road and up hill, 1.5 miles northwest of Peytonville, Williamson County; (10) on hill, 1.6 miles east of Bethesda, Williamson County; (11) 1.0 mile south of Allisona; (12) along Bear Creek Pike on west side of Loftin Hill, 8.0 miles east of Columbia; (13) near Pulaski; (14) from Aspen Hill to Prospect, along hill 2.0 miles southeast of Lester, Giles County; (15) Fayetteville; (16) Clear Creek, 2.0 miles west of Deray, Giles County; (17) Edgefield Junction; (18) near Hartsville; (19) 4.5 miles east of Hartsville; (20) 3.5 miles south of Alexandria; (21) 4.0 miles northwest of Carthage; (22) along hill on Hartsville-Carthage Pike just north of Carthage—calcareous algae, sponges, hydrozoans, corals, cystoids, bryozoans, brachiopods, gastropods, pelecypods, cephalopods, ostracods, and annelids.

Catheys Formation: (1) Columbia; (2) along Big Bigby Creek, at crossing of Mount Pleasant–Hampshire Pike, Maury County; (3) Rhodes quarry, 1.5 miles southwest of Franklin; (4) about five miles northwest of Franklin; (5) Nashville; (6) 4.0 miles east of Liberty, De Kalb County; (7) Pulaski; (8) 1.0 mile south of Allisona, southwest corner of Rutherford County—calcareous algae, corals, sponges, starfish, bryozoans, brachiopods, gastropods, pelecypods, cephalopods, ostracods, and trilobites.

Leipers Formation: (1) Columbia; (2) ridge 3.0 to 4.0 miles north of Gallatin; (3) Fort Negley, Nashville—sponges, hydrozoans, corals, brachiopods, bryozoans, crinoids, cystoids, gastropods, cephalopods, pelecypods, annelids, and trilobites.

THERE IS LITTLE SILURIAN in the Central Basin, except local occurrences (with Devonian) around the margin of the Nashville Dome, where the rocks have been exposed by erosion: (1) along Long Hollow Pike, about eight miles northeast of Goodlettsville; (2) White's Creek post office, Davidson County; (3) south side of hill two miles southwest of Southall, Williamson County; (4) north side of ridge three to four miles north of Gallatin; (5) along Pulaski–Brick Church Pike at milepost three miles northeast of Pulaski; (6) on Memphis to Bristol highway, fourteen to fifteen miles west of Nashville, and 1.5 miles north-west of Newsom—brachiopods, bryozoans, gastropods, and cri-noids.

Very important in the Central Basin is the Mississippian system of shale, limestone, and sandstone—with its oldest mem-ber, Chattanooga shale, long thought to be Devonian. The change in dating came about because the shale contains no conodonts like those of the well-established Devonian of New York, but does have many like those of the Mississippian in Ohio. Chat-tanooga black shale, the characteristic fossils of which are frag-ments of water-worn bones of large fishes, conodonts (which are abundant), and plant remains (abundant in some places) can be found in the following localities: (1) Baker's; (2) White's Creek Springs; (3) along Morgan Branch, 2.0 miles north of Totty's Bend, Duck River, Hickman County; (4) hill 4.0 miles west of Mount Pleasant; (5) Gordonsburg.

A special study of the geology of Nashville emphasizes the fact that Ordovician (deposited by shallow seas) occurs through-out the city, and sometimes on tops of high hills. Among the fossils, long famous for having weathered out freely from the limestone, are sponges, stromatoporoids, corals, ostracods, and many bryozoans. In 1948 these were exposed in: (1) old quarry behind City Pumping Station north of Lebanon Pike and east of mouth of Brown's Creek, (2) quarry across Lebanon Pike from Mount Olivet Cemetery, (3) along bluff north of Davidson Street at south end of South 12th Street, (4) in cut made for tracks along east side of Nolensville Pike at crossing of Tennes-see Central RR, and opposite State Fair Grounds, (5) along tracks of Nashville, Chattanooga and St. Louis RR, northwest of Woody Crest Road overpass; and in scores of other sites un-doubtedly no longer accessible.

A thin veneer of Pleistocene occurs in the Nashville area, and in 1920 the Carnegie received fossils from a pit dug in the floodplain east of the Cumberland river, upstream from Lock No. 1, in the vicinity of Lower City Island, at a depth of about thirty feet. From the lowest level came the lower left molar of *Equus leidyi,* the left femur and part of the right metatarsal of *E. complicatus,* and an antler of a small deer; from higher clay, indeterminate bones of turtle, lower molar of a young mastodon, bone of *Camelops,* and lower left molar of the ground sloth *Mylodon harlani.* Pleistocene bones were also found in alluvial sediments along valley of Factory Branch, west of Gallatin Pike, in excavations made for L & N RR tracks. In a drained swamp area south of the intersection of Buchanan Street and 18th Avenue North, were several teeth, some bones, and part of the tusk of a mastodon.

Almost all of Tennessee's Devonian is exposed in numerous small irregular areas in the Western Valley and certain tributaries, in Benton, Decatur, and Hardin, and portions of Wayne, Perry, Humphreys, and Henry counties. It stretches across the state in a narrow belt from north to south, and important localities are on Indian, Horse, Birdsong, and Cypress creeks, and along the lower course of Big Sandy River in Benton County. There are small outcrops of Lower Devonian in Wells Creek basin near Cumberland City, and at Sneedville in the mountains of eastern Tennessee; of mid-Devonian near Pegram and Newsom, a few miles west of Nashville. Though the surface of the deeply incised valley as a whole is rough and broken, sedimentary strata are approximately horizontal. Early Devonian appears as follows:

Rockhouse shale—greenish gray—brachiopods and gastropods.

Olive Hill—Hardin County and adjacent portions of Alabama and Mississippi, but best at type locality. Also in bluffs along river at Grandview, along Smith's Fork and lower Indian Creek, and Horse Creek—sparingly fossiliferous.

Birdsong—shaly—weathered into barren hillside slopes or "glades," which are good places to collect; west of Tennessee River and north of Perryville, especially in northern Decatur and southern Benton counties. This is richly fossiliferous, and preservation is scarcely equalled in any other deposit of Lower Devonian in North America. Brachiopods predominate; there are also crinoids, but rarely with calices; many bryozoans; four species of corals (two tetracorals and two favosites). Of the ninety-nine invertebrate species here, sixty-six had been found also in New York at the time of this report.

Decaturville chert—yellowish to gray—extremely fossiliferous. Specimens are preserved as natural casts and molds, many of unusual size, some very rare.

Oriskany in two formations: (1) land of Jim Quall in valley of Dry Creek at Walnut Grove, in road between house and barn, and in bluffs nearby—highly fossiliferous—often free pseudomorphs; (2) most widely in Perryville and Parsons—hills unevenly fossiliferous—best and biggest specimens at Cypress Creek.

Middle Devonian appears in Camden chert and Pegram limestone, which contain: (1) sharp natural molds and casts of exterior and interior, with details in unusual perfection—small variety of brachiopods predominant; (2) many corals.

A study of the Foraminifera of the state reveals that Eocene formations, investigated in Henry, Hardeman, Hornsby, Bolivar, and Chester counties, are virtually barren, but Cretaceous are rich, especially at these localities: (1) Jim Wilkin's property, 300 yards northwest of Union Church, Hardin County; (2) New Corinth Highway, 13.5 miles south of Selmer, McNairy County; (3) 0.5 mile west of the town of Guys, McNairy County; (4) 1.5 miles west of Sardis on Sardis-Henderson road, Henderson County; (5) Blue Cut, N & O RR at state line, McNairy County; (6) Coon Creek on Dave Weeks's property, near Enville, Chester County.

The Coon Creek locality contains a great deal besides forams! And, with written permission from the Memphis Museum of Natural History, it is possible to hunt there—in one of the most fabulous of all sites for Cretaceous fossils of many kinds, which has supplied specimens for museums all over the world.

The creek runs through a forty-foot-wide ravine with steep sides thirty-three feet deep, and is not easy to find. Adamsville, on U.S. 64, 104 miles west of Memphis and about twenty miles north of the Mississippi border, is the nearest town of any size. One turns north on a poorly paved road about two miles west of Adamsville, proceeds approximately ten miles to the village of Leapwood, and turns right onto the unmarked "Milledgeville road." Taking the right branch of the first fork, and the left branch of the second, and going for perhaps a mile and a half, brings one to an abandoned farm, known as "Dave Weeks's place." A badly eroded lane, which runs by the farm, goes to the creek, some three hundred yards behind the house.

The blue-gray sandy clay sides are packed with fossils. From various parts of its five-mile length, Coon Creek has given up more than four hundred species, often in a spectacular state of preservation, ranging from one-celled organisms to forty-foot reptiles, and including more than a hundred new species of gastropods.

Among the types already found are mosasaurs and sea turtles, seven classes of fish, thirty species of bryozoans, 175 kinds of gastropods (more than anywhere else in the world), 120 species of pelecypods, four species of scaphopods, five of marine crabs or related crustaceans, two genera of starfish, two of worms, two of corals, one of brachiopods, and many teeth of carnivorous reptiles.

Coon Creek runs through a sedimentary layer of the Upper Cretaceous, in a region that obviously lay just off the coast of a Cretaceous sea, and specimens found there have furnished much information about the period.

TEXAS

Texas is as big for fossils as it is for everything else.

The first discoveries were made in 1878, in Wichita and Archer counties by Prof. Jacob Boll, collecting for Edward Drinker Cope (see Wyoming). Cope was assisted by various other persons, including W. E. Cummins, who, in 1880, began a series of collecting trips to Texas and other parts of the Southwest; and by C. H. Sternberg, who was very successful between 1896 and 1917. Among other names associated with important finds in the state are those of Barnum Brown, for many years curator of fossil reptiles at the American Museum of Natural History, New York; E. C. Case of the University of Michigan; and Paul C. Miller of the University of Chicago. Some of the

most remarkable discoveries of fossils in the entire United States
have been made in Texas, and there are very few sections where
some sort of fossils cannot be found. Numerous museums display them, and much technical literature has been written about
them.

Every type of rock, from Precambrian to Pleistocene, is
found on the surface somewhere in the state, and in almost every
type, except the very early, there are likely to be rich deposits of
fossils. Texas is especially rich in Permian and Cretaceous rocks.

Cretaceous and other Mesozoic rocks cover a large part of
the center of the state, with different ages of the Cenozoic occurring in bands between them and the Gulf of Mexico. A broad
area of Tertiary runs up alongside New Mexico. Quaternary
(which borders the Gulf) outcrops also in the southwest part of
the state, beyond the Pecos River; and Permian (sandwiched
between Triassic and Carboniferous rocks) occupies the north-
central.

A handbook issued by the University of Texas tells and
shows where outcrops of different periods appear (illustrated on
a colored generalized geologic map), and what the chances are
for fossils, especially in two of the three major regions. Best
chances are in the Trans-Pecos (land beyond the Pecos River),
where, in very rugged country, are the Van Horn, Solitario, and
Marathon uplifts and the Big Bend area; and in the Texas Plains
—divided into the High Plains (a high plateau), the North-
Central Plains (east of the High Plains), the Edwards Plateau
(in the south-central part of the state), the Grand Prairie (in the
northeast), and the Llano Uplift (in almost the exact center of
the state). The third region—the Gulf Coastal Plain, with its
broad river valleys and low uplands—is relatively unfossiliferous but produces some fossils from the Upper Cretaceous and
certain marine formations of the Tertiary. The broad geologic
and paleontological picture shows:

CAMBRIAN (late)
Conglomerates have no fossils; sandstones, shales, lime-
stones, and some dolomites in the Franklin Mountains, near El
Paso, and in the Marathon, Llano, and Solitario uplifts have

poor fossils, the best of which—brachiopods, gastropods, and trilobites—are in the Llano Uplift.

ORDOVICIAN

Sandstones, limestones, dolomites, and cherts are found in the Llano Uplift and in Solitario, El Paso, Marathon, and Van Horn areas. There are many graptolites in the Marathon; other areas have brachiopods, gastropods, cephalopods, trilobites, corals, and sponges, but these are hard to reach and usually poorly preserved.

SILURIAN

Little outcropping except in Van Horn and El Paso, with brachiopods and corals from a few localities.

DEVONIAN

Best developed rocks are in Trans-Pecos, especially in El Paso, Van Horn, and Marathon areas—chiefly radiolarians and brachiopods, usually fragments and poorly preserved. In minor exposures of the Llano Uplift—brachiopods, gastropods, trilobites, corals, and bryozoans, plus a few conodonts and primitive armored fishes, usually not well preserved.

MISSISSIPPIAN

In Hueco Mountains of the Trans-Pecos Region—brachiopods and a few gastropods and bryozoans; in the Llano Uplift—many fossils, including brachiopods, gastropods, trilobites, crinoids, ostracods, and cephalopods.

PENNSYLVANIAN

Fossils in many parts of the state: in the Hueco and Diabolo Mountains—algae, brachiopods, gastropods, pelecypods, fusulinids, corals, and crinoids; in the Llano Uplift—fossils of many varieties; in the north-central area (the best collecting ground) —abundant plants, invertebrates on banks of streams and in gullies, and corals, brachiopods, and mollusks in highway and railroad cuts. Most typical are fusulinids, horn corals, lacy and branching bryozoans, pelecypods, gastropods, coiled cephalopods (chiefly nautiloids and goniatites), and crinoids (often in thick crinoidal limestone). Also some very early reptiles.

PERMIAN

Found in many parts of the state, with especially fine deposits in the Glass Mountains (often silicified fossils)—brachio-

pods, corals, bryozoans, mollusks; in the North-Central Plains
Region—marine and terrestrial fossil remains including those of
invertebrates and many amphibians and primitive reptiles. This
is one of the finest collecting areas in the world for marine life,
with more than 320 kinds of crinoids (among the most difficult
invertebrates to collect), and fifty blastoids.

Triassic

Glass Mountains, parts of other west Texas counties, and
parts of the High Plains—mostly sandstones, shales, and conglomerates, and some gypsum—almost exclusively vertebrates,
including fish, amphibians, crocodiles, and phytosaurs, and a
few poorly preserved plants and invertebrates.

Jurassic

Found only in the Malone Mountains, where limestones,
sandstones, shales, and conglomerates contain fresh-water ammonites and gastropods and marine and fresh-water pelecypods.

Cretaceous

Widely distributed deposits, appearing on the surface in
more than a quarter of the state, and underlying many of the
larger cities as marls, shales, limestones, and chalks, with sands
and conglomerates in some places, provide excellent fossil hunting, especially in chalky limestone and chalk along roads, highways, and small gullies. The most common finds are gastropods,
pelecypods, cephalopods, and echinoids. Many vertebrates have
been found in the Cretaceous rocks.

Tertiary

Many fossils in bands of clay, sands, and limestones over
Cretaceous rocks across Gulf Coastal Plain. Invertebrates common in certain areas—in sands, marls (often glauconitic), and
clays, which contain corals, clams, and snails; these are easiest
to find on banks of rivers and creeks, especially in bluffs along
the Brazos, Sabine, and Trinity rivers.

Quaternary

Pleistocene sands, clays, and gravels are found in many
parts of the state, especially in a band fifty to a hundred miles
wide along the Gulf, and also farther south and in the Trans-
Pecos Region. A few invertebrates may be collected; vertebrates
—including mammoths, horses, camels, and other mammals—
are often abundant.

Types of fossils found in Texas deposits include:

PLANTS / Usually poorly preserved and fragmentary—
from coal deposits in dumps around abandoned mines in north-
central parts of the state, and in other Pennsylvanian rocks in
north and Trans-Pecos; leaves from the east part of the state;
Upper Cretaceous varieties in the north—fairly well preserved;
fossil wood from almost all ages, and in most parts; seeds,
spores, pollen, and other minute fossils from deep wells.

INVERTEBRATES / Some of the most dramatic are the
large ammonoids locally abundant in many rocks, sometimes
with ammonite sutures that look like leaf patterns on the surfaces. Found also are belemnoids from Upper Cretaceous; ostracods, which are particularly abundant in Cretaceous and Tertiary marine deposits; *Ophiuroidea* (echinoderms)—usually segments; numerous echinoids, especially heart-urchins and biscuit-
urchins from Lower Cretaceous, and sea cucumbers, which are
locally abundant; graptolites, from Cambrian in central parts of
the state, and Ordovician in west—especially common in certain
Trans-Pecos formations.

VERTEBRATES / Giant fishes, primitive amphibians, many
types of dinosaurs, and all kinds of extinct mammals. An especially good exhibit of extinct vertebrates is on view in the
Texas Memorial Museum in Austin.

Fish—three out of the four classes of fish are represented.
Placoderms are rare, but fragments are found in Devonian rocks
in central Texas. Sharks' teeth (probably the commonest of
Texas fossils) represent the Chondrichthyes, and are found in
sediments ranging from Pennsylvanian through Miocene, usually in thin-bedded marine limestones or clays. Remains of
Osteichthyes (true bony fishes) come from many localities,
chiefly from Cretaceous rocks; most often these remains are
teeth, vertebrae, or scales, though occasionally a well-preserved
skeleton is found.

Amphibians—mostly in upper Paleozoic and lower Mesozoic, in north and west parts of the state, associated with primitive reptiles—chiefly in Archer and Baylor counties (Permian),
and where the red beds are exposed from Big Spring north along
edge of the High Plains. Certain authorities say that these beds

have provided the world's most complete record of early Permian amphibians and reptiles. From Baylor County came *Seymouria,* about twenty inches long, forming a link between amphibians and reptiles.

Reptiles—from Baylor and nearby counties have come early true reptiles; from Permian red beds somewhat more developed types, such as *Dimetrodon* and *Edaphosaurus.* The famous dinosaur tracks in the American Museum of Natural History were found by Dr. Brown in Lower Cretaceous rocks near Glen Rose, Somervell County. Other dinosaur tracks have been collected from the Lower Cretaceous of central Texas, and from Upper Cretaceous beds in Big Bend National Park in the Trans-Pecos. Actual remains of many types of more developed reptiles are known, usually from Cretaceous beds. All sorts of reptiles from the seas have been discovered. A Cretaceous mosasaur was found near Austin, and its skull is on view in the Texas Memorial Museum. Plesiosaur fossils come from the Cretaceous, and one short-necked type, found near Waco, is in the Strecker Museum of Baylor University at Waco. The crocodilelike creatures known as phytosaurs come from Triassic rocks along the margin of the High Plains. Many crocodiles and alligators have been collected, including the crocodile *Phobosuchus,* the largest ever discovered, from Upper Cretaceous along the Rio Grande. Finds continue. For example, in 1964 Bob Slaughter of Dallas found two genera of mosasaurs in the Bardwell basin south of the city, and also got much Miocene and Pleistocene material from the Livingston Reservoir basin.

Mammals—found in various places, in rocks from Paleocene to Pleistocene. Finds have included giant ground sloths, glyptodonts, saber-tooths, dire wolves, mammoths, mastodons, "giant pigs" (Miocene of the Coastal Plain), uintatheres (Big Bend National Park), titanotheres (Trans-Pecos), camels (Oligocene to Pleistocene, in many parts of the state), and horses showing the animal's development—*Eohippus* (Big Bend National Park), later (Trans-Pecos), and Pleistocene (in many areas).

UTAH

Reptiles of the mesozoic are shown in unusually spectacular fashion, in their natural setting, at Dinosaur National Monument, which lies in the Badlands of northeastern Utah and northwestern Colorado. A museum has been built there, over the face of a quarry approximately four hundred feet long, forty feet wide, and forty feet deep, and visitors can look out from a balcony, onto a fossil-filled cliff, to see such sights as a giant reptile lying like a bas-relief in the rock where it was buried and from which it has been partly excavated. More than a dozen species of dinosaurs, of all sizes—from the tiny *Laosaurus*, no bigger than a cat, to the enormous *Apatasaurus*, weighing forty tons have been taken out. Other finds in the area have included remains of primitive mammals, crocodiles, turtles, shells, cycads, leaves, and petrified wood.

Geologists say that the deposit of dark sandstone containing the dinosaur fossils was probably a sand bar in an ancient river, onto which the bodies were washed, and where they remained until the rock was tilted and eroded into view.

This wonderful cache was discovered in 1909 by Dr. Earl Douglass of the Carnegie Musuem. The Carnegie had sent Dr. Douglass into the Utah Basin in 1908, looking for fossil mammals, and ranchers called his attention to dinosaur bones protruding from bluffs near Green River. When he went back the next year for reptiles, he saw the tail of a large dinosaur exposed on the face of a sandstone ledge, and discovered that it was that of the saurischian form, now named *Apatasaurus*.

The area in which he found it is one of the richest deposits of dinosaur bones in North America. Between the time of the discovery and 1923 nearly a million tons of rocks and bones were taken out by the Carnegie, and excavation was continued by others, including the Smithsonian Institution and the University of Utah. In 1924 Dr. Frederick J. Pack, professor of geology at the university, carried nineteen wagonloads of dinosaur bones to

Salt Lake City. In 1931 the American Museum of Natural History became actively interested, and in 1934 Dr. Barnum Brown became consulting paleontologist for the monument. The program of development has been under the National Park Service since 1933. Twenty-two complete skeletons and thousands of individual bones have been removed, and some of them have gone to almost every important museum in the country.

Dinosaur National Monument lies in the midst of some of the grandest and most dramatic natural scenery in this country, with weirdly shaped cliffs and rugged canyons. Green River runs through the area, and the quarry lies near beautiful Split Mountain Canyon, where there are picnic grounds, and trails leading upward. By presidential proclamation, the monument was established in Utah in 1915, on sixty acres, for the protection of the rich and important natural display, and was enlarged in 1938 to take in seventy-eight square miles in Utah and 325 in Colorado. A bitter controversy arose when the Bureau of Reclamation announced in 1947 that it was going to build Echo Park Dam near Steamboat Rock, and Split Mountain Dam in the canyon—both on the Green River, *inside* the monument. Engineers admitted that the dams could equally well be constructed outside, and conservationists protested sufficiently so that in 1956 an amendment was made to the Colorado River Storage Project Act, saying, "It is the intention of Congress that no dam or reservoir constructed under the authority of this Act shall be within any national park or monument." Even that did not end the fight, and the National Park Association (an association of nonofficial persons much concerned with conservation) announced its intention of trying to have the monument redesignated, giving it national park status, for better protection against any encroachment. After a controversy that lasted six years, it was finally agreed that the Echo Park and Split Mountain dams would not be built, and the irreplaceable exhibit of fossils was saved.

The monument is approached by State Highway 149, going north of Jensen, on U.S. 40. It is open all year, and admission is free.

In Utah, dinosaur remains are not confined to this region.

They have been found also in the San Raphael Swell (rounded elevation) in the central part of the state; in the Cleveland-Lloyd Quarry in Emery County; and in the Escalante Valley, in the south-central part of the state. In fact, fragments of Jurassic dinosaurs are likely to be found wherever the Morrison Formation occurs. Such bones may take on beautiful colors from the minerals in which they lie, and are sometimes cut and polished to make semiprecious jewelry.

The state has rock of every geologic period, and fossils are found to represent each period. Some of the other well-known sites, as furnished by the department of geology of the University of Utah, are:

CAMBRIAN
Antelope Springs, House Range, Millard County in west-central Utah—trilobites (with *Elrathia* commonly sold commercially and traded extensively) and brachiopods.

TRIASSIC
Fossil wood, of the same age as that in Petrified Forest National Park—wherever the Chinle Formation is found; cephalopods (*Meekoceras* especially, but much picked over)—from Cephalopod Gulch near Salt Lake City.

CRETACEOUS
Mollusks (especially *Scaphites*, a cephalopod)—wherever Frontier and Ferron sandstones appear near the base of Upper Cretaceous.

EOCENE
Fossil insects, leaves, fish, bird tracks, and miscellaneous remains in Tertiary Green River Formation around Uinta Basin, near Wyoming.

Among recent finds by the geology museum of Brigham Young University are cervical vertebrae (previously unknown from North America) of what appears to be *Brachiosaurus* (the largest of the dinosaurs); the previously unknown skull of *Apatasaurus* (more commonly known as *Brontosaurus*); and the partly articulated skeleton of a *Camarasaurus*-like sauropod. The bones of the last included the column of dorsal and cervical vertebrae, and a four-clawed foot, though only three-clawed ones had been found before. *This* is the skeleton the amateur fossil hunters ruined! (See p. xiv.)

Dinosaur National Monument has added a turtle to its display, and a museum of natural history has been established on the campus of the University of Utah, with anthropological, biological, geological, and paleontological material.

VERMONT

THOUGH FEW FOSSILS HAVE BEEN FOUND IN VERMONT, THOSE that do come to light are often important. For example, the most primitive early Cambrian trilobite yet known, *Olenellus vermontanus,* was found near Georgia Center. A complete Cambrian ostracoderm from Franklin County is in the geological museum at Princeton, New Jersey. Ordovician specimens have come from near Northfield—crinoid columnals, and from north-northeast of Montpelier—cup corals. Silurian or Devonian crinoids and cystoids have been found near Westmore; and in 1950, from a spot on the Connecticut River three miles southwest of Claremont, New Hampshire, came many specimens—corals, brachiopods, crinoids, cephalopods, and possibly a trilobite—of the same age.

In general, it is to be expected that whatever fossils are found should come from that portion of the state west of the Green Mountains, which run down the middle, dividing areas of granite and other extremely hard rocks on the east from the less crystalline deposits on the west.

Two of the earliest finds were the tusk, bones, and teeth of a mastodon, made in 1848 by workmen on the railroad in Rutland County, and the entire skeleton of an archaeocete in 1849, in a Rutland Railroad cut, in Chittenden County, near Charlotte.

Trilobites, crinoid fragments, corals, and other fossils have been, and still are being, found on islands in Grand Isle County. There are many trilobites, and coral is abundant in the Highgate area of Franklin County; coral, trilobites, crinoid columns, those "written stones" called graptolites, and various kinds of shells come from Addison County, which lies along lower Lake Champlain.

VIRGINIA

VIRGINIA MAY BE DIVIDED INTO THREE DISTINCT GEOGRAPHIC provinces: the Coastal Plain (or Tidewater), the Piedmont Region, and the Appalachian Mountains. The first of these extends from the Potomac, Chesapeake Bay, and the Atlantic to the fall line that runs through Alexandria, Fredericksburg, Richmond, and Petersburg, making an area that is about a hundred miles wide at the North Carolina border, and narrows to a point below the Great Falls of the Potomac. It is bounded by three long peninsulas, is all fairly level, and contains the Dismal Swamp in the southeast. Rocks are Cretaceous to Quaternary. The Piedmont, which is immediately west of the Coastal Plain, slopes upward toward the west to an elevation of about one thousand feet near the Blue Ridge, and is manteled with red clays and sandy loams (chiefly derived from crystalline and Precambrian rocks), sharply cut into by streams that have left a hilly and rocky surface. The granite, gneiss, and greenstone of the Blue Ridge, outcropping along the west edge of the Piedmont, were thrust up violently along a fairly sharp and narrow ridge widening from northeast to southwest. Between the Blue Ridge and the Alleghenies, a great valley extends more than 350 miles, from the Potomac to the Tennessee border. That valley, plus the adjacent part of the Appalachian Plateaus, containing the coal fields of the southwestern part of the state, is considered a separate geologic province, with rocks ranging from Cambrian to Quaternary. The valley portion forms a part of the great Appalachian Valley that is a major physiographic feature from central Alabama to central Pennsylvania.

In general, guidance to fossil localities in Virginia must be culled (sometimes with great difficulty) a bit at a time, from USGS Professional Papers, state bulletins, and other scientific publications. However, through the courtesy of the Virginia Department of Conservation and Economic Development, we give a list of up-to-date localities. Asterisks indicate particularly good ones. No Cambrian localities are included because formations of that period are sparsely fossiliferous and no rewarding collecting sites are known at the present time. Triassic collecting is described later in this section.

ORDOVICIAN

1. Tumbling Run section, 1.0 mile southwest of Strasburg, just west of U.S. 11, Shenandoah County—many characteristic species.

2. North environs of Staunton, U.S. 11, Augusta County—graptolites in shale.

3. Rye Cove, 8.0 miles northwest of Gate City, Scott County—brachiopods, bryozoans, sponges, corals, and echinoderms.

SILURIAN

Big Moccasin Gap, near Gate City—brachiopods.

DEVONIAN

*1. Southeast slope of Bull Pasture Mountain, 3.0 miles east of McDowell, along U.S. 250, Highland County—brachiopods, corals, and bryozoans.

2. Peters Hill, 3.0 miles west of New Castle, Craig County—bryozoans.

*3. East city limits of Clifton Forge, in cemetery at intersection of Highways 60 and 220—fossil reef with many species.

*4. Road cut one-quarter mile west of Gainsboro, Frederick County—ostracods, brachiopods, trilobites, and crinoids.

5. Road cut 2.0 miles northeast of Van Buren Furnace, Shenandoah County—numerous species.

*6. Massanutten Mountain, one-quarter mile west of Detrick, Shenandoah County—numerous large brachiopods.

MISSISSIPPIAN

1. Along U.S. 19, south of bridge over Holston River, 2.0 miles north of Greendale, Washington County—brachiopods and plecypods.

2. U.S. 23, 2.0 miles south of Gate City—corals, brachiopods, gastropods, algae, and crinoids.

3. State Route 85, 0.5 mile southeast of Falls Mills, Bland County—pelecypods, ostracods, and brachiopods.

MISSISSIPPIAN and PENNSYLVANIAN PLANTS

1. Brushy Mountain, north of Price Forks, Montgomery County.

2. Lewis Tunnel, 0.75 mile east of Alleghany, Alleghany County.

3. Mine tailings from many strip mines in Wise, Dickenson, and Buchanan counties.

EOCENE

Fairview Beach, on Potomac River above Colonial Beach, Westmoreland County—gastropods and pelecypods.

MIOCENE

1. Along York River, 1.0 to 2.0 miles southeast of Yorktown, York County—pelecypods, gastropods, sharks' teeth.

2. Old Camp Penniman, east of Williamsburg, on York River, York County—pelecypods, gastropods, sharks' teeth, whale bones.

3. James River Beach at Kings Mill, off U.S. 60 in James City County—pelecypods, gastropods, foraminifers.

A PAPER DATED 1956 ANNOUNCED that seventeen species of nautiloids, divided among ten genera (two of them new) have come from limestone of the Chepultepec-Stonehenge transition unit, which lies between Cambrian and Ordovician. Many of the nautiloids are closely related to those found in adjacent states. Specific localities include: (1) Strasburg, 2.7 miles north, 12 degrees east of the center of Woodstock, and 1.7 miles south, 69 degrees west of Mauertown—abundant specimens along east side of Pughs Run, in highly carbonaceous beds, but fossils are likely to be deformed; (2) Roanoke Quadrant, in abandoned quarry on east side of Carvin Creek, 0.6 mile north and 64 degrees west of confluence of Carvin and Tinker creeks, 3.5 miles north of center of Roanoke—poor exposures.

The oldest Mesozoic strata of Virginia are all east of the Blue Ridge, lying in narrow strips isolated from each other, apparently deposited in fresh, or possibly brackish, water. Some of those areas were once marsh where coal eventually formed. The region that has yielded almost all plants from the older part of that era is about thirty miles long and has an average width of six miles; its eastern edge is about ten miles west of Richmond, beginning at the south on the Appomattox River, and ending at the north in Caroline County, approximately three miles north of Hanover Junction. The main body is the Richmond Coal Field, south of the James River. Within it, classic localities are: (1) near Manakin, on the north bank of the James; (2) Carbon Hill, about six miles north of the James; (3) Deep Run, about 3.0 miles east of Carbon Hill, in small detached strip; (4) Clover Hill, at the southeastern end of the coal field. Fossils found include *Equisetales*, gymnosperms, *Cycadales*, fruits of cycads, and a few conifers. This flora is essentially the same as that of the same period in North Carolina.

Because of unfavorable geologic conditions at the time, fossils of the Triassic in Virginia are scarce at best, compared with those of other periods; but various kinds have been systematically collected since 1840. As recently as between 1920 and 1923 paleontologists gathered many plants, dinosaur tracks, trails, brachiopods, and a few fish scales. These came from five isolated regions (the first three of continental, or residual, origin; and the last two of swamp, or mesophytic), with the bulk from the Richmond and Farmville areas. These five regions are:

Potomac: Plants found: (1) 1.0 mile east of Manassas; (2) at Bull Run Quarry, 2.5 miles north of Manassas; (3) at Bull Run Battlefield, south of crossroads 3.0 miles west of Manassas; (4) on Hoppen Run, 5.5 miles south of Bealeton. Trails found: (1) 3.0 miles east of Leesburg on Potomac River bluffs; (2) 0.75 mile south of Ashburn on north side of Beaver Run; (3) near Ryan on public highway; (4) west of Auburn in Old Dominion RR cut; (5) at crossroads on Bull Run Battlefield 4.0 miles west of Manassas; (6) 1.0 mile east of Buckland on north side of Broad Run; (7) 1.0 mile east of Batna.

Scottsville—south of Somerset and just north of Barboursville—conifer stems and numerous fossil trails.

Danville—same type of conifers, and a few trails, but large numbers of the plant *Araucarioxylon* (some very big): (1) ten miles northwest of Danville—Rocky Mountain road; (2) ten miles southwest of Danville and 2.0 miles southeast of Hall's Corner; (3) 8.5 miles west of Danville, near Lebanon.

Farmville—1.0 mile northwest of Farmville—*Araucarioxylon* fragments; throughout area, poorly preserved coal plants.

Richmond: (1) pit of Murphy Coal Corporation, 1.0 mile south of Midlothian—beautiful plants in black shales, slates, and sandstones; (2) 1.0 mile west of Otterdale—large fragments of *Araucarioxylon*.

ACCORDING TO THE MONOGRAPH on Miocene and Pliocene pelecypods, collecting localities for these invertebrates in 1943 included (by counties): Westmoreland—Horsehead, Stratford, and Nomini cliffs; Northumberland—east bank of Hull Creek; Richmond—(1) 1.5 miles west of Carter Wharf, (2) Union Mill; Essex—(1) 1.0 to 2.0 miles and 2.5 miles below Bowler's Wharf; (2) 0.25 mile above Jones Point; Middlesex—(1) Urbanna, (2) Burhan's Wharf; King and Queen—3.0 miles northeast of Walkerton; New Kent—Lanexa; James City—King's Mill Wharf; York—(1) 0.75 mile above Yorktown, (2) Bellefield; Gloucester—Ware River; Prince George—near mouth of Bailey's Creek; Surry—(1) Claremont, (2) old Claremont Wharf, (3) Claremont Wharf, (4) 6.75 miles below Claremont, (5) Sunken Marsh Creek, (6) 8.5 miles below Claremont Wharf, (7) 7.0 to 7.5 and 8.0 to 8.5 miles below Zuni; Greensville—Hitchcock; Southampton—(1) Biggs Farm, (2) Delaware Park, (3) Sycamore Church; Nansemond—(1) 0.5 mile north of Chuckatuck, (2) 0.5 mile east of Everets, (3) Exit, (4) 6.5 miles southeast of Reid's Ferry, (5) 1.25, 1.5, 2.5, and 5.5 miles northwest of Suffolk, (6) 1.5 miles north of Suffolk, (7) 1.0 mile west of Suffolk, (8) 0.5 mile below Suffolk Waterworks Dam, (9) 1.0 and 1.5 miles southeast of Suffolk, (10) drainage ditch of Norfolk and Western RR just east of Jericho Ditch.

Through a library, it is possible to inspect a 1941 Bulletin (see Bibliography) consisting of plates and identifications of invertebrate and plant fossils of the Appalachian Valley, with information on the places where they were found. Some of those sites may still be accessible.

WASHINGTON ·

It is uncertain whether there are silurian rocks in the state of Washington; Pennsylvanian and Mississippian are so slightly differentiated that they are best lumped as Carboniferous; and Jurassic fossil localities are hard to find and relatively inaccessible. Otherwise, every kind of rock in the geologic column is present—and supplies fossils. Fossiliferous localities are widely separated, but productive.

The methods by which Washington's fossils have been created are unusually varied: carbonization—in sandstones and shales near Wenatchee, Spokane, and Cle Elum; petrifaction—wood found in Ginkgo Petrified Forest State Park, near Vantage in Kittitas County; permineralization—for the fossil clams in sea bluffs west of the West Twin River in Clallam County. Mold sand casts were made, yielding the rhinoceros impression found in 1935 in basalt near Blue Lake in Sun Lakes State Park, Grant County, and trees in lava in such places as the lava tunnel in the NE¼ sec. 19, T. 7 N., R. 5 E., on the south flank of Mount St. Helens, and near the ranger station at Spirit Lake on the north side of the mountain; covering by lakes and swamps led to the preservation of leaf and insect remains in fresh-water deposits of the Latah Formation near Spokane.

Paleozoic fossils are most abundant in the northeastern part of the state. Tertiary invertebrate remains are most abundant in the western part, and Tertiary vertebrates, in the central and southern parts; Tertiary leaf fossils are widely distributed and occur from north of Winthrop in Okanogan County, south to the Oregon border, and from Puget Sound to Idaho.

According to the state's geologists, good places to look for fossils of the various ages are:

CAMBRIAN
Large areas in Stevens and Pend Oreille counties—trilobites, brachiopods. Some specific sites: (1) quarries of the Lehigh

Portland Cement Company, 0.5 mile southeast of Metaline Falls, Pend Oreille County; (2) south end of low ridge opposite Addy, Stevens County, on west side of Colville River in SW¼ sec. 13, T. 33 N., R. 39 E. (in very platy, sandy orgillite that crops out along north side of road), a little more than 0.2 miles south of west end of bridge over river at Addy; (3) near center of sec. 14, T. 33 N., R. 38 E., about 0.4 mile up east fork of Stranger Creek from where road crosses it on Dunn Mountain, about seven miles due west of Addy. Archaeocyathids (sponge-like masses), the oldest fossils in the state, are best found just past the Vista House road, about 1.3 miles north of the intersection of Main and 5th streets in Colville, Stevens County.

ORDOVICIAN

In Pend Oreille and Stevens counties—graptolites most abundant. Specific sites: (1) cuts along King road 0.2 mile northwest of its junction with McKern road east of Rice in Stevens County; (2) west bank of Pend Oreille River below Pend Oreille mine, about one mile north of Metaline Falls; (3) stream banks at confluence of Slate Creek and Pend Oreille, about five miles northwest of Metaline Falls; (4) highway cuts for about one mile south of Ledbetter Lake, Pend Oreille County.

DEVONIAN

On both sides of Cascade Mountains, and possibly mixed with Silurian—brachiopods and corals most common fossils. A good collecting spot is the limestone outcrop on hillside in sec. 16, T. 40 N., R. 43 E., just northwest of where road crosses Fence Creek in Pend Oreille County.

CARBONIFEROUS

Brachiopods, corals, and bryozoans are found in limestone rocks that crop out between towns of Springdale and Valley in Stevens County—especially along Jackel Road, sec. 19, T. 31 N., R. 41 E., about 0.9 mile north of Jumpoff School and about 0.7 mile south of Stroven Road. On west side of road, outcrops are several hundred feet away, in cultivated field; on east side, in old Kulzer clay pits.

PERMIAN

Gastropods, corals, and fusulinids are found in outcrops in hills just north of Kettle Falls in Stevens County, and in limestone near center of sec. 16, T. 36 N., R. 38 E., on west side of

and above Vanasse Road; gastropods and corals are found in
W½ SW¼ sec. 10, T. 36 N., R. 38 E., on hillside above the
Vanesse Road.

TRIASSIC

In both eastern and western Washington pelecypods are
common. Two good localities in Ferry County: (1) hillside above
and on east side of Kettle River, immediately north of White
Creek, about 3.5 miles north of Curlew on Highway 4A; (2) east
side of road into headquarters area of Shasket Creek about 1.6
miles from its junction with Highway 4A and near center of
sec. 17, T. 40 N., R. 34 E. In western Washington, best locality
is on Davidson Head at northwest side of San Juan Island, San
Juan County.

CRETACEOUS

In northern Cascades and San Juan Islands—best locality
is Sucia Island—pelecypods and both coiled and straight
cephalopods.

TERTIARY

Covers southern half of state and narrow band that projects
north along eastern edge of Puget Sound toward Canada. The
only Tertiary marine sediments are found west of the Cascade
Range; sediments, probably from fresh-water embayments, near
Bellingham, Cle Elum, Wenatchee, Black Diamond, Morton, and
Packwood; lake deposits, near Spokane; and deposits interbedded
with Columbia River basalt flow, at various places in the Columbia Basin and Yakima Valley.

Marine fossils—pelecypods, gastropods, and scaphopods—
are found in many places. The best and most accessible localities
are in bluffs along Highway 9 in Grays Harbor County between
Porter and Malone, and extending beyond the towns (where
echinoderms and microscopic foraminifers are also found); and
along banks of Olequa and Stillwater creeks, above and below
their confluence, at Vader, Lewis County.

Leaves—such as those of sequoia, ginkgo, oak, willow,
poplar—are found in black or platy shale, siltstone, or sandstone
at the following sites: (1) along Chuckanut Drive, just south of
Bellingham, Whatcom County; (2) just south of section line
betwen secs. 27 and 34, T. 39 N., R. 6 E., on Primary State Highway No. 1, not quite 1.1 miles south of Boulder Creek bridge, up

Nooksack River in Whatcom County—large palm leaves; (3) bank on southwest side of Wenatchee River in NE¼ NW¼ sec. 17, T. 24 N., R. 18 E., about one and one quarter miles up river from Peshastin bridge; (4) road cut in SW¼ sec. 22, T. 22 N., R. 20 E., a little more than 0.4 mile down Squillchuck Canyon road from its intersection with Pitcher Canyon road near Wenatchee; (5) along old highway between Cashmere and Wenatchee, where road breaks over Sunnyslope Hill in NE¼ NE¼ sec. 19, T. 23 N., R. 20 E., at old roadside park; (6) along Deep Creek, 0.5 mile above its mouth, northwest of Spokane; (7) cuts of Spokane, Portland and Seattle RR and Chicago, Milwaukee, St. Paul and Pacific RR tracks in Spokane and west of Latah Creek (fossil insects also); (8) bank on north side of Highway 1R, 0.4 mile west of Coal Bank bridge over Toutle River, in sec. 19, T. 10 N., R. 1 E., in Cowlitz County; (9) road cuts along Highway 1Q a little less than 1.1 miles north of its intersection with Highway 1R, in SW¼ sec. 3, T. 10 N., R. 1 E., Cowlitz County; (10) road cut above Coweman River in S½ SW¼ SE¼ sec. 30, T. 8 N., R. 1 W., about 0.7 mile from end of Allen Street Road, just east of Kelso, Cowlitz County; (11) Steel's Crossing, where old Steel's Bridge ran over Great Northern RR, in SW¼ sec. 11, T. 23 N., R. 4 E., in King County; (12) sandstone quarry in SE¼ NE¼ SE¼ sec. 12, T. 14 N., R. 4 E., reached from Elbe by turning first west after Mineral Junction, going about 1.1 miles to where road forks, and taking left fork for about 0.2 mile.

Vertebrate bones are not nearly so abundant as shells and leaves. Therefore there are few good collecting localities. The best are in eastern Washington, where it is sometimes possible to find the horse *Hipparion*, bison, oreodonts, camels, caribou, and various rodents. Fossil hunters are advised to try (1) along the east side of the Columbia River north of Richmond, especially near Ringold; and (2) along both sides of Wenas Valley, Yakima County, especially in SW¼ sec. 10, and NE¼ sec. 35, T. 14 N., R. 18 E. Other possible areas are in sandstones and siltstones on both sides of Ahtanum Valley, in hills north of Naches, and in the hill between Rattlesnake Creek and Nile Creek on the Naches River—all in Yakima County; and in hills north of Ellensburg in Kittitas County.

QUATERNARY

Found as far south as Spokane and Coulee City in eastern part of the state, and to just south of Olympia in western.

Vertebrates are rare, and mostly such cold-weather forms as woolly mammoth, bison, and caribou. A small mastodon was found by a farmer excavating a reservoir near Port Angeles; mammoth and mastodon teeth and tusks have been taken from scattered localities in both eastern and western parts of the state; and there is the rhinoceros mold in Sun Lake State Park.

Invertebrates are also usually cold-weather forms and have come from (1) marl around Booher Lake, secs. 3 and 10, T. 35 N., R. 26 E., about four miles north of Riverside on Highway 97 in Okanogan County—with abundant gastropods; (2) small lake on Orcas Island, at NW corner sec. 17, T. 36 N., R. 2 W., San Juan County—excellent pelecypods and worm tubes; (3) south side of Chambers Creek Valley at elevations of 30 and 110 feet, about 700 and 1,000 feet respectively from mouth of Chambers Creek, just north of Steilacoom in Pierce County— pelecypods; (4) Whatcom County, where pelecypods have been found in the following locations: road cut 2,008 feet north from intersection of Smith Road and road that passes Harmony School, sec. 26, T. 39 N., R. 3 E., about six miles northeast of Bellingham; road cut just west of intersection of Van Wyck and Dewey Roads, at SE cor. sec. 4, T. 38 N., R. 3 E., about three miles northeast of Bellingham; road cut about 0.7 mile west from intersection of Birch Bay and Blaine-Ferndale Roads, in sec. 31, T. 40 N., R. 1 E., about 0.2 mile east of Birch Bay; road cut 0.5 mile northeast from intersection of Smith Road and Mount Baker Highway, in sec. 28, T. 39 N., R. 3 E., about 0.6 mile southwest of North Cedarville; high sea banks on Fish Point about 0.7 mile from intersection of Cagey and Lummi Bay Roads, in sec. 19, T. 38 N., R. 2 E., on Lummi Indian reservation.

GINKGO PETRIFIED FOREST STATE PARK contains one of the best exhibits of petrified wood in the world, and the best of the ginkgo. It covers some seven thousand acres of Columbia Lava Plateau; the trees appear to have grown between flows of lava, to have later been submerged, and to have been protected by water from lava during ensuing eruptions. Although the forest is best known for its ginkgoes, there is the Trail of the Petrified Logs (two miles from the park's little museum), where there are also elm, cedar, hemlock, spruce, and Douglas fir. Pleistocene fossils of such animals as the saber-tooth, wild pig, and elephantine creatures have been found thereabouts. The park is about thirty miles east of the town of Ellensburg and may be reached by U.S. 10; or from Spokane on State Highway 7, via Odessa and Ephrata.

WEST VIRGINIA

THE PERSON WHO IS GOING TO COLLECT PLANT FOSSILS—AND do it seriously—would do well to get hold of a well-illustrated guide published in 1960 by the West Virginia Geological and Economic Survey (see Bibliography).

The state is famous for its fossil plants—as it should be, of course, when it is also famous for its coal. The majority of such plants are found in the rocks of the Pennsylvanian system—which are the rocks usually associated with coal seams, but sometimes plant fossils are found (less abundantly) in rock and clay quarries or in drill cores. The beginner should start looking in the shaly rocks just above the coal, or in the partings that often separate the individual "benches" (elevated shelves) of the seam, digging the material from an outcrop or exposure in a highway or railway cut. Or he may (and more easily) split open the blocks of refuse rock that are found in dumps near the mouths of deep mines, or all around on any strip mine.

There are four series of Pennyslvanian rocks in West Virginia—Monongahela, Conemaugh, Allegheny, and Pottsville, with the last divided into three groups. As part of these series there are nearly fifty coal seams, of which the most important are the Waynesburg, Pittsburgh, Bakerstown, Upper Freeport, Upper and Middle Kittanning, Stockton, Campbell Creek, Sewell, Beckley, and Nos. 3 and 4 Pocahontas.

The 1960 guide very helpfully explains the terminology that

is used for fossil plants, which are much more difficult to treat intelligently than are other fossils, because plants have almost never been preserved in their entirety, and "each individual fragment, such as a leaf or a stem, when first discovered is assigned a Latin generic name." This results in what are called *form genera,* to distinguish them from what we usually think of as genera, and they "can not be assigned to a family. Whenever separate fragments named as form genera are found attached to other form genera (such as leaves to a stem), then the oldest published name has priority for both structures. Nevertheless, the form genus name is usually retained for naming the separate detached parts even after they have been proved to belong to the same plant. In some cases a plant will have seven or eight names for the various organs."

This, one disconcertingly discovers, has resulted in such classifications as, for example, that for the parts of *Lepidodendron: Lepidophyllum* for the leaves when found alone; *Lepidostrobus* for the cones as a whole, but *Lepidostrobophyllum* for cones found alone; *Stigmaria* for roots; and *Lepidophloios* for lycopod stems of a certain kind!

Fossil plants of West Virginia may be put into three main categories:

1. Compressions and impressions—created when leaves, twigs, seeds, and other fragments fell to the bottom of a swamp or lake, were covered by sand, clay, or some other fine sediment, and then were compressed for so long by such weight that all water and air were squeezed out and the organic substance was gradually converted into coaly material. Frequently, when such a matrix is split open, one surface will bear a nearly perfect "compression" of the fragments, while the other has an impressed counterpart—the positive and negative. Microscopic spores or pollen grains can also be separated from coal, and literally are minute compressions.

2. Casts and molds—created when the root, seed, or some other bulky part of a plant was buried in loose sediment, which hardened around it. As the plant material decayed, it left a cavity, its exact shape and size, in the hard matrix. That is a mold. If other material later filled the mold, it formed a cast.

3. Petrified (rarest kind)—created when, at the beginning,

the fragments were in water that contained mineral substances in solution. Those substances gradually were deposited as a solid filling in the cells of the fragment, while the water in the cells was driven out by the weight of the sediments above. The whole thing—sediments and plant—became solid. Such fossils make important specimens because the original cell structure is often preserved.

THE MAJOR TYPES OF FOSSIL FORM GENERA found in the coal measures of West Virginia are:

1. Stems. *Calamites* (represented in modern flora only by the horsetails), commonly preserved as pith casts (cavities from one node to another); *Lepidodendron* (modern "ground pines"), one hundred feet tall, chief growth in Carboniferous coal swamps; *Psaronius* (Mississippian to Triassic tree ferns); *Sigillaria*, which is among the largest of the Carboniferous trees, as much as six feet in diameter at the base.

2. Leaves. The fernlike foliage seen as compressions or impressions on mine dumps is better known to the layman than are any other fossils. There are *Alethopteris* (foliage of seed ferns)—throughout Pennsylvanian system, in an unknown number of species; *Alloiopteris* (special type of fronds)—comparatively rare, but sterile pinnae (divisions of a pinnate leaf) are found in the Pocahontas and New River groups; *Annularia* (one of two types of leaves on *Calamites*)—at least five species found, throughout the coal-bearing horizons; *Aphlebia* (large leaflike structures, perhaps protective devices for young buds); *Asterophyllites* (leaves on *Calamites*)—at least three species in the state, occurring from the Pocahontas group up into the Dunkard strata; *Callipteridium* (a seed fern)—frequent small specimens throughout the upper third of the Pennsylvanian; *Callipteris* (probably a seed fern)—not reported lately; *Cordaites* (leaves borne in spiral sequence on smaller branches of a Carboniferous gymnosperm)—complete specimens rare; *Danaeites* (oblong blunt pinnules)—in Monongahela and Dunkard strata; *Lescuropteris* (probably a seed fern, with scythe-shaped pinnules)— in roof shales of Pittsburgh coal; *Megalopteris* (plant with strap-shaped pinnules)—rare, and usually fragmentary; *Neuropteris* (a fern-like plant) from lower Pottsville through Dunkard;

Linopteris (a seed fern); *Odontopteris* (a seed fern)—from Pottsville through Dunkard; *Pecopteris* (genus covering several ferns)—dozens of species from Pottsville through Dunkard; *Sphenophyllum* (small plants similar to *Calamites*)—at least six of the twenty-one North American species, scattered through coal measures of West Virginia. Other genera include *Mariopteris, Diplothmena, Sphenopteris, Eremopteris,* and *Aneimites*.

3. Seeds, cones, and other detached fructifications. *Aulacotheca* (pollen-bearing organ) in Pocahontas and New River groups; *Carpolithus* (small, egg-shaped compression or cast, looking like a seed)—common; *Dolerotheca* (large pollen-bearing organ)—found in roof shales associated with *Alethopteris* foliage in roof shales of Pittsburgh coal; *Holcospermum* (compression of a seed)—common; *Trigonocarpus* (inclusive term to cover casts of radially symmetrical seeds with three prominent longitudinal ribs)—almost anywhere among abundant fossil plants. Cones are rare, and difficult to identify accurately.

WISCONSIN

COMPARED WITH MANY STATES, WISCONSIN HAS VERY FEW FOSsils. What fossils there are, however, are extremely ancient. Most commonly they are found in dolomites, limestones, and shales; a few are in Cambrian sandstones. Fossil-bearing rocks occur chiefly in a wide belt bordering the igneous core of the north-central portion of the state, and sedimentary rocks lie in layers that dip away from the core, with the youngest strata near Lake Michigan. Wisconsin fossils range in age from something more than 300 million to nearly 500 million years, and the best places to find them exposed are abandoned quarries, cliffs, and bluffs along rivers, and in highway cuts, especially in the southwestern part of the state. (Because of very recent changes of dating in the geologic time schedule, some of the dates given below may need enlargement.)

According to the state's geological survey, there are good
local sites in the following deposits in the eastern part of the
state:

Niagara dolomite (about 340 million years old)—in which
fossils are found in quarries, road cuts, stream cuts, lake bluffs,
and rock fence rows of the following counties:

1. Door—many localities—especially corals; also brachiopods, gastropods, and pelecypods (Casco Quadrangle map).

2. Manitowoc—in quarries near Valders and Reedsville,
west of Manitowoc—tabulate corals, stromatoporoids, and shelled
animals (Reedsville Quad.).

3. Fond du Lac—in abandoned quarry near Oakfield
(NW¼, sec. 23, T. 14 N., R. 16 E.)—calcified and silicified
corals, bryozoans, and brachiopods (Waupun Quad.); other
quarries toward east (Campbellsport Quad.)

4. Dodge—in quarries near and south of Mayville—abundant corals, sponges, and brachiopods (Horicon Quad.)

5. Ozaukee—in quarries and outcrops in banks of Milwaukee River, between Cedarburg and Grafton—large brachiopods, gastropods, trilobites, corals, bryozoans, stromatoporoids,
and poorly preserved crinoids (Port Washington Quad.); and
in outcrops and small quarries north of Saukville (especially sec.
26, T. 11 N., R. 21 E.)—rock described as a crinoid coquina,
containing both plates and columnals (Port Washington Quad.).

6. Waukesha—in quarries near Lannon about twenty miles
northwest of Milwaukee—huge cephalopods (Waukesha Quad.).

7. Milwaukee—in low railroad cut about 20 feet high and
140 feet long on north side of Rapid Transit tracks along north
side of Menomonee Valley in Milwaukee (SE¼, sec. 25, T. 7 N.,
R. 21 E.)—corals, stromatoporoids, bryozoans, brachiopods, mollusks, trilobites (Milwaukee Quad.); in outcrops about one and
an eighth miles east of west Granville (secs. 20 and 29, T. 8 N.,
R. 21 E.)—various fossils (Waukesha Quad.); in low bluff extending east from quarry along north side of Menomonee River
in Wauwatosa, just northeast of intersection of State Street and
Eighth Avenue—many corals, stromatoporoids, bryozoans, brachiopods, mollusks, and trilobites (Waukesha Quad.); southwest part of the county in small quarries north of Hale's Corners,

(SW¼, sec. 28, T. 6 N., R. 21 E.)—abundant coral heads, crinoids, and trilobites, and possibly in other quarries between Hale's Corners and Franklin (Muskego and Bayview Quads.).

8. Waukesha and Racine—in small quarries along Highway 83, between the cities of Waukesha in the county of that name, and Burlington in Racine County—large trilobite *Bumastus imperator* (here alone in Wisconsin), and excellent crinoid stems (Eagle and Muskego Quads.).

9. Racine—in quarries in city of Racine and its vicinity— cystoids and crinoids (Bayview and Racine Quads.).

Maquoketa shale (about 360 million years old) is found in Brown County (sec. 7, T. 24 N., R. 22 E.) in road cut on Highway 57 north of Green Bay near wayside—abundant fossils, particularly bryozoans, in shale overlain by dolomite, especially in stream cuts (New Franken Quad.); and similar fossils are found in intermittent exposures southward from Green Bay to near Stockbridge at east shore of Lake Winnebago (New Franken, DePere, Chilton, and Neenah Quads.).

Upper Cambrian sandstone (about 460 million years old): in Green Lake County, in road cuts along State Highway 44 near Kingston (SE¼, NW¼, sec. 24. T. 14 N., R. 11 E.)—brachiopods and trilobites near top, and about six feet of fossiliferous limestone near bottom (Randolph Quad.).

Galena dolomite (390 million years old) in: two small quarries along U.S. 151, about 4 miles northeast of Sun Prairie, Dane County (NE¼, NE¼. sec. 34, T. 9 N., R. 11 E.)—brachiopods, trilobites, and algal beads (Sun Prairie Quad.).

In the western part of the state there are good localities:

Upper Cambrian sandstone in the following counties:

1. St. Croix—in road cut and adjacent hill in south part of Hudson, along State Highway 35 (C of sec. 25, T. 29 N., R. 20 W.)—worm borings near top, and brachiopods, trilobites, and worm tubes below (Hudson and River Falls Quads.).

2. Dunn—in quarry and outcrops near Colfax (sec. 9, T. 29 N., R. 11 W.) about thirty feet exposed, all fossiliferous— brachiopods and trilobites (New Auburn, Ridgeland, Menomonie, and Elk Mound Quads.).

3. Eau Claire—outcrop in Mount Washington (north part of sec. 25, T. 27 N., R. 10 W.)—in upper seventy feet of ex-

posure, beginning near top—abundant brachiopods and trilobites (Elk Mound Quad.).

4. Trempealeau: in road cuts along highway north of
Whitehall (on line betwen secs. 11, 12, 13, and 14, T. 22 N.,
R. 8 W.)—brachiopods and trilobites, about 140 feet below top
of section and about fifty feet above Trempealeau River (Whitehall Quad.); and in bluff at Trempealeau (NE¼, sec. 28, T. 18
N., R. 9 W.)—about seventy-five feet above base, in two-foot
zone—trilobites and brachiopods (Galesville Quad.).

5. Monroe—in quarry near Tunnel City (NE¼, sec. 23,
T. 18 N., R. 2 W.)—seven feet above floor—trilobites, brachio-
pods, and gastropods (Millston Quad.); in road cuts along
County Trunk Highway Z, southwest of Wilton (secs. 7, 17 and
18, T. 15 N., R. 1 W.)—gastropods and trilobites (Tomah
Quad.).

6. Vernon—roadside cliff on secondary road on northwest
side of Coon Valley (NE¼, sec. 7, T. 14 N., R. 5 W.), in upper
five feet of exposure—trilobites and brachiopods (Stoddard
Quad.).

7. LaCrosse—in section at Middle Ridge, about four miles
east of St. Joseph (SW¼, sec. 2, T. 15 N., R. 5 W.) in ten-foot
zone about thirty-five feet above base—abundant worm tubes
and trilobites (Sparta Quad.).

8. Juneau—in road cut on State Highway 80, about six
miles north of Elroy (SE¼, sec. 3, T. 15 N., R. 2 E.) upper
twenty feet of exposure—trilobites, brachiopods, and worm borings (Mauston Quad.); in road cuts along Highway 82 at Good-
enough Hill, about six miles west of Mauston (NE¼, sec. 13, T.
15 N., R. 2 E.)—trilobites and brachiopods in upper four feet,
and a variety of fossils between thirty-five and 140 feet below
top (Mauston Quad.).

9. Richland—in quarries southeast of Richland Center
(sec. 21, T. 10 N., R. 1 E.), in seventeen-foot siltstone about
eighty-five feet below top—trilobites and brachiopods (Richland
Center Quad.).

10. Iowa—exposures near Lone Rock, along Wisconsin
River, from fifteen feet of siltstone overlying thirteen feet of
dolomite, about 180 feet above river—brachiopods and trilobites
(Richland Center Quad.).

11. Dane—in bluffs at School Section Bluff (N½, sec. 16, T. 8 N., R. 6 E.); and Ferry Bluff (SW¼, sec. 20, and NW¼ NW¼, sec. 29, T. 7 N, R. 6 E.)—algal beads in nine-foot bed about sixty feet below top of exposure; and in twenty-eight-foot silt-stone bed above dolomite—trilobites and brachiopods (Blue Mounds Quad.).

Galena dolomite (about 390 million years old) in the following counties:

1. Grant—in road cut about three and a half miles northwest of Dickeyville, on Highways 35 and 61—brachiopods, sponges, ostracods, etc. (Potosi Quad.); and in road cut about seven miles southwest of Platteville on U.S. 151—brachiopods, gastropods, corals, trilobites, and sponges (Lancaster Quad.).

2. Lafayette—in outcrop in steep ravine from west into Galena River, northeast of Benson (near center of east line of sec. 4, T. 1 N, R. 1 E.)—some very fossiliferous zones (New Diggings and Cuba City Quads.); in quarries near Calamine on County Trunk Highway G (sec. 8, T. 3 N., R. 3 E.)—brachiopods, gastropods, ostracods, and corals (Calamine and Mineral Point Quads.); and in abandoned quarry on west side of State Highway 78, south of Blanchardville—abundant horn coral (Blanchardville Quad.).

3. Green—in road cut on main highway west of junction of Highways 92 and 69, about three miles north of New Glarus (SW¼, sec. 36, T. 5 N., R. 7 E.)—brachiopods, ostracods, gastropods, and trilobites (New Glarus Quad.).

4. Dane—in shallow road cuts on County Trunk Highway P, about a mile and a half north of Pine Bluff (sec. 15, T. 7 N., R. 7 E.)—brachiopods, gastropods, ostracods, and corals (Cross Plains Quad.).

Maquoketa shale (about 360 million years old) in outcrop at junction of County Trunk Highways O and W, about two miles south of Shullsburg, in Lafayette County (SW¼, sec. 22, T. 1 N., R. 3 E.)—abundant loose fossils at base (Shullsburg Quad.).

WYOMING

IT IS DIFFICULT TO POINT OUT SPECIFIC FOSSIL LOCALITIES IN Wyoming, because there are so many of them. Moreover, geologists are justifiably wary about giving precise directions to amateurs. As one specialist says, "When they do stumble onto something of scientific importance, the specimens are often destroyed by their poor collecting techniques. And if the amateur does manage to collect a fine specimen, it is frequently sold to some curio collector or dealer, and thus lost to science." Wyoming has laws similar to those established by the federal government prohibiting the collecting of fossils on public land without a permit. So the amateur should be careful; be as scientific as he can; and mind his manners!

Wyoming's fossils range from Precambrian to sub-Recent, and from the most primitive of invertebrates to advanced mammals. They are scattered widely throughout the state, with several localities world famous since the early days of collecting in this country.

The history of dinosaur collecting in Wyoming goes back to the 1870s, and has continued ever since, with such prodigious results that almost all the vertebrate paleontologists of America have collected remains of the terrible reptiles from the state's sediments. There are none from the Permian or Triassic. All are either Cretaceous or what is known as Comanchean. In an official 1930 bulletin, *Dinosaurs of Wyoming*, Roy L. Moodie said, "The dinosaurs of several types occur in Wyoming in abundance in what is called the Morrison Formation, or Como or Atlantasaurus beds, belonging either in the Upper Jurassic, Lower Cretaceous or representing a separate period—the Comanchean [the name comes from a town near which the beds are found]. The chief dinosaurs are the huge sauropods—the long amphibian animals. . . . Cretaceous dinosaurs as found in and near Wyoming are armored, beaked, aquatic, horned and huge carnivores." Those types outdo all others in variety as well as numbers, and the rocks in which they occur compete in importance with those of Utah, Montana, and Alberta.

Up to 1870, though some of their bones had been found in Wyoming, they were not recognized. Then, in 1877, came the realization that great numbers were buried in the Rocky Mountain area, and chiefly in that state. Three men were largely responsible for bringing them to the attention of the scientific world: Prof. Arthur Lakes (then a teacher at the Colorado School of Mines); O. Lucas (a teacher, and later a clergyman); and William H. Reed (then section foreman of the Union Pacific Railroad in Como). After their revelations, several huge deposits were opened up in the Rocky Mountain region. One was seven miles north of Canon City, Colorado, at the south end of Garden Park, where Edward Drinker Cope, who went into the West frequently after 1869, found his sauropod, *Camarasaurus,* now in the American Museum of Natural History. *Diplodocus* was found in a quarry nearby, opened by Othniel C. Marsh, and later worked by John Bell Hatcher for the Carnegie. An immense cache was opened back of the Como station by Samuel W. Williston, who excavated in Wyoming at intervals until 1918; and many hundreds of tons of dinosaurs were taken from the state's Rock Creek, and Freezeout Mountains, to go to museums all over the world. Williston and Prof. Benjamin F. Mudge worked with and for Prof. Marsh, who began to send out parties after 1870. Hatcher was at Yale, and spent some twenty years in the field, shipping more than fifteen hundred boxes to Yale, the National Museum, and the Carnegie.

In the early days, paleontologists had to sleep with guns in their hands, but after 1880 they were able to establish permanent camps, and more and more parties went out. Even today, it is the expected thing that any great museum will send its representatives to Wyoming as often as possible.

G. R. Wieland of Yale began to search about 1898, and it was he who found the *Barosaurus* in the Black Hills of South Dakota, to the northeast of Wyoming. He also made remarkable collections of cycads.

Hatcher, who invented new techniques during his collecting, was responsible for the first ceratopsians (horned dinosaurs). In 1889, he found a horned skull near Lusk, Wyoming,

in Niobrara County. It was identified by Marsh, and by 1892
Hatcher had collected remains of fifty such creatures—thirty-
three of them including skulls. Among the nine hundred boxes
he shipped to Yale between 1884 and 1892, one, containing a
three-horned dinosaur, weighed three tons.

Among other paleontologists whose names are closely
associated with the finding of reptiles in Wyoming are Leidy of
Philádelphia; Prof. Wilbur C. Knight, who went out for the
museum at the University of Wyoming, and described the plesiosaurs; E. S. Riggs of the Field Museum, Chicago, who super-
vised the collecting of sauropods; Dr. Earl Douglass who worked
for the Carnegie; Charles W. Gilmore, who increased the collection of the National Museum; and Charles H. Sternberg,
who found many of the monsters, got the famous dinosaur
mummy now in the American Museum of Natural History, sent
Triceratops to the British Museum, and supplied various forms
to many other foreign centers. A Princeton expedition of 1877–
78 consisted of Henry Fairfield Osborn, W. E. Scott, Thomas
Speer, and a large party. The finest and best collection of dinosaurs in the world is at the American Museum of Natural History, for which many were gathered by Barnum Brown, Walter
Granger, W. D. Matthew, J. L. Wortman and Osborn.

Cretaceous deposits come down from Alberta into Montana,
North Dakota, Minnesota, Iowa, Nebraska, Colorado, Utah, Arizona, New Mexico, and Wyoming, and the best place to look for
fossils anywhere is "talus" slopes, in gullies or in cliffs, where
they are exposed by erosion. Some dinosaur bones have,
strangely, been found in marine deposits, and scientists assume
that the creatures died near what was then the shore, and their
bodies were swept into the sea.

The most famous dinosaur specimens from Wyoming are
those of:

Mummies found in the Cretaceous of Niobrara County.

Duckbills—an almost complete one, encased in an impression cast of its skin, found by George F. Sternberg (son of C. H.)
in 1908, and now in the AMNH; another, which was found in
1910, and went to Germany.

Stegosaurus—one of the great finds, from Como Bluff, and
now at Yale.

Sauropods—one of the largest, from near Medicine Bow, now in the AMNH, is sixty-six feet long and weighed thirty-eight tons; the brontosaur now in the AMNH is composed of parts from Nine Mile Crossing of Little Medicine Bow River, from Como Bluff, and from Bone Cabin Quarry.

Allosaurus—collected in 1879 in Como Bluff near Medicine Bow River by F. F. Hubbell for Cope. It is thirty-four feet long and eight feet tall, was complete when found, and lay in packing boxes for twenty years, until after the AMNH acquired Cope's collection.

Ornitholestes ("bird-catcher")—from Bone Cabin Quarry for the AMNH.

Triceratopsian—the first known, from Cope's 1875–76 collection; it came from Niobrara County's sandstone beds (with some plant impressions) and is now in the AMNH.

WYOMING'S EXPOSURES, from Precambrian through Eocene, have revealed such specimens as the following:

PRECAMBRIAN

Stromatolites—from beds in Medicine Bow Mountains.

CAMBRIAN

Plants and vertebrates—from Beartooth Bluff near Yellowstone. Upper Cambrian calcareous algae in great masses—from Gros Ventre Formation in the Grand Teton Quadrangle.

ORDOVICIAN

Ostracoderms—from Big Horn Mountains; found in typical marine strata similar to those in Canon City, Colorado.

EARLY MESOZOIC

Fish—from banks of Green River.

JURASSIC

Protosuchus (an ancestral crocodilian) and abundant remains of mammal-like reptiles—from Dinosaur Canyon, where they were found by a Navajo Indian. Dinosaurs found by Barnum Brown.

CRETACEOUS

Dinosaurs (see foregoing); dozens of mammal jaws and hundreds of teeth—discovered, in Lance beds, by a recent party from the University of California. Dinosaur eggs—from Lance beds, near Powell, near the northern boundary of the state.

PALEOCENE

From Big Horn Basin—characteristic mammals not common in other localities. In 1953 a party under C. Lewis Gazin of the Smithsonian went into Bison Basin and came back with an unusually good collection of Paleocene mammals. Among the most important finds were remains of plesiadapids—small primates, classified in the superfamily with lemurs, and perhaps fairly closely related to them. At least four species and two genera of plesiadapids are represented by jaws and teeth found by the expedition. The largest—and most primitive—of them are from a fairly small creature (known as *Pronothodectes*) that was perhaps a precursor of true *Plesiadapis*. Not far away was a specimen representing the most advanced of the plesiadapids. Other finds included those archaic, sub-ungulate animals, the herbivorous condylarths, which are thought to have preceded the hoofed types. Most of the condylarths found are very small, but one—the *Phenacodus*—is more than four feet long. From the Bison Basin also came examples of creodonts, ancestors of the carnivores; and clenodonts, which looked something like small bears, but were really no relation.

EOCENE

Chlorellopsis (blue-green algae)—from shores of three Eocene fresh-water lakes; *Diatryma* (a flightless bird, seven feet tall); from the Green River, near Bridger—the best-preserved fresh-water fish skeletons ever found; a creodont from Henry's Fork, near the Utah state line, and along with it a large insect fauna from which we derive much of our knowledge of Eocene forests. From the Bridger Basin also have come the most complete sequence of early Tertiary mammalian fauna known anywhere in the world, including *Uintatherium*, and ancestors of the elephant, camel, horse, rodents, whales, true carnivores, and primates.

A *Uintatherium* WAS THE PRIZE of the 1940 season for a party from the Smithsonian led by C. L. Gazin. Parts of such an animal are not uncommon, but this one was almost complete, with nothing lacking but one hind leg, part of one foreleg, and the neck vertebrae. The skull was a yard long, and in good condition except that the lower jaw was somewhat crushed. The party came on this rare specimen in the side of a steep hill about a half mile from the road, and had to drive a truck up a dry creek and drag the bones out on canvas. When the fossil was shipped to Washington, it filled four 500-pound cases.

Particularly productive and famous localities in Wyoming include:

1. Bone Cabin Quarry—one of the greatest fossil caches ever found. It is in Albany County, south-central Wyoming, and was accidentally discovered in 1897 by Walter Granger. From it, a carload of specimens was sent each year for six years to the AMNH, which thus acquired remains of seventy-three animals—all dinosaurs except five turtles and four crocodiles. Dinosaur bones were so common that a Mexican sheepherder had used gigantic vertebrae as foundation material for his cabin.

2. Niobrara Formation. Three-horned dinosaurs, along with Cretaceous mammals, have been found at six locations on the Niobrara River. Among the distinguished collecting expeditions that have searched here have been parties from the AMNH, the Carnegie Museum, the Field Museum, and Kansas State and Princeton universities.

3. Como Bluff and other quarries in the Morrison Formation. When George Gaylord Simpson was at the AMNH, he wrote a monograph about Como Bluff—a ridge several hundred feet above the surrounding country, and consisting of a hogback with its scarp facing slightly west of north. Rocks in the face of the bluff are Triassic to Cretaceous, and include several sections of late Jurassic marine Sundance and continental Morrison formations. Como Bluff is on the line between Carbon and Albany counties, in the Laramie Basin, about forty-five miles north-northwest of Laramie, and five miles east of Medicine Bow.

In the early days, when Samuel Williston was excavating for Marsh, a tiny Mesozoic mammal, *Dryolestes,* was found near the surface, and other Morrison mammals were found later in Quarry 9. The area remains unique for Jurassic mammals. Of the nearly three hundred known, all but three (from near Canon City) are from Como, almost all from Quarry 9. W. H. Reed, who was in charge for Marsh after July 1878, opened the three most famous Como Bluff quarries, and continued to work in the area until 1883, when he went into sheep herding. Between 1878 and 1880, Arthur Lakes painted some remarkable watercolors of the area, which may be seen in Yale's Peabody Museum. And in 1882 Marsh turned responsibility for the Como project over to the USGS.

In 1887, when Osborn, then of the AMNH, turned to the locality for dinosaurs, Walter Granger prospected northward from Como Bluff, and opened up Bone Cabin Quarry. For many years thereafter, little collecting was done at Como; but few localities have contributed so much to knowledge of American vertebrate paleontology, or to the training of so many specialists. Its fame is based altogether on fossil vertebrates found in the Morrison. It is the discovery site of American Jurassic ichthyosaurs, and has a fairly rich invertebrate fauna.

4. Green River basin. Probably no area of comparable size has attracted so many paleontologists as have flocked to the Green River basin. It lies athwart the great migratory route across the Rockies, and even at the beginning of the nineteenth century was known to have fossils. The first record of collecting them there is of finding fossil shells, in the 1812–13 journal of Robert Stuart, who collected shells. The first vertebrates were credited to a trapper, Jack Robinson; and James Hall of New York wrote of Green River fossils in 1848. In 1856 John Evans, educator and engineer, sent to Leidy a fish he had picked up where thousands were to be found later; and many finds were made during the Territorial Survey period, 1868–78. Controversy concerning the type of fossils known as Green Mountain vertebrates touched off a climax to one of the most bitter rivalries in the entire history of paleontology—that between Edward Drinker Cope and Othniel C. Marsh.

For Cope, who was made professor of vertebrate zoology at Haverford College when he was in his early twenties, digging for fossils was an inconquerable obsession, and he made some of the most dramatic discoveries in our West, which was still largely unexplored. Marsh, professor of paleontology at Yale, had been making equally important finds somewhat earlier, in Kansas and Wyoming, and resented it when Cope began to explore what

Marsh thought of as his own territory. Both sent fossils back to museums in the East, and each tried to outdo the other.

The climax came when Cope found a strange monster with tusks, which he named *Loxolophodon* Cope (using the accepted system of adding his own name as discoverer). Two days after he sent back a telegram about the find, Marsh came on a fossil of the same beast, naming it *Tinoceras* Marsh, and sent his own wire. Because the telegrapher had mixed up Cope's message, credit for being first went to Marsh. The row that ensued echoed throughout the country, and the two men never forgave each other.

On July 12, 1872, Cope left Fort Bridger in the extreme southwest corner of the state on a vertebrate-collecting tour in the Badlands south of the fort, and went up Bitter Creek to Black Butte, then to Vermilion, and into the Washakie Basin. Later he went up the Fontenelle and, in the course of his explorations, collected one hundred specimens of Eocene vertebrates—sixty of them new. Marsh left Fort Bridger in August 1870, with twelve Yale students and a military escort, and went down Henry's Fork, across the Green River to Brown's Hole, along the lower White River, up the Uinta River to Fort Uinta, and back to Bridger. In 1871 and 1872 he was in Kansas and Wyoming for six weeks, and in 1873 spent ten days in Wyoming.

The Green River is especially noted for its fossil fish, and few museums are without fish from its deposits. They first came to the attention of the scientific world in 1856, when Leidy described the herring sent to him by John Evans. Then, after the Union Pacific Railroad went through in 1868, the Green River station became important, and a long cut was made in the shale along the river, at the west end of town—an area that came to be known as Petrified Fish Cut. The Hayden Geological Survey made a collection that was described in 1870 by Cope, who also wrote a series of papers between 1877 and 1884. In his "Bible," he described thirty species of fossil fish, and others have been added from time to time. Cope spoke of Petrified Fish Cut, and of one locality "near the main line of the Wasatch Mountains," by which he may have meant Twin Creek, which has supplied the majority of the specimens found in the area since the 1870s. The main locality on Twin Creek is Fish Cliffs, on the west side of

Twin Creek Valley, 1.0 mile north of Fossil station on the Oregon Short Line Railroad.

Actually, fish fossils are scattered throughout the formation, though most of them come from a few localities. The fish are thought to have died from fouling of the water by dead plankton or algae. In order to extract fossil fish from Twin Creek, where the fish layer is about fifty feet below the top of the main bluffs, collectors find it best to select an area bounded on the sides by "settling cracks," with joint cracks in between, about two to four feet apart. The collectors quarry, then blast away the overburden and raise the blocks from between the joint cracks so that they may be split. Fish are found usually *between* the bedding planes, covered by a thin layer of matrix. Among the most common types are the small *Piscarara serrata* ("sunfish") and the *Diplomystus* (small herring). *Pharodus* (a deep-bodied fish with many plates) is fairly common. Garfish and the fresh-water ray are rare. Very few birds or reptiles are found in this Eocene formation. But a skeleton of the bird *Gallinoides* has been found, as have feathers of other birds, a toad, a thirteen-inch crocodile, insect eyes still attached to bodies, and the most complete fossil snake ever found in North America—*Boavus ideimani,* thirty-eight inches long.

Anyone driving through southwest Wyoming can easily recognize the hills where fossils are still to be found. Those hills are weathered in a characteristic fashion, usually gray-buff, and show horizontal bands. Even a brief stop along the route is likely to produce at least a leaf or a fish.

THE SUBJECT OF FOSSILS IN WYOMING is obviously an inexhaustible one, to which both professionals and amateurs are constantly adding material, and about which much has been written.

In 1960 and 1961 Wyoming laymen and geologists and Harvard archeologists recovered the carcass of a young seventeen-foot, five-ton woolly mammoth (*Mammuthus columbi*) not far north of the Colorado border. The creature's skull was fractured in two places, and he had three broken vertebrae. His bones were scientifically dated as 11,280 years old, plus or minus 350 years, and with him were stone hammers, scrapers, and other tools, including an awl for working on leather, along with some big quartzite rocks. It seems certain that he had had his head bashed in and been eaten by the people who made the weapons and tools. About three quarters of the mammoth is now in the University of Wyoming, where the skeleton has been reconstructed; the tools that show evidence of man's handiwork are in Harvard's Peabody Museum of Archeology.

A very important find was made more recently by Prof. John H. Ostrom and an expedition from Yale, which for four years had been investigating the Big Horn Basin of Wyoming and Montana. It was almost the entire skeleton of a dinosaur twenty-five feet long, and about 116 million years old, which fills a gap between *Camptosaurus* (a bird-hipped European Jurassic reptile dated 20 million years earlier) and the duck-billed type, which appeared 30 million years afterward. This newly discovered dinosaur had short front legs, was covered by coarse, scaly skin, and is said to be closer to the European *Iguanodon* than anything else found heretofore in North America.

One of the latest important finds was a crocodile skull, discovered near Kemmerer in the summer of 1966. This skull, which is about twenty-eight inches long, was unearthed when a group was looking for mammal fossils in Eocene sediment, and is dated at about 50 million years. The searchers, graduate students at the University of Wyoming, were James Anderson of Cheyenne, Donald Doehring of Laramie, and Bruce Wilkinson of Lancaster, Pennsylvania. Larry Johnson, another graduate student, has been preparing the specimen for the university's museum, under the supervision of Dr. Paul O. McGrew, acting head of the department of geology.

The area in which the crocodile skull was found seems to be a prolific one, and students have already found in it several other Eocene creatures, including a uintathere and a taeniodont, both of which are rare. The site will be investigated further during ensuing summers.

Wyoming's greatest fossil-hunting period has been glorified by the publication (after nearly seventy-five years) of lithographs of sauropods and stegosaurs made by Othniel Marsh. These were put out by Yale's Peabody Museum, and the publication includes a history of Como Bluff, with much material drawn from letters that Marsh wrote between 1877 and 1889.

It is officially announced that visitors are welcome, between July 1 and September 1, to visit the quarry in south Wyoming, on the north side of Wyoming Highway 789, near where famous faunas were collected.

ALGA (pl. algae)—any plant of a group, Algae, comprising virtually all seaweeds and allied fresh-water or nonaquatic forms.

AMOEBA—a protozoan of the genus *Amoeba*, one of the simplest forms of animal life.

AMOEBOID—like an amoeba.

ANGIOSPERM—a flowering plant of a class, Angiospermae, having seeds in a closed ovary.

ANTICLINE—an uplift or arch of stratified rock.

ARCHEOCETI—ancient ancestors of aquatic mammals such as the whale.

ARGILLACEOUS—resembling clay; argillaceous substances are usually associated with other substances, and emit a peculiar odor when breathed on.

ARTHROPOD—a member of a phylum, Arthropoda, of animals with articulated body and limbs, which include insects, arachnids, and crustaceans.

ARTIODACTYL—hoofed mammal with even number of toes.

ASTHENOSPHERE—the more or less plastic and shifting layer around the globe, just under the crust.

BASIC OR BASAL—applied to igneous rocks such as basalt that are comparatively low in silica and high in iron and magnesium.

BASIN—a depression of the earth in which sediments accumulate; an inverted dome.

BATHOLITH—a mass of magma moving upward, lifting or engulfing the older rocks above it and often forming the core of a mountain range.

BEDDING PLANE—surface between two layers of stratified rock, along which layers are easily separable.

BIOCLASTIC—of rock or similar material that attained its present form through the action of living organisms.

BIOHERM—a body of rock built up or composed of many sedimentary organisms, as corals, algae, or mollusks, enclosed or surrounded by rock of different origin.

BLOCK MOUNTAINS—mountains produced by enormous segments of earth's crust and having no associated folding.

BRACHIOPOD—one of a class, Brachiopoda, of marine animals with shells made up of two unlike and unequal valves.

CALICHE—a crust of calcium carbonate formed on stony ground in arid regions.

CARAPACE—bony or horny case or shield covering all or part of the back of an animal.

CARNIVORE—a meat-eating animal.

CATASTROPHISM (or the cataclysmic theory)—the doctrine that at intervals in the earth's history all living things have been destroyed by cataclysms (floods, earthquakes, etc.) and replaced by entirely different populations. A version of this long-denied theory has recently become respectable, because we now know that the earth's magnetic fields have been reversed every now and then through the eons, the last occasion being about 700,000 years ago. At that time, the earth's atmosphere was disturbed, cosmic radiation from the sun and outer space hit the globe, and a huge comet exploded. Scientists have found that the age of the resultant shower of tektites (glass hailstones—bits of the exploded comet) is exactly the same as that of certain sea-bottom sediments containing significant mutations of previously known species. Thus, it is reasoned, radiation (during this cataclysm and others) may have accounted for the extinction of living species and for mutations that sent life along new pathways.

CETACEAN—of or pertaining to an order, Cetacea, of aquatic, mostly marine, mammals, consisting of whales, dolphins, etc.

CHAMSOSAUR—a five-foot reptile with slender jaws like those of the phytosaurs.

CHARAPHYTE (or chara)—a bushy microscopic plant, either fresh-water or marine; member of a family of grass-green algae.

CHLOROPHYLL—green coloring matter present in growing plants.

CLASTIC—conglomerate made up of fragments of pre-existing rocks.

COELACANTH—a primitive fish long thought to have become extinct at the end of the Mesozoic, but discovered in living specimens since 1938.

COELENTERATE—any member of a phylum of invertebrate animals, including corals, sea anemones, jelly fishes, and hydroids.

COLUMNAR SECTION—succession of rock formations in a given place, when shown in a vertical chart.

COMPRESSION—a specimen in which external form has been modified by weight of overlying sediments and almost all internal structure has been destroyed.

CONCRETION—a nodule of any size or shape, produced by chemical precipitation around a nucleus such as a grain of sand or a fossil.

CONDYLARTH—an archaic herbivorous sub-ungulate.

CONGLOMERATE (rock)—cemented gravel in which fragments may be of any kind of rock.

CONULARIAN—an early jellyfish.

CRINOID (sea lily)—one of the echinoderms or spiny-skinned marine animals, which looks like a plant.

CRUSTACEAN—any of a large class, Crustacea, of arthropods, principally aquatic, commonly covered by a horny shell.

CYCAD—a fernlike tropical gymnosperm of the family Cycadaceae.

CYSTOID ("bladderlike")—a primitive echinoderm with an egg-shaped or spherical body.

DIATOM—any of a class of microscopic unicellular or colonial algae, the silicified skeletons of which form kieselguhr.

DICOTYLEDONOUS—having two cotyledons, or seed leaves, as most deciduous trees and most herbs and shrubs.

DICYNODONT—an herbivorous offshoot of pelycosaurs, which left no descendants.

DISCONFORMITY—a geologic structure in which beds are parallel above and below an unconformity.

ECHINODERM—a spiny-skinned marine animal.

EDROASTER ("seated star")—a rare kind of echinoderm.

EXOSKELETON—hard supporting or protective structure developed on or secreted by the outside of a body, as the shell of a crustacean.

FAVOSITE—honeycomb coral.

FOLDED MOUNTAINS—a system of ranges that appear as series of alternating ridges and valleys.

FORAMINIFER—a one-celled amoeboid protozoan especially important in the search for oil.

GAMETOPHYTE—in the alternation of generations in plants, the generation that bears sex organs.

GASTROPOD—a snail or one of its kin with shell consisting of one main structure.

GENE—an entity concerned with the transmission and development or determination of hereditary characteristics.

GENUS (pl. genera)—the category of classification between family and species.

GEOLOGIC COLUMN—composite geologic record in which columnar sections from a number of localities are brought together.

GEOSYNCLINE—a great subsiding trough of sedimentation which originated along the margin of a stable region. All great mountain ranges have risen out of geosynclines.

GLAUCONITIC—containing glauconite, a mineral that is essentially a hydrous silicate of iron and potassium, green in color.

GRAPTOLITE ("written stone")—a very early primitive animal, the nature of which is not entirely understood.

GRAPTOLOIDEA—advanced order of graptolites.

GYMNOSPERM—a plant having seeds naked, or not enclosed in an ovary.

HERBIVORES—plant-eating animals.

HORIZON—the geological deposit of a particular time, usually identified by distinctive fossils.

HYDROZOAN—any of a class, Hydrozoa, of coelenterates that includes various kinds of polyps and jellyfish.

IGNEOUS ROCK—rock formed by solidification of molten magma; may be *intrusive* (formed within the earth's crust) or *extrusive* (formed from cooling lava at surface of the earth).

INSECTIVORE—an insect-eating animal.

INVERTEBRATE—an animal without a backbone.

ISOTOPE—one of two or more forms of the same element, distinguished by radioactive transformations or differences in atomic weight.

LAVA—magma that erupts in a molten state through fissures or volcanoes, and hardens on the surface, forming extrusive rock.

LENS—a reeflike accumulation of limestone, shale, and fossils; a deposit shaped like a lens.

MAGMA—underground molten rock which in cooling forms the igneous rocks.

MARSUPIAL—a mammal of the order Marsupialia, the females of which have a pouch for carrying their young.

MATRIX—the natural material in which any fossil is imbedded.

METAMORPHIC ROCKS—igneous and sedimentary rocks that (without melting) have been changed so that they are characterized by new textures, new minerals, or both; gneiss, schist, phyllite, slate, quartzite, marble, serpentine, soapstone, and amphibolite are examples.

MICROSPORE—an asexually produced spore of small size compared to that of others produced by the same species.

MILLIPEDE (or millepede)—any of numerous myriapods (a group of arthropods), chiefly with a round body of numerous segments, covered with hard integument (external skin).

MULTITUBERCULATE—animal having many tubercles, such as teeth.

MUTATION—a sudden variation, in which, because of changes within the genes, offspring differ from their parents in some well-marked character or characters.

NONCONFORMITY—structure in which upper rocks lie on the eroded surface of a major rock of a different type (*e.g.*, sedimentary rocks on igneous or metamorphic). When the lower sequence or stratum was folded or tilted before the upper sequence was deposited, the result is an angular nonconformity.

OPALIZED—having the original substance replaced by silica and some water.

ORNITHISCHIA—reptiles with four-pronged pelvis.

OSTRACOD (or ostracode)—a short-bodied crustacean.

PELECYPOD—a clamlike invertebrate.

PELYCOSAUR—a reptile (usually carnivorous) thought to be an early ancestor of mammals.

PENEPLAIN (or peneplane)—a land surface worn down nearly to a plain; to erode to a peneplain.

PERISSODACTYL—hoofed mammal with odd number of toes.

PLACENTAL—mammal that nourishes the fetus by means of a placenta in the uterus.

PLUTONIC ROCK—rock formed by solidification within the earth of molten magma.

POLLEN—the mass of microspores in seed plants, usually a fine yellow dust.

PROSOBRANCH—an order of gastropods having the gills in front of the heart.

PROTOPLASM—the essential substance of both the cell body and the nucleus of the cell in animals and plants.

PROTOTHERIA—egg-laying mammals.

PROTOZOAN (pl. protozoans) or protozoon (pl. protozoa)—a member of the phylum Protozoa, of animals that have bodies consisting of a single cell and that reproduce by fission.

PSEUDOMORPH—an irregular or deceptive form.

PSEUDOPOD—a temporary protrusion or retractile process of the protoplasm of a cell, for moving about or taking up food.

SAURISCHIA—reptiles with three-pronged pelvis.

SCAPHOPOD—a tusk-shaped shell.

SCOLECODONT—jaw of a kind of earthworm.

SEDIMENTARY ROCK—rock formed by or from deposits of sediments; especially (1) rock formed from fragments of other rocks transported from their sources and deposited in water, as sandstone or shale; (2) rock formed by precipitation from solution, as rock salt or gypsum; (3) rock formed from calcareous remains of organisms, as limestone.

SERIES—rocks of a given epoch, often differentiated as Lower, Middle and Upper, or receiving geographical names.

SHIELD—an area (*e.g.*, the Canadian Shield) that has been neither thickly covered nor profoundly eroded since the Precambrian.

STEGOCEPHALIAN—an early amphibian which had its head covered by bones.

STRATUM (pl. strata)—a sheet-like mass of sedimentary rock of one kind, usually in layers between beds of other kinds.

STROMATOPOROID—a fossil hydrozoan of the most abundant type, made up of limy layers held together by pillars, and found in colonies; Cretaceous or earlier.

SYNCLINE—a downfold or trough.

THERAPSIDS—carnivorous descendants of pelycosaurs, with teeth approaching those characteristic of mammals.

THERIODONT—a reptile descendant of pelycosaurs that developed characteristics later made use of by mammals.

TRICONODONTS—largest of the Mesozoic mammals, and aggressively carnivorous.

TRILOBITE—any of numerous extinct marine arthropods characterized by a body longitudinally divided into three lobes by furrows on the dorsal surface.

UNCONFORMITY—(1) a lack of continuity between strata in contact, corresponding to a gap in the stratigraphic record; or (2) a surface of contact between unconformable strata.

UNGULATE—a hoofed mammal.

UNIFORMISM (or Uniformitarianism)—a geological theory stated as a law by Sir Charles Lyell, stressing the thesis that what is going on now in the physical world is just a continuation of what has been going on since the beginning.

VERTEBRATE—an animal with a backbone.

Bibliography

Guides, Pamphlets, Professional Papers, and Other Documents

ALABAMA

Ala. GS Bull. No. 1, Truman H. Aldrich ("Tertiary Marine Invertebrates"), Otto Mayer ("Eocene Marine Invertebrates"), 1886.

Upper Cretaceous Floras of the Eastern Gulf Region in Tennessee, Mississippi, Alabama and Georgia, Edward Wilber Berry, USGS Prof. Paper 112, 1919.

Curious Creatures in Alabama Rocks, Charles H. Copeland, Jr., Ala. GS Circ. 19, 1963.

List of Fossil Collecting Sites, courtesy Geological Survey of Alabama.

ALASKA

The Iniskin-Chinitna Peninsula and Snug Harbor District, Alaska, Fred H. Moffet, USGS Bull. 789, 1927.

The Upper Cretaceous Floras of Alaska, Arthur Hollick and George C. Martin, USGS Prof. Paper 159, 1930.

The Tertiary Floras of Alaska, Arthur Hollick and Philip S. Smith, USGS Prof. Paper 182, 1936.

Callovian (Jurassic) Ammonites from the United States and Alaska, Ralph W. Imlay, USGS Prof. Papers 249-A and 249-B.

Characteristic Jurassic Mollusks from Northern Alaska, Ralph W. Imlay, USGS Prof. Paper 274-D, 1955.

Cenozoic Megafossils of Northern Alaska, F. Stearns MacNeil, USGS Prof. Paper 294-C, 1957.

Landscapes of Alaska: Their Geologic Evolution, Howel Williams, ed., U. of Calif. Press, 1958.

Succession and Speciation of the Pelecypod Aucella, Ralph W. Imlay, USGS Prof. Paper 314-G, 1959.

Late Paleozoic Gastropods from Northern Alaska, Ellis J. Yochelson and J. Thomas Dutro, Jr., USGS Prof. Paper 334-D, 1960.

Upper Cretaceous Pelecypods of the Genus Inoceramus from

Northern Alaska, David L. Jones and George Gryc, USGS Prof.
Paper 334-E, 1960.
*Characteristic Lower Cretaceous Megafossils from Northern
Alaska,* R. W. Imlay, USGS Prof. Paper 335 (in coop. with
U.S. Dept. of Navy, Off. of Petroleum and Oil Shale Review),
1961.
The Bajocian Ammonites from the Cook Inlet Region, Alaska,
Ralph W. Imlay, USGS Prof. Paper, 418-A, 1962.

ARIZONA

The Petrified Forests of Arizona, USGS, 1900.
The Paleontological Literature of Arizona: A Review, Halsey W.
Miller, Jr., department of geology, University of Arizona,
1960.

ARKANSAS

Fauna of the Moorefield Shale of Arkansas, George H. Girty,
USGS Bull. 439, 1911.
"Localities for fossil-collecting in Arkansas," courtesy Arkansas
Geological and Conservation Commission.

CALIFORNIA

"California Mosasaurs," Charles L. Camp, U. of Cal. *Memoirs,*
Vol. 13, No. 1, 1942.
Geologic Guidebook of the San Francisco Bay Counties, parts IV
and V, R. S. Stirton, Leo George Hertlein, Ralph W. Chaney,
G. Dallas Hanna, *et al.,* Cal. Dept. of Nat. Rsrcs. Bull. 154,
1951.
"Outline of Stratigraphic Record of California," article in Cal.
Min. Info. Srvcs., news release, Vol. 5, No. 3, Mar. 1, 1952.
"Use of Fossils in Geological Exploration," article in Cal. Min.
Info. Srvcs. news release, Vol. 5, No. 6, June 1, 1952.

COLORADO

*Geological Examinations in Southern Colorado and Northern
New Mexico During the Years 1878 and 1879,* John J. Steven-
son, C. A. White, *et al.,* USGS Surveys of 100th Meridian.
Colorado Springs: A Guide Book, George Irving Finlay, Out West
Co., 1906.

Fossil Mammals, Harvey C. Markman, Denver Mus. of Nat. Hist. Pictorial No. 4, 1952.

Fossils, Harvey C. Markman, Denver Mus. of Nat. Hist. Pop. Ser. No. 3, repr. ed., 1954.

Geology of the Front Range Foothills West of Denver: Deer Creek to Ralston Creek, Jefferson County, Colorado, Ben H. Parker, ed., Rocky Mt. Assoc. of Geologists, 1955.

Guide to the Geology of Colorado, Robert J. Weimer and John D. Haun, eds., Geol. Soc. of America, Rocky Mt. Assoc. of Geologists, and Colo. Scientific Soc., 1960.

CONNECTICUT

Triassic Life of the Connecticut Valley, Richard Swann Lull, Conn. Geol. and Nat. Hist. Survey Bull. 81, rev. ed., 1953.

DELAWARE

Marine Upper Cretaceous Formations of the Chesapeake and Delaware Canal, Johan J. Groot, Donna M. Organist, and Horace G. Richards, Del. GS Bull. 3, 1954 (out of print).

An Invertebrate Macrofauna from the Upper Cretaceous of Delaware, Horace G. Richards and Earl Shapiro, Del. GS Report of Investigations No. 7, 1963.

FLORIDA

A List, Bibliography, and Index of the Fossil Vertebrates of Florida, Clayton E. Ray, Fla. GS Spec. Pub. No. 3, 1957.

Fossil Mammals of Florida, Stanley J. Olsen, Fla. GS Spec. Pub. No. 6, 1959.

Trichecodon huxlei in the Pleistocene of Southeastern United States, Clayton E. Ray, *Bulletin* of Mus. of Comp. Zool. at Harvard, Vol. 122, No. 3, Mar. 1960.

Vertebrate Fossil Localities in Florida, Stanley J. Olsen, Fla. GS Spec. Pub. No. 12, 1965.

GEORGIA

Ga. GS *Mineral News Letter,* articles in Vol. VIII, Nos. 1, 2, and 3, 1955.

Fossils of Northwest Georgia, ed. by Lewis Lipps for NSF In-Service Inst., 1961.

IDAHO

The Fauna of the Phosphate Beds of the Park City Formation in Idaho, Utah and Wyoming, USGS Bull. 436, 1910.
USGS Water-Supply Paper 774 (with Ida. Bur. Mines and Geol.), Harold T. Stearns, Lynn Crandall and Willard J. Steward, 1938.
Idaho, Am. Guide Series, New York, Oxford University Press, 1950.
Lists of Fossil-Collecting Localities, courtesy Dept. of Geol. and Geog., U. of Ida., and department of geology of Idaho State College.

ILLINOIS

Guide for Beginning Fossil Hunters, Charles W. Collinson, Ill. GS, rev. ed., 1959.
Pennsylvanian Plant Fossils of Illinois, Charles W. Collinson and Romayne Skartvedt, Ill. GS Field Book, 1960.
Geological Science Field Trips, Ill. GS, 1961–62.

INDIANA

"Exploring an Ancient Seafloor," T. G. Perry, in *Outdoor Indiana,* Ind. GS, Apr. 1956.
Adventures with Fossils, Robert H. Shaver, Ind. GS Circular No. 6, June 1959.
Fossil Plants of Indiana, James E. Canright, Ind. GS Report of Progress No. 14, Aug. 1959.
Fossils: Prehistoric Animals in Hoosier Rocks, T. G. Perry, Ind. GS Circular No. 7, Dec. 1959.
"Fossils: Numbers on the Pages of Time," Robert H. Shaver, in *Outdoor Indiana,* Ind. GS, Nov. 1960.

IOWA

Fossil-Collecting Areas in Iowa, courtesy Iowa Geological Survey.

KANSAS

"Kansas Coal Measures New Labyrinthodont," Roy L. Moodie, in Natl. Mus. *Proceedings,* Vol. 39, 1910.
The Kansas Rock Column, Raymond C. Moore, *et al.,* State Geol. Sur. of Kansas Bull. 89, 1951 (out of print).

Announcement, Fort Hays (Kan.) State Coll. Museums, Vol. 1, No. 5, Apr. 12, 1961.

KENTUCKY

The Paleontology of Kentucky: A Symposium, Willard Rouse Willson, ed., Ky. GS, 1931 (out of print).

LOUISIANA

Geology of Grant and La Salle Parishes, H. N. Fisk, La. Dept. of Conservation Bull. 10, Jan. 1938.

MARYLAND

The Pleistocene Vertebrate Fauna from Cumberland Cave, James W. Gidley and C. Lewis Gazin, U.S. Natl. Mus. Bull. 171, 1938.

MASSACHUSETTS

Triassic Life of the Connecticut Valley, Richard Swann Lull, Conn. Geol. and Nat. Hist. Survey Bull. 81, rev. ed., 1953.

MICHIGAN

Guide to Michigan Fossils, Robert W. Kelley, Mich. Dept. of Conservation.
Outline of the Geologic History of Michigan, Helen M. Martin, Mich. GS, 1952.

MINNESOTA

Paleontology, Leo Lesquereux, Charles Schuchert, *et al.,* Minn. Geol. and Nat. Survey, 1895.
Minnesota's Rocks and Waters, George M. Schwartz and George A. Thiel, Minn. GS Bull. 37, 1954.
Lower Paleozoic Geology of the Upper Mississippi Valley, Geol. Soc. of Am. Guide Book, Field Trip No. 2, 1956.
Southeastern Minnesota Field Trip Guide Book, Geol. Soc. of Am., 1956.

MISSISSIPPI

The Upper Cretaceous Deposits, Lloyd W. Stephenson and Watson H. Monroe, Miss. GS Bull. 40, 1940; repr. 1959.

Scott County, Harlan R. Bergquist and Thomas E. McCutcheon, Miss. GS Bull. 49, 1942.
Clay County, Virginia M. Kline, *et al.,* Miss. GS Bull. 53, 1943.

MISSOURI

Common Fossils of Missouri, A. G. Unklesbay, U. of Mo. Handbook, No. 4, 1955.
Missouri's Ice Age Mammals, M. G. Mehl, Mo. Div. of Geol. Srvy. and Water Rsrcs., Educ. Ser. No. 1, 1962.

MONTANA

Vertebrate Fossils from the Fort Union Beds, Earl Douglass, *Annals* of Carnegie Mus., Vol. 4, 1908–1909.
The Fort Union of the Crazy Mountain Field, Montana, and Its Mammalian Fauna, George Gaylord Simpson, U.S. Natl. Mus. Bull. No. 169, 1937.
Stratigraphic Section of Upper Paleozoic and Mesozoic Rocks in South-Central Montana, L. S. Gardner, *et al.,* Mont. Bur. of Mines and Geol. Memoir 24, 1946.
Cambrian Stratigraphy in Southwestern Montana, Alvin M. Hanson, Mont. Bur. of Mines and Geol. Memoir 33, 1952.
The Rocks and Fossils of Glacier National Park: The Story of Their Origin and History, Clyde P. Ross and Richard Rezak, USGS Prof. Paper 294-K, 1959.
The Montana Almanac, 1959–60, and statistical suppl., 1962–63, Mont. State U.
"The Tertiary Flora of the Ruby-Gravelly Basin in Southwestern Montana," Herman F. Becker, reprint from proceedings of Billings Geol. Soc. 11th Ann. Field Conf., 1960.
"Additions to the Tertiary Ruby Paper Shale Flora of Southwestern Montana," Herman F. Becker, Torrey Bot. Club *Bulletin,* Vol. 87, No. 6, Nov. 1960.
Oligocene Plants, Upper Ruby River Basin, Montana, Herman F. Becker, Geol. Soc. of Am., Memoir 82, 1961.
"Two New Species of Mahonia from the Grant-Horse Prairie Basin in Southwestern Montana," Herman F. Becker, Torrey Bot. Club *Bulletin,* Vol. 89, No. 2, Mar.–Apr. 1962.

NEBRASKA

Museum Notes, U. of Neb. State Mus., Feb. 1959, Feb. 1960, Mar. 1960, Mar. 1961, Apr. 1962.

NEVADA

Structural Geology of the Hawthorne and Tonopah Quadrangles, Henry G. Ferguson and Siemon W. Muller, USGS Prof. Paper 216, 1949.

Nevada, Am. Guide Ser., Portland, Oregon, Binfords and Mort, 1957.

Pre-Tertiary Stratigraphy and Upper Triassic Paleontology of the Union District, Shoshone Mountains, Nevada, N. J. Silberling, USGS Prof. Paper 322, 1959.

NEW HAMPSHIRE

The Geology of New Hampshire (*Bedrock Geology,* Part II), Harland P. Billings, N. H. Planning and Development Comm., 1956.

NEW JERSEY

New Jersey Miocene Formations, Robert Parr Whitefield, USGS, 1894.

New Jersey, Am. Guide Series, 1946.

The Cretaceous Fossils of New Jersey, Horace G. Richards, *et al.,* N. J. Bur. of Geol. and Topog. Bull. 61; Part I, 1958; Part II, 1962.

General Fossil-Collecting Localities, courtesy N. J. Bureau of Geology.

NEW MEXICO

Permo-Carboniferous Deposits of New Mexico, S. W. Williston, E. C. Case, and M. G. Mehl, Carnegie Inst., 1913.

Permian Sedimentary Facies, Central Guadalupe Mountains, Donald Wilkin Boyd, N. M. Inst. of Mines and Tech., 1958.

"New Mexico's Fossil Record" (U. of N. M. 8th Ann. Research Lecture, Apr. 7, 1961), Stuart A. Northrop, in New Mexico *Quarterly,* Vol. 32, Nos. 1 and 2, 1962.

NEW YORK

Handbook of Paleontology for Beginners and Amateurs, Winifred Goldring, Part II, *The Fossils,* N. Y. State Mus. Handbook No. 9, 1929 (out of print).

A Popular Guide to the Nature and the Environment of the Fossil Vertebrates of New York, Roy L. Moodie, N. Y. State Mus. Handbook No. 12, 1933.

General Guide to the American Museum of Natural History, Sc. Guide No. 118, rev. ed., 1958.

"Coral Growth and Geochronometry," John W. Wells, article in *Nature,* Vol. 197, No. 4871, March 9, 1963.

"Devonian Flora of New York State," Harlan P. Banks, article in Empire State Geogram of NYGS, Vol. 4, No. 3, spring 1966.

NORTH CAROLINA

Mollusca from the Miocene and Lower Pliocene of Virginia and North Carolina, Part I, *Pelecypoda,* Julia Gardner, USGS Prof. Paper 199-A, 1943.

Geology of the Coastal Plain of North Carolina, Horace G. Richards, in *Trnsctns.* of the Am. Philos. Soc., New Series, Vol. 40, Part I, Aug. 1950.

NORTH DAKOTA

The Geology of Emmons County, Stanley P. Fisher, NDGS Bull. 26, 1952.

"The Status of Paleontology in North Dakota" (invitation paper read before N. D. Acad. of Sciences, May 5, 1961), F. D. Holland, Jr., in *Proceedings* of the NDAS, Vol. 15, 1961.

Guidebook for Geologic Field Trip in the Minot Area, North Dakota, Wilson M. Laird, NDGS Misc. Series No. 2, 1957.

Guidebook for Geologic Field Trip in the Devils Lake Area, North Dakota, Wilson M. Laird, NDGS Misc. Series No. 3, 1957.

Guidebook for Geologic Field Trip in the Williston Area, North Dakota, F. D. Holland, Jr., NDGS Misc. Series No. 6, 1957.

Guidebook for Geologic Field Trip in the Jamestown Area, North Dakota, F. D. Holland, Jr., NDGS Misc. Series No. 7, 1957.

Guidebook for Geologic Field Trip Fargo to Valley City, F. D. Holland, Jr., NDGS Misc. Series No. 8, 1957.

Guidebook for Geologic Field Trip Grand Forks to Park River, F. D. Holland, Jr., NDGS Misc. Series No. 9, 1957.

NDGS Misc. Guide Series (guidebooks) Nos. 11 (1958) and 14 (1962).

General Fossil Collecting Localities, courtesy Dept. of Geol., U. of North Dakota.

OHIO

Ohio Fossils, Aurèle la Rocque and Mildred Fisher Marple, Ohio GS Bull. 54, 1961.

OKLAHOMA

"Late Pleistocene Fossils from Harper County, Oklahoma," John J. Stevens, Geol. Soc. of Am. *Bulletin*, Vol. 71, Nov. 1960.
List of Fossil-Collecting Localities, courtesy Dept. of Geology, U. of Oklahoma.

OREGON

"Geology of the John Day County, Oregon," Margaret L. Steere, *The Ore-Bin*, Ore. Dept. of Geol. and Min. Inds., July 1954.
"Fossil Localities of the Sunset Highway Area, Oregon," Margaret L. Steere, *The Ore-Bin*, Ore. Dept. of Geol. and Min. Inds., May 1957.
"Fossil Localities of the Eugene Area, Oregon," Margaret L. Steere, *The Ore-Bin*, Ore. Dept. of Geol. and Min. Inds., June 1958.
"Fossil Localities of the Salem-Dallas Area," Margaret L. Steere, *The Ore-Bin*, Ore. Dept. of Geol. and Min. Inds., June 1959.
"Fossil Woods of Oregon," Wallace Eubanks, *The Ore-Bin*, Ore. Dept. of Geol. and Min. Inds., July 1960.
"Plant Fossils in the Clarno Formation, Oregon," Herbert L. Hergert, *The Ore-Bin*, Ore. Dept. of Geol. and Min. Inds., June 1961.

PENNSYLVANIA

Swatara Gap, Lebanon County, Pa. GS Earth Sc. Field Trip Guide.
Plant Fossil Locality, Lebanon County, Pa. GS Earth Sc. Field Trip Guide.
Selected Fossil-Collecting Localities in Pennsylvania, courtesy Pa. Bureau of Topographic and Geologic Survey.

RHODE ISLAND

Insect Forms in the Rhode Island Coal Fields, Samuel Hubbard Scudder, USGS Bull., 1893.
Rhode Island, American Guide Series, Houghton Mifflin, 1937.

SOUTH CAROLINA

Geology of the Coastal Plain of South Carolina, USGS Bull. 867,
  1936.
"Oligocene Fossils from the Old Bolton Phosphate Mine Near
  Charleston, S. C.," Horace G. Richards and Arthur H. Hopkins,
  in S. C. Dev. Bd. *Geol. Notes*, Vol. 4, No. 3, May–June 1960.
Good Collecting Localities, courtesy Dept. of Geol. and Geog.,
  U. of South Carolina.

SOUTH DAKOTA

Preliminary Report on the Paleontology of the Black Hills, R. F.
  Whitfield, USGS Survey of the Rocky Mountain Region, 1877.
Titanotheres of Ancient Wyoming, Dakota and Nebraska, Henry
  Fairfield Osborn, U.S. Govt. Printing Office, 1919.

TENNESSEE

*Upper Cretaceous Floras of the Eastern Gulf Region in Tennes-
  see, Mississippi, Alabama and Georgia*, Edward Wilber Berry,
  USGS Prof. Paper 112, 1919.
Tenn. Div. of Geol. Bulletins: No. 21, *Stratigraphy and Correlation of the Devonian of Western Tennessee*, Carl O. Dunbar,
  1919; No. 38, *The Stratigraphy of the Central Basin of Tennessee*, R. S. Bassler, 1932; No. 41, *A Preliminary Report on
  the Foraminifera of Tennessee*, Joseph A. Cushman, 1931;
  No. 51, *The Geology of Nashville, Tennessee*, Charles W. Wilson, Jr., 1948; No. 56, *Pre-Chattanooga Stratigraphy in Central Tennessee*, Charles W. Wilson, Jr., 1949.

TEXAS

Texas Fossils: An Amateur Collector's Handbook, William H.
  Matthews III, Bur. of Econ. Geol., U. of Tex., 1960.

UTAH

List of Fossil-Collecting Localities, courtesy Dept. of Geol., U.
  of Utah.

VIRGINIA

Older Mesozoic Fauna of Virginia, William M. Fontaine, USGS
  Monograph, Vol. 6, 1883.

"Early Ordovician Nautiloids from Virginia," A. G. Unklesbay and Robert S. Young, *Journal of Paleontology*, Vol. 30, No. 3, May 1956.

"Lower Canadian Brachiopods from Virginia," Robert S. Young, *Journal of Paleontology*, Vol. 30, No. 5, Sept. 1956.

"The Microfauna of the Yorktown Formation from James River, Surry County, Virginia," Joseph W. Sabol, *Bull. of Am. Paleontology*, Vol. 41, No. 191, Nov. 25, 1960.

Virginia Geological Survey Bulletins: No. 29, *Geology of the Virginia Triassic*, Joseph K. Roberts, 1928 (supply depleted); Nos. 46 and 51, *Contributions to Virginia Geology: Symposium*, Part I, 1936, Part II, 1939 (supply depleted); No. 52, *Geology of the Appalachian Valley in Virginia*, Charles Butts, Part I, 1940, Part II, 1941 (supply depleted).

List of Fossil-Collecting Localities, courtesy Virginia Department of Conservation and Economic Development.

WASHINGTON

Fossils in Washington, Vaughn E. Livingston, Jr., Wash. Dept. of Conservation Information Circular 33, 1959.

WEST VIRGINIA

A Guide to the Common Fossil Plants of West Virginia, W. H. Gillespie and I. S. Latimer, Jr., W. Va. Geological and Economic Survey, June 1960.

WISCONSIN

Fossil Collecting in Wisconsin, Meredith E. Ostrom, Wis. GS, 1961.

WYOMING

Dinosaurs of Wyoming, Roy L. Moodie, Wyo. GS Bull. 22, 1930.

Geological Society of America Bull. Vol. 57, June 1946.

Wyoming Geological Association Guidebooks 10th Ann. Field Conf. of Green River Basin, 1955 and 1956.

Titanotheres of Wyoming, Dakota and Nebraska, Henry Fairfield Osborn, Govt. Printing Office, 1919.

Special Material

"New Method of Handling and Preserving Soft-Matrix Fossils,"
Herman F. Becker, in *Asa Gray Bull.,* Gray Memorial Bot.
Assn., Vol. 3, No. 1, spring 1955.
Midwest Gem Trails, June Culp Zeitner, Mineralogist Publishing
Co., Spokane, Wash., 1960.
News Bulletins, Society of Vertebrate Paleontology, Feb. 1964
through June 1966.

General Bibliography

Adams, Frank D., *The Birth and Development of the Geological
Sciences,* Baltimore, Williams and Wilkins, 1938.
Andrews, Henry N., Jr., *Studies in Paleobotany,* New York,
Wiley, 1961.
Andrews, Roy Chapman, *An Explorer Comes Home,* Garden City,
N. Y., Doubleday, 1947.
———, *Ends of the Earth,* Garden City, N. Y., Garden City Books,
1929.
———, *This Business of Exploring,* New York, Putnam, 1935.
Ardrey, Robert, *The Territorial Imperative,* New York, Atheneum,
1966.
———, *African Genesis,* New York, Atheneum, 1961.
Augusta, Josef, and Burian, Zdenek, trans. by Margaret Schiel,
A Book of Mammals, London, 1963 (Russian ed. 1962).
———, *Prehistoric Animals* (same series).
———, *Prehistoric Man* (same series).
———, *Prehistoric Reptiles and Birds* (same series).
———, *Prehistoric Sea Monsters* (same series).
Ball, Max W., *This Fascinating Oil Business,* Indianapolis, Bobbs-
Merrill, 1949.
Barzun, Jacques, *Darwin, Marx and Wagner,* Boston, Little,
Brown, 1941.

Bates, Marston, *The Forest and the Sea*, New York, New American Library, Mentor Book, 1960.

Beerbower, James R., *Search for the Past*, Englewood Cliffs, N. J., Prentice-Hall, 1960.

Brewster, Edwin Tenney, *This Puzzling Planet*, New York, New Home Library, 1928; revised by Ralph Emerson Esarey, 1942.

Buchsbaum, Ralph, and Milne, Lorus J., *The Lower Animals: Living Invertebrates of the World*, Garden City, N. Y., Doubleday, 1960.

———, *Animals Without Backbones*, Chicago, U. of Chicago Press, rev. ed., 1938.

Camp, Charles L., and Hanna, G. Dallas, *Methods in Paleontology*, Berkeley, University of California Press, 1937.

Carrington, Richard, *Mermaids and Mastodons*, New York, Rinehart, 1957.

Carson, Rachel L., *The Sea Around Us*, New York, New American Library, Mentor Book, 1950.

Colbert, Edwin H., *Dinosaur Book*, New York, McGraw-Hill, 1945.

———, *Triumph of the Mammals*, American Museum of Natural History, Science Guide No. 112, 1953.

Darwin, Charles, *Autobiography*, Sir Francis Darwin, ed., with introductory essay by G. G. Simpson, New York, Henry Schumann, 1950.

———, *Journal of Researches into the Geology and Natural History of the Various Countries Visited by H. M. S. Beagle* (orig. ed., 1839), New York, Hafner, 1952.

———, *The Origin of Species* (orig. ed., 1859), New York, P. F. Collier, 1909.

Delevoryas, Theodore, *Morphology and Evolution of Fossil Plants*, New York, Chicago, San Francisco, Toronto, and London, Holt, Rinehart and Winston, 1962.

Dunbar, Carl O., *Historical Geology*, New York, Wiley, 1960.

Eiseley, Loren C., *Darwin's Century*, Garden City, N. Y., Doubleday, 1958.

———, *The Firmament of Time*, New York, Atheneum, 1960.

———, *The Immense Journey*, New York, Modern Library, 1946.

Emmons, William H., Thill, George A., Stauffer, Clinton R., and Ellison, Ira S., *Geology: Principles and Processes*, New York, McGraw-Hill, 1949.

Farb, Peter, *Living Earth*, New York, Pyramid, 1959.

Fenton, Carroll Lane, and Fenton, Mildred Adams, *The Fossil Book*, Garden City, N. Y., Doubleday, 1958.

Fitzenmayer, E. W., *Siberian Man and Mammoth*, London, Blackie and Sons.

Gamow, George, *Biography of the Earth: Its Past, Present, and Future* (orig. Ed., 1941), New York, Viking, 1959.

Hapgood, Charles H., *Earth's Shifting Crust*, New York, Pantheon, 1958.

Hibben, Frank C., *The Lost Americans*, New York, Apollo, 1961.

Hotton, Nicholas, III, *Dinosaurs*, New York, Pyramid, 1963.

Hurley, Patrick M., *How Old Is the Earth?* Garden City, N. Y., Anchor Books, 1959.

Hussey, Russell C., *Historical Geology: The Geological History of North America*, New York, McGraw-Hill, 1949.

Kahn, Fritz, *Design of the Universe*, New York, Crown, 1954.

Klein, Alexander, *Grand Deception: The Real Story of the Cardiff Giant*, Philadelphia, Lippincott, 1955.

Krutch, Joseph Wood, *Grand Canyon: Today and All Its Yesterdays*, New York, Sloane, 1958.

Kummel, Bernhard, and Raup, David, eds., *A Handbook of Paleontological Techniques*, San Francisco and London, W. H. Freeman and Co., 1955.

Lucas, Jeanette May, and Carter, Helene, *The Earth Changes*, Philadelphia, Lippincott, 1937.

McDougall, Curtis D., *Hoaxes*, New York, Macmillan, 1940.

Milne, Lorus J. and Margery, *The Senses of Animals and Men*, New York, Atheneum, 1962.

Moore, Ruth, *Man, Time and Fossils: The Story of Evolution*, New York, Knopf, 1953.

———, *The Coil of Life*, New York, Knopf, 1959.

Pearl, Richard M., *Geology: An Introduction to Principles of Physical and Historical Geology*, New York, Barnes and Noble, 1960.

Robinson, W. W., *Beasts of the Tar Pits*, Los Angeles, Ward Ritchie, 1932.

Romer, Alfred Sherwood, *The Vertebrate Story*, Chicago, U. of Chicago Press, 4th ed., 1959.

Sanderson, Ivan T., *The Continent We Live On*, New York, Random House, 1961.

Schnacke, Stewart, and Drake, N. D'Arcy, *Oil for the World* (orig. ed., 1950), New York, Harper (for Standard Oil Co.), 1960.

Scheinfeld, Amram, *The New You and Heredity*, Philadelphia, Lippincott, 1950.

Senet, André, *Man in Search of His Ancestors*, trans. by Malcolm Barnes, New York, McGraw-Hill, 1955.

Shimer, H. H., and Schrock, R. R., *Index Fossils of North America*, New York, Wiley, 1945.

Simpson, George Gaylord, *The Meaning of Evolution*, New Haven, Conn., Yale, 1950.

——, Pittendrigh, C. S., and Tiffany, L. H., *Life: An Introduction to Biology*, New York, Harcourt, 1957.

Sinnott, Edmund W., Dunn, Leslie C., and Dobzhansky, Theodosius, *Principles of Genetics*, New York, McGraw-Hill, 1950.

Stirton, R. A., *Time, Life and Man*, New York, Wiley, 1950.

Vercours, Jean Bruller, *You Shall Know Them*, trans. by Rita Barisse, Boston, Little, Brown, 1953.

Verrill, A. Hyatt, *The Strange Story of Our Earth*, New York, Grosset and Dunlap, 1952.

Weiner, J. S., *The Piltdown Forgery*, New York, Oxford University Press, 1955.

Worth, C. Brook, and Enders, Robert K., *The Nature of Living Things*, New York, Signet, 1953.

Wright, H. E., Jr., and Frey, D. G., eds., *The Quaternary of the United States*, Princeton, N. J., Princeton University Press, 1965.

Zumberger, James H., *Elements of Geology*, New York, Wiley, 1958.

Museums Containing Paleontological Specimens

HERE ARE SOME OF THE MUSEUMS, UNIVERSITIES, AND OTHER
centers that display fossils. In addition to the places listed, there
are numerous institutions that show fossils but place less emphasis on them. Many states have children's museums; and if
the ancient rocks of nearby areas contain many fossilized remains, there are certain to be specimens on view.

ALABAMA

Regar Memorial of Natural History, 1411 Gurnee Street, Anniston

ALASKA

University of Alaska Museum, Fairbanks

ARIZONA

John Wesley Powell Memorial Museum, 6 North 7th Avenue,
Page
Museum of Northern Arizona, Fort Valley Road, Flagstaff

ARKANSAS

Arkansas State University Museum, State University
University of Arkansas Museum, Fayetteville

CALIFORNIA

California Division of Mines and Geology, Ferry Building, San
Francisco
Museum of Paleontology, University of California, Earth Sciences
Building, Berkeley
Riverside Municipal Museum, 3720 Orange Street, Riverside

COLORADO

Denver Museum of Natural History, City Park, Denver
Dinosaur Quarry Visitor Center, Dinosaur
University of Colorado Museum, Boulder

CONNECTICUT

Dinosaur Park, Rocky Hill
Peabody Museum of Natural History, 170 Whitney Avenue, New Haven
Stamford Museum and Nature Center, 39 Scofieldtown Road, Stamford

DISTRICT OF COLUMBIA

National Museum of Natural History (Smithsonian Institution), Constitution Avenue at 10th Street N.W., Washington

FLORIDA

Florida State Museum, University of Florida, Gainesville
Science Center of Pinellas County, 7701 22nd Avenue North, St. Petersburg
Science Museum and Planetarium, West Palm Beach

IDAHO

Idaho State University Museum, Pocatello

ILLINOIS

Burpee Natural History Museum, 813 North Main Street, Rockford
Field Museum of Natural History, Roosevelt Road at Lake Shore Drive, Chicago
Illinois State Museum, Spring and Edwards Streets, Springfield
Museum of Natural History, University of Illinois, Urbana

INDIANA

Hanover College, Department of Geology, Hanover
Indiana State Museum, 202 North Alabama Street, Indianapolis

IOWA

Museum of History and Science, 503 South Street, Waterloo
University of Northern Iowa Museum, 31st Street and Hudson
 Road, Cedar Falls

KANSAS

Benedictine College, Department of Biology, Atchison
Natural History Museum, University of Kansas, Lawrence
Sternberg Memorial Museum, Fort Hays Kansas State College,
 Hays

KENTUCKY

Kentucky Museum, Western Kentucky University, Bowling Green
University of Louisville, Department of Geology, Louisville

LOUISIANA

Museum of Geoscience, Louisiana State University, Baton Rouge

MAINE

Nylander Museum, Caribou

MARYLAND

Maryland Academy of Sciences, 7 West Mulberry Street, Baltimore

MASSACHUSETTS

Museum of Comparative Zoology, Harvard University, Cambridge

MICHIGAN

Exhibit Museum, University of Michigan, 1109 Geddes Street,
 Ann Arbor
Grand Rapids Public Museum, 54 Jefferson Street, Grand Rapids
The Museum, Michigan State University, East Lansing

MINNESOTA

Bell Museum of Natural History, University of Minnesota, 17th Street and University Avenue S.E., Minneapolis
Science Museum of Minnesota, 30 East 10th Street, St. Paul

MISSOURI

Kansas City Museum of History and Science, 3218 Gladstone Boulevard, Kansas City

MONTANA

Carter County Museum, Ekalaka
Natural History Museum, Northern Montana College, Havre
Yellowstone County Museum, Logan Field, Billings

NEBRASKA

Cook Museum of Natural History, Agate
University of Nebraska State Museum, 101 Morrill Hall, Lincoln
University of Nebraska Trailside Museum, Fort Robinson

NEVADA

Ichthyosaur State Park, Nye County
Nevada State Museum, Carson City

NEW HAMPSHIRE

Dartmouth College Museum, Hanover

NEW JERSEY

Museum of Natural History, Guyot Hall, Princeton University, Princeton
Museum of Natural History, Rutgers University, New Brunswick

NEW MEXICO

Ghost Ranch Museum, Abiquiu
Natural History Museum, Carlsbad Caverns National Park
University of New Mexico, Biology Department, Albuquerque

NEW YORK

American Museum of Natural History, Central Park West at 79th Street, New York City
Buffalo Museum of Sciences, Humboldt Park, Buffalo
Museum of Petrified Wood, 106 Thomas Street, Rochester
New York State Natural History Museum, State Education Building, Albany
Paleontological Research Institution, 1269 Traumansburg Road, Ithaca

OHIO

Cincinnati Museum of Natural History, 1720 Gilbert Avenue, Cincinnati
Cleveland Museum of Natural History, University Circle, Cleveland
Dayton Museum of Natural History, 2629 Ridge Avenue, Dayton
Geology Museum, University of Cincinnati, Cincinnati

OKLAHOMA

East Central State College Museum, Ada
Northwestern State College Museum, Alva
Stovall Museum of Science and History, University of Oklahoma, Norman

OREGON

Museum of Natural History, University of Oregon, Eugene
Oregon Museum of Science and Technology, 4015 Southwest Canyon Road, Portland

PENNSYLVANIA

Academy of Natural Sciences of Philadelphia, 19th Street and Parkway, Philadelphia
Carnegie Museum, Carnegie Institute, Pittsburgh

South Dakota

Geology Museum, Petrified Forest, Piedmont
Museum of Geology, South Dakota School of Mines and Technology, Rapid City
Zeitner Geological Museum, Mission

Texas

Dallas Museum of Natural History, Dallas
El Paso Centennial Museum, University of Texas at El Paso
Houston Museum of Natural Science, 5800 Caroline Street, Houston
Panhandle-Plains Museum, 2401 Fourth Avenue, Canyon
Southern Methodist University, Department of Geology, Dallas
Texas Memorial Museum, 24th and Trinity Streets, Austin
University of Houston, Department of Geology, 3801 Cullen Boulevard, Houston

Utah

Dinosaur Quarry Visitor Center, Dinosaur National Monument, north of Jensen
Utah Museum of Natural History, University of Utah, Salt Lake City

Washington

Ginkgo Petrified Forest State Park, Vantage

Wisconsin

Greene Memorial Museum, University of Wisconsin, Milwaukee
Milwaukee Public Museum, 800 West Wells Street, Milwaukee

Wyoming

Geological Museum, University of Wyoming, Laramie

Where To Study

THIS PARTIAL LIST OF COLLEGES and universities currently offering courses in vertebrate paleontology was prepared by the Smithsonian Institution.

Amherst College, Amherst, Massachusetts.
University of Arizona, Tucson, Arizona.
University of California, Berkeley, California.
University of California at Los Angeles, Los Angeles, California.
University of Chicago, Chicago, Illinois.
Columbia University, New York, New York.
Dartmouth College, Hanover, New Hampshire.
University of Florida, Gainesville, Florida.
Harvard University, Cambridge, Massachusetts.
University of Kansas, Lawrence, Kansas.
University of Michigan, Ann Arbor, Michigan.
University of Nebraska, Lincoln, Nebraska.
University of Oklahoma, Norman, Oklahoma.
Princeton University, Princeton, New Jersey.
South Dakota School of Mines and Technology, Rapid City, South
    Dakota.
University of Texas, Austin, Texas.
University of Wyoming, Laramie, Wyoming.
Yale University, New Haven, Connecticut.

ALABAMA

Geological Survey of Alabama
P.O. Drawer O
University, Alabama

ALASKA

State Division of Mines and Minerals
Territorial Building, Box 1391
Juneau, Alaska 99801

ARIZONA

College of Mines
Arizona Bureau of Mines
University of Arizona
Tucson, Arizona 85725

ARKANSAS

Arkansas Geological and Conservation Commission
State Capitol
Little Rock, Arkansas

CALIFORNIA

Division of Mines and Geology
Department of Conservation
Ferry Building
San Francisco, California 94111

COLORADO

Colorado Metal Mining Fund Board
204 State Office Building
Denver, Colorado 80202

CONNECTICUT

Connecticut Geological and Natural History Survey
Judd Hall, Wesleyan University
Box 128, Wesleyan Station
Middletown, Connecticut 06457

DELAWARE

Delaware Geological Survey
University of Delaware
Newark, Delaware 19711

FLORIDA

Florida Geological Survey
P.O. Box 631
Tallahassee, Florida 32302

GEORGIA

Department of Mines, Mining, and Geology
State Division of Conservation
19 Hunter Street S.W.
Atlanta, Georgia 30303

IDAHO

Idaho Bureau of Mines and Geology
University of Idaho
Moscow, Idaho 83843

ILLINOIS

State Geological Survey Division
121 Natural Resources Building
University of Illinois
Urbana, Illinois 61801

INDIANA

Indiana Geological Survey
Department of Conservation
Owen Hall, Indiana University
Bloomington, Indiana 47401

IOWA

Iowa Geological Survey
Geology Annex
Iowa City, Iowa 52240

KANSAS

State Geological Survey
University of Kansas
Lawrence, Kansas 66045

KENTUCKY

Kentucky Geological Survey
307 Mineral Industries Building
120 Graham Avenue
Lexington, Kentucky 40506

LOUISIANA

Louisiana Geological Survey
P.O. Box 8847, University State
Baton Rouge, Louisiana 70803

MAINE

Department of Economic Development
Division of Geology
State House
Augusta, Maine 04330

MARYLAND

Department of Geology, Mines and Water Resources
102 Latrobe Hall
Johns Hopkins University
Baltimore, Maryland 21218

MICHIGAN

Geological Survey Division
Department of Conservation
Lansing, Michigan 48926

MINNESOTA

Minnesota Geological Survey
University of Minnesota
Minneapolis, Minnesota 55414

MISSISSIPPI

Mississippi Geological, Economic and Topographical Survey
2525 N. West Street
P.O. Drawer 4915
Jackson, Mississippi 39206

MISSOURI

Division of Geological Survey and Water Resources
P.O. Box 250
Rolla, Missouri 65401

MONTANA

Montana Bureau of Mines and Geology
Montana School of Mines
Butte, Montana 59701

NEBRASKA

Conservation and Survey Division
Nebraska Hall
University of Nebraska
Lincoln, Nebraska 68508

NEVADA

Nevada Bureau of Mines
University of Nevada
Reno, Nevada 89507

NEW HAMPSHIRE

New Hampshire State Planning and Development Commission
Conant Hall
University of New Hampshire
Durham, New Hampshire 03824

NEW JERSEY

Department of Conservation and Economic Development
Bureau of Geology
520 East State Street
Trenton, New Jersey 08625

NEW MEXICO

State Bureau of Mines and Mineral Resources
New Mexico Institute of Mining and Technology
Socorro, New Mexico 87801

NEW YORK

Geological Survey
State Education Building
Hawk Street
Albany, New York 12224

NORTH CAROLINA

Division of Mineral Resources
Department of Conservation and Development
State Office Building
Raleigh, North Carolina

NORTH DAKOTA

North Dakota Geological Survey
University of North Dakota
Grand Forks, North Dakota 58201

OHIO

Ohio Division of Geological Survey
1207 Grandview Avenue
Columbus, Ohio 43212

OKLAHOMA

Oklahoma Geological Survey
University of Oklahoma
Norman, Oklahoma 73069

OREGON

State Department of Geology and Mineral Industries
1069 State Office Building
Portland, Oregon 97202

PENNSYLVANIA

Bureau of Topographic and Geologic Survey
Department of Internal Affairs
Harrisburg, Pennsylvania 17120

SOUTH CAROLINA

Division of Geology
State Development Board
P.O. Box 927
Columbia, South Carolina 29201

SOUTH DAKOTA

State Geological Survey
State University
Union Building, Lock Drawer 351
Vermillion, South Dakota 57069

TENNESSEE

Division of Geology
Department of Conservation
G-5 State Office Building
Nashville, Tennessee 37203

TEXAS

Bureau of Economic Geology
University of Texas
Austin, Texas 78712

UTAH

Utah Geological and Mineralogical Survey
103 Civil Engineering Building
University of Utah
Salt Lake City, Utah 84102

Vermont

State of Vermont Development Department
East Hall
University of Vermont
Burlington, Vermont 05401

Virginia

Department of Conservation and Economic Development
Division of Mineral Resources
Natural Resources Building
Box 3667
Charlottesville, Virginia 22901

Washington

Division of Mines and Geology
Department of Conservation
335 General Administration Building
Olympia, Washington 98501

West Virginia

West Virginia Geological and Economic Survey
P.O. Box 879
Morgantown, West Virginia 26505

Wisconsin

Geological and Natural History Survey
Science Hall
University of Wisconsin
Madison, Wisconsin 53706

Wyoming

Geological Survey of Wyoming
University of Wyoming
Laramie, Wyoming 82070

    States not included in this list have no state geologist or
state mineral agency.

INDEX

Index

NOTE: Most of this index is based on material in chapters I through VI and the portions of the Fifty Chapters on States. There is no attempt to refer to specific fossils found in individual localities.